Compliments of the . . .

ED WELLS
INITIATIVE

Phone: 425/393-2626
Fax: 425/393-2616
http://EdWells.web.boeing.com

A Joint Boeing/SPEEA Program
for the application of Technical Excellence

Pocius
Adhesion and Adhesives Technology

Alphonsus V. Pocius

Adhesion and Adhesives Technology

An Introduction

Hanser Publishers, Munich Vienna New York

Hanser/Gardner Publications, Inc., Cincinnati

The Author:

Dr. Alphonsus V. Pocius, 445 Highpoint Curve, Maplewood, MN 55119, U.S.A.; or c/o 3M Adhesive Technologies Center, 3M Center, St. Paul, MN 55144-1000, U.S.A.

Distributed in the USA and in Canada by
Hanser Gardner Publications, Inc.
6915 Valley Ave., Cincinnati, OH 45244, USA
Fax: +1 (513) 527 8950
http://www.hansergardner.com

Distributed in all other countries by
Carl Hanser Verlag
Postfach 86 04 20, 81631 München, Germany
Fax: +49 (89) 99 830-269
http://www.hanser.de

Library of Congress Cataloging-in-Publication Data
Pocius, Alphonsus V.
    Adhesion and adhesives technology : an introduction / Alphonsus
V. Pocius.
        p. cm.
    ISBN 1-56990-212-7
    1. Adhesion.   2. Adhesives.   3. Chemistry, Physical and
theoretical.   4. Chemistry, Organic.   I. Title.
    QC183.P72   1997
    668′.3–dc20   96-31003

Die Deutsche Bibliothek – CIP-Einheitsaufnahme
Pocius, Alphonsus V.:
Adhesion and adhesives technology : an introduction /
Alphonsus V. Pocius. - Munich ; Vienna ; New York : Hanser ;
Cincinnati : Hanser-Gardner, 1997
    ISBN 3-446-17616-0

© Carl Hanser Verlag, Munich, Vienna, New York, 1997
Typeset in England by Alden Bookset, Didcot
Printed and bound in Germany by Schoder Druck GmbH & Co. KG, Gersthofen

This book is dedicated to my wife, Janice, and to my children,
Nick and Amanda

Preface

Adhesion science is a multidisciplinary field which encompasses aspects of engineering as well as physical and organic chemistry. The broadness of the field is probably the reason that there have been so few books written on the subject by a single author. The books in this area have tended to be handbooks, treatises or other compilations by multiple authors. In this volume, I have attempted to provide a broad view of the field, but with a consistent style that leads the reader from one step to another in the understanding of the science.

The text assumes that the reader has little or no knowledge of the science of adhesion. The bulk of the book is written with the supposition that the reader has had courses in college level calculus as well as college level organic and physical chemistry. The book has also been written in such a fashion that even a person who has a meager knowledge of these subjects can learn something about adhesion science from reading this book. That is, the emphasis is on *understanding* the science rather than a complete and detailed exposition on any part of it. An attempt has been made to describe as much as possible in words and examples rather than in detailed mathematical derivation. The mathematics has been included in those sections where more detail seemed necessary. Each section or chapter starts with a simple view of the subject area, starting at the same point an entry level textbook would begin. Each section or chapter then builds to a point at which more detail is available for the reader who is or wants to be a practitioner of the art and science of adhesion. Each section also includes helpful practical suggestions about how measurements can be made, how surfaces can be modified or how adhesives can be formulated to lead to a useful result. The wish of the author is to produce a well-rounded introductory view of each of the fields which form adhesion science no matter what the technical background of the reader may be.

I would like to acknowledge some of the people at 3M who have assisted me either by reviewing this manuscript or by providing the support to pursue my study of the science of adhesion. These people include Sam Smith, Bill Schultz, Dave Wangsness, Ted Valentine, Brian Smillie, Dick Hartshorn, Don Theissen, George Allen, Tom Savereide, Morgan Tamsky, Larry Clemens, Rich Newell, and Mike Engel. Without their friendship and support, it is doubtful that I would have had the opportunity to build the base of expertise necessary to prepare a book such as this. I would also like to acknowledge Prof. Bob Kooser at Knox College who inspired me to pursue a career in physical chemistry. Finally, I would like to thank my wife, Janice, for proofreading this text and for her love and support.

Contents

1 Introduction

1.1 Introduction and Chapter Objectives

Adhesive bonding is a method by which materials can be joined to generate assemblies. Adhesive bonding is an alternative to more traditional mechanical methods of joining materials, such as nails, rivets, screws, etc. Although adhesive bonding is not a new joining method (use of adhesives is described in ancient Egypt [1] and in the Bible [2]) widespread use of adhesives as a joining medium is a relatively recent phenomenon.

All joining methods have their advantages and disadvantages and adhesive bonding is not an exception. This introductory chapter explores some of the positive and negative features of adhesive bonding as a joining method. Exploring these features sets the stage for many of the chapters to follow. The objectives of this chapter are to acquaint the reader with the basic definitions used in adhesion science, to provide the reader with a basis for understanding the advantages and disadvantages of using adhesive bonding, and to discuss the place of adhesive technology in our economy as well as provide examples of where adhesives are utilized. The final objective of this chapter is to describe sources of information about adhesion and adhesives for those who are becoming practitioners of the art and science of adhesive bonding.

1.2 Basic Definitions

The assembly made by the use of an adhesive is called an *adhesive joint* or an *adhesive bond*. The solid materials in the adhesive joint other than the adhesive are known as the *adherends*. The phenomenon which allows the adhesive to transfer a load from the adherend to the adhesive joint is called *adhesion*. There is also the phenomenon of *abhesion* which is the condition of having minimal adhesion. This property is important when an assembly is needed from which the adhesive can be removed on demand. Materials that exhibit abhesion are also known as *release materials* and they are used to make certain pressure-sensitive adhesive constructions. Pressure-sensitive adhesives are described in Chapter 9.

The actual strength of an adhesive joint is primarily determined by the mechanical properties of the adherends and the adhesive. The term we apply to the measured physical strength of an adhesive bond is *practical adhesion*. It is a primary purpose of this book to describe the phenomenon of adhesion and to describe the chemistry and properties of adhesives and to discuss the current understanding of the relationship between practical adhesion, adhesion and the mechanisms of energy dissipation in the adhesive joint.

1.3   Advantages and Disadvantages of Adhesive Bonding

One major differentiation between an adhesive joint and a mechanical joint is that in the second, the adherend, in general, must be pierced by a mechanical fastener to execute the assembly. When an adherend is pierced by a mechanical fastener or if the adherend is pierced before the installation of mechanical fastener, a hole is created in the adherend (Fig. 1.1).

In Fig. 1.1 we see two examples of an adherend. In Fig. 1.1(a), the adherend is intact. If a load is applied to the adherend, the lines of force propagating through the adherend would be continuous. If instead, the adherend had a hole in it (such as depicted in Fig. 1.1(b)), the lines of force could not be continuous through the adherend and would have to go around the hole. Thus, at the edges of the hole, the

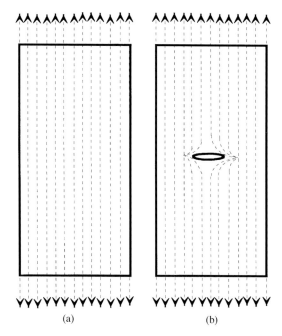

(a)   (b)

Figure 1.1   Diagram showing lines of force through a monolithic body (a) and a body containing an elliptical hole (b). The lines of force pass continuously through (a) but are unable to do so in (b). This results in a stress concentration at the edges of the elliptical hole

force experienced by the material is much larger than the force experienced by the material remote from the hole. The edges of the hole not only have to support the force that is applied to those edges but also must support the force that should have been supported by the material which would have been in the hole. As we will find in Sections 2.4 and 3.5.1 on fracture mechanics, this situation is known as a *stress concentration*. A stress concentration can cause a decrease in many physical properties of the adherend as well as those of the mechanical joint. In contrast, if an adhesive is used to generate an assembly no hole is generated in an adherend. Therefore, the physical properties of the adherend are maintained after the assembly has been created.

The presence of stress concentrations generated by the use of mechanical fasteners in a joint can lead to several problems which are not present when adhesives are used. First, the overall strength of the joint can be reduced. Second, the joint can experience early fatigue failures. Third, if either of the adherends is sensitive to shock, the act of applying the mechanical fastener could cause the assembly to fail.

Adhesive bonding, when executed in a properly designed adhesive joint, does not exhibit high stress concentrations, so the properties of the adherends can be fully utilized. However, adhesive joints do require a much larger area of contact between the adherends and the adhesive in order to carry the same load as a mechanical fastener. Some of the criteria for the proper design of an adhesive joint are described in Chapters 3 and 11.

For the most part, adhesives are polymeric materials which exhibit *viscoelastic* properties. Materials which display viscoelasticity have both a viscous character as well as an elastic character. These terms are described in more detail in Chapters 2 and 5. Polymer based adhesives absorb mechanical energy applied to the joint and dissipate that energy as heat. Hence, fatigue failures are delayed in comparison to mechanical fastening. The viscoelastic properties of adhesives and the role they play in the adhesive bonding and debonding process are discussed in Chapters 2, 5, 6 and 9.

Finally, many adhesives do not require input of mechanical energy to effect an assembly. Hence, shock-sensitive materials can be easily made into an assembly. For example, one would not consider joining of dynamite sticks with nails. However, dynamite sticks can be easily joined by pressure-sensitive adhesive-backed tape.

The primary disadvantage of adhesive bonding is that it relies on adhesion for the transfer of load through the assembly. Adhesion is a surface physico-chemical phenomenon which is discussed in Chapters 4 and 6. Since adhesion is a surface phenomenon, it follows that the physical properties of the adhesive joint depend strongly on the character of the surface of the adherend and how the adhesive interacts with that surface. Thus, an adherend with an improper surface could lead to lower joint strengths than might be predicted from the mechanical properties of the adhesive and the adherend. Surface problems are even more important when one tries to generate adhesive bonds that are durable in adverse environments. The need for a proper surface, and the fact that it is not always available is one disadvantage of adhesive bonding in comparison to mechanical fasteners which are not affected by the state of the surface of the members of a joint. Practical methods by which one can generate surfaces that are amenable to adhesive bonding are discussed in Chapter 7.

Adhesives display several other advantages over mechanical fastening. One of these advantages is reason for the widespread use of adhesives in the aerospace industry, specifically the ability of adhesives to not only form a joint but also to seal the assembly in one step. Mechanical fastening often requires separate sealing steps to create a pressurizable assembly. Adhesives also allow galvanically dissimilar materials to adhere to one another without leading to accelerated corrosion. For example, the mechanical joining of steel and aluminum would be a disaster in the making. Aluminum would act as an anode to steel and corrode rapidly in corrosive environments. Since most polymeric adhesives are non-ionic and electrical insulators, a properly effected adhesive bond would electrically separate the members of the galvanic couple while still joining them structurally.

However, mechanical fastening does have a number of advantages over adhesive bonding. Once a mechanical fastener is applied, one certainly knows that it is there. Adhesives, by their nature, are internal to the joint. In most cases, it is not easy to determine (without destructive testing) whether the adhesive was properly applied. This lack of non-destructive quality control has led to entire studies on methods by which adhesive bonds can be inspected in a non-destructive fashion. One other advantage of mechanical fasteners over adhesive bonding is that the engineering of mechanically fastened assemblies is part of many schools' curricula. However, there is a paucity of courses on the engineering of adhesively bonded structures. Thus, there may be a certain lack of confidence in the use of adhesives among engineers and designers. It is hoped that this book increases confidence in the use of adhesives and potentially lays the groundwork for an engineering curriculum in this area.

1.4   Uses of Adhesive Bonding in Modern Industry

For thousands of years, adhesive bonding has been used in the production of veneered furniture. Many examples of veneered furniture from Egyptian and Roman times are found in museums. Adhesives were also used for the generation of wooden musical instruments. In more recent times, adhesives have been used in many industries and are still used in the generation of veneered wood. Adhesives are used in a far wider array of applications than could have been imagined by our ancestors. The primary boost in the use of adhesives came with the advent of synthetic polymeric materials with improved mechanical properties.

There are many types of adhesives, both organic and inorganic. The inorganic adhesives are familiar to most people and include materials such as Portland cement and solder. The chemistry and physical properties of these adhesives are not discussed in this book although the sections on mechanical properties and surfaces for organic materials apply just as well to these adhesives. Rather, the adhesives which

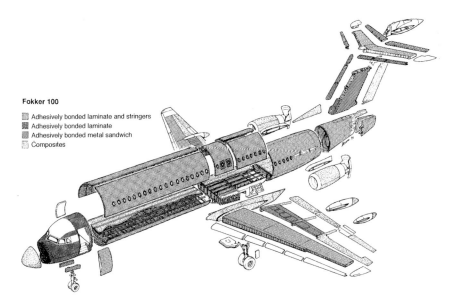

Fokker 100

- Adhesively bonded laminate and stringers
- Adhesively bonded laminate
- Adhesively bonded metal sandwich
- Composites

Figure 1.2   Diagram of a Fokker F-100 aircraft showing the sections of the aircraft that are adhesively bonded. Note that a substantial amount of the fuselage is constructed using structural adhesives. (Diagram courtesy of the Fokker Aircraft Company, The Netherlands, reprinted with permission)

we discuss in this book are those which are based entirely or primarily on organic materials. The chemistry and physical properties of these polymer based adhesives are discussed in Chapters 8–11.

Since these adhesives are organic in nature, they normally have a lower specific gravity than either the inorganic adhesives mentioned above or most adherends. Thus, assemblies produced with polymer-basis adhesives weigh less than those produced with inorganic adhesives, a major advantage in the aerospace industry where lightweight structures are of paramount importance.

Despite the fact that the use of adhesives is not part of many engineering curricula, there are many examples of the use of adhesive bonding in industry. The aerospace industry uses adhesive bonding to great advantage in the construction of many components. Figure 1.2 is a diagram of a Fokker F-100 passenger aircraft, indicating the areas which are adhesively bonded. It is easy to see that much of the fuselage, the wing structure, and the engine housing are at least partially adhesively bonded. What is not apparent from the figure is that many of the internal components in the aircraft cabin are also adhesively bonded. For example, floor panels are a special construction of a material known as Nomex[1] honeycomb core adhesively bonded to fiberglass panels. The overhead compartments are made in a similar way. These constructions are not only lightweight but they are also stiff.

---

[1] "Nomex" is a trademark of E. I. DuPont de Nemours and Co.

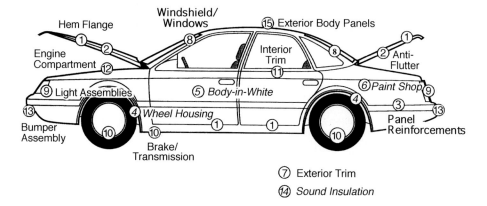

Figure 1.3   Diagram of an automobile body showing at least 15 locations in which adhesives and sealants could be used or are being used. Particular note should be made of the windshield (8) which is considered a load bearing structure in modern automobiles and is adhesively bonded. Also attention should be paid to hem flange bonding (1) in which adhesives are used to bond and seal. Adhesives are used to bond friction surfaces in brakes and clutches (10). Anti-flutter adhesive bonding (2) helps control deformation of hood and trunk lids under wind shear. Thread-sealing adhesives are used in engine applications (12)

Many of the types of adhesives that are used in the aerospace industry are discussed in Chapter 8.

The automobile industry also uses adhesives extensively. Figure 1.3 shows locations of an automobile where adhesives are used. For example, automobile hoods are typically constructed of a top panel and a stiffener. The stiffener is joined to the top panel by "anti-flutter" adhesives which allow the hood to maintain its shape even under high stresses and wind shear. In newer automobiles, the windshield is part of the overall structure of the roof and is fastened by adhesives to the frame. Automobile doors are often adhesively bonded in an assembly known as the "hem-flange" in which the outer door is bonded to an inner shell. The outer door is crimped around the inner shell and the two pieces are joined and sealed by adhesive bonding. Figure 1.4 shows the use of adhesives in the manufacture of frame for an autobus. The potential weight savings inherent in adhesive bonding are a major reason for their increased use as automotive technology advances.

Great use of adhesives is found in the wood products industry. Plywood manufacturers use tank car quantities of various types of adhesives, ranging from those made with natural products to those made from synthetic materials, such as phenol-formaldehyde polymers. Similar materials are used to make press board and chip board, both of which are used extensively in home construction. Figure 1.5 shows a construction worker applying adhesives to joists in a home construction project.

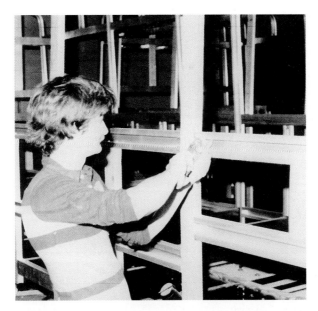

Figure 1.4 A production worker applies a paste adhesive to struts which form the frame for an autobus

Figure 1.5 A construction worker applies a mastic adhesive to the joists in a home construction project. The use of a mastic adhesive in such an application provides for a quieter floor

Figure 1.6   Photographs of a spray adhesive used in a lamination line. The top photograph shows a spray head applying a rubber-based adhesive to an adherend. The lower photograph shows a factory worker placing adherends to be sprayed onto a conveyor belt for passage under the spray head

When floor boards are adhesively bonded to joists, the floor tends to be stiffer and quieter then when nails are used exclusively in a similar construction.

Adhesives are also used in the manufacture of furniture and cabinets. In particular, adhesives are used to make laminates incorporating materials such as Formica[1] bonded to pressboard. Figure 1.6 shows how a rubber-based adhesive is spray-applied to a veneer and a base wood. The two materials are later laminated to

---

[1] "Formica" is a registered trademark of the Formica Corporation

generate the furniture article. Adhesives are widely used in other aspects of home construction, as well. Floor and wall tile is applied with rubber-based mastic cements. These materials are discussed in Chapter 9. Similar adhesives are used to apply paneling. Wall coverings are also attached by adhesive bonding. The paper industry, which might be considered a subset of the wood products industry, also uses large quantities of adhesives. Hot melt adhesives, which are discussed in Chapter 10, are used to seal cartons as well to bind paper-back books. Moisture-activatable adhesives are applied to envelopes and postage stamps. A newer adhesive application is the Post-it[1] repositionable note.

Consumer usage of adhesives is a growing portion of the market for adhesive technology. In fact, in some cases, the consumer-oriented adhesive tradename has become synonymous with the adhesive technology. For example, cyanoacrylate adhesives (discussed in Chapter 8) are widely known as Super-Glue[2]. One type of pressure-sensitive adhesive-backed tape (discussed in Chapter 9) is recognized as Scotch[3] tape. Poly(vinyl acetate) emulsions which are used as wood bonding and paper adhesives are often called Elmer's Glue[4]. Other adhesive products are also well accepted in the consumer marketplace. Vinyl adhesives used to repair such items as vinyl inflatables are not only widely sold to consumers but are also a very good example of one of the primary theories of adhesion, the diffusion theory, which is discussed in Chapter 6. Epoxy adhesives, which are widely used in the aerospace industry, also are found in the consumer marketplace as two-part adhesives which come in tubes or applicator packages.

1.5   Economics of Adhesives Technology

A measurable percentage of chemical production is associated with the generation of adhesives and related products. In 1992, the worldwide adhesive and sealant industry produced 17 trillion pounds of formulated products with an estimated value of more than $16.3 billion [3]. This number does not include the rather significant amounts of adhesives used in plywood and chipboard manufacture. The bulk of this production and usage was in North America, Europe and the Far East.

The single major use of adhesives comes under the heading of "converting" which includes the generation of various types of packaging and labeling. The second major use of adhesives is in the construction industry which includes many of the applications discussed earlier. The adhesive industry is considered a "fragmented" industry. There are an extremely large number of adhesive companies with

---

[1] "Post-it" is a registered trademark of the 3M Company
[2] "Super-Glue" is a registered trademark of Loctite Corporation
[3] "Scotch" tape is a registered trademark of the 3M Company
[4] "Elmer's Glue" is a registered trademark of Borden Co.

fewer than 50 employees. Only a few adhesive companies have more than 1000 employees. However, the industry saw a substantial consolidation through the 1980's and the emergence of several large companies which grew through the acquisition of smaller ones.

1.6   Literature

Literature regarding adhesives and adhesion technology can be found primarily in patents, which can be difficult to read. However, review of the patent literature is indispensable for anyone wishing to produce innovative adhesive products.

There are many journals devoted to polymeric materials which are essential ingredients used in the adhesives discussed in this book. Journals such as *Macromolecules, Journal of Applied Polymer Science*, and *Polymer Science and Engineering,* etc., are indispensable for keeping up with progress in this field. Also important are the mechanical properties of materials. Thus, reading journals such as the *Journal of Material Science* and the *Journal of Rheology* is very important. Adhesion science also deals with surfaces, so journals such as *Langmuir* and the *Journal of Colloid and Interface Science* often have articles of importance to the adhesiologist.

There are a number of journals strictly related to the science of adhesion and the understanding of adhesives. The oldest of these journals is the *Journal of Adhesion* which has been published for more than 25 years. A newer journal is the *Journal of Adhesion Science and Technology.* Both of these journals include articles which cover all aspects of adhesion science and technology. The *International Journal of Adhesion and Adhesives* has articles primarily written by European authors. These three journals are published in English. Other journals important to adhesiologists are published in German (*Adhaesion*) and in Japanese.

There are a number of excellent texts in adhesion science. Notable is *The Handbook of Adhesives* [4] edited by Skeist. This volume, now in its third edition, is a compilation of contributed articles describing almost every aspect of adhesive technology. Another important series of books is the *Treatise on Adhesion and Adhesives* [5], which has had several editors. This series of books is important because the articles, even though they are written by many authors, are written in greater depth than those in the *Handbook*. A useful series of books is entitled *Adhesion* [6] and *Aspects of Adhesion* [7]. These books are compilations of articles taken from the proceedings of an annual adhesives meeting in the United Kingdom. The *Handbook of Pressure Sensitive Adhesive Technology* [8] is similar to the *Handbook of Adhesives* but is devoted solely to pressure-sensitive adhesives. There are a few books written by individual authors covering adhesion and adhesives technology most notably Kinloch's *Adhesion and Adhesive Technology* [9].

For the beginning practitioner of adhesive technology, an indispensable tool is the trade literature provided by adhesive and adhesive raw material manufacturers.

In many cases, detailed descriptions are given of the materials offered as well as starting formulations for many types of adhesives. For the user of adhesives, trade literature can often provide useful methodology for the application of the adhesive as well as surface preparation methods. Trade literature also includes the properties of the adhesive.

1.7   Summary

This introductory chapter provides basic definitions which are used throughout this book plus an idea of the impact of adhesives and adhesive technology on world industry and economy. The advantages and disadvantages of the use of adhesives to generate assemblies are discussed, as well. A recounting is given in Table 1.1. The chapter ends with a discussion of useful literature references for the experienced and beginning practitioner of adhesion science.

Table 1.1   Advantages and Disadvantages of Adhesive Bonding

Advantages	Disadvantages
No stress concentrations due to piercing of the adherend	Strength is dependent upon the condition of the adherend surface
Improved fatigue resistance	Lack of non-destructive quality control methods
Lighter weight structures	
Ability to join and seal simultaneously	Lack of engineering curricula describing adhesive bonding
Ability to join shock-sensitive substrates	
Ability to join galvanically problematic metals	Can be more expensive than mechanical fastening
Can be less expensive than mechanical fasteners	

References

1. Inscription in an ancient Egyptian tomb in Thebes, circa 1500 BC
2. Quote from the Apocrypha, Jesus ben Sirach (Ecclesiasticus, C22)
3. "The Global Adhesive and Sealant Industry 1992–1997" (May, 1993), Chem Research GmbH and DPNA International, Frankfurt, Germany
4. Skeist, I., ed., *Handbook of Adhesives* (1990) Van Nostrand Reinhold, New York
5. Patrick, R.L., ed., *Treatise on Adhesion and Adhesives,* vols. 1–6 (1967–1990), Marcel Dekker, New York
    Minford, J.D., ed., *Treatise on Adhesion and Adhesives,* vol. 7 (1991) Marcel Dekker, New York
6. Allen, K.W., ed., *Adhesion,* vols 1–15 (1977–1991) Applied Science Publishers, London

7. *Aspects of Adhesion*, vols 1–8 (1963–1975) University of London Press, London
8. Satas, D., ed., *Handbook of Pressure Sensitive Adhesive Technology*, 2nd ed. (1989) Van Nostrand Reinhold, New York
9. Kinloch, A.J., *Adhesion and Adhesives: Science and Technology* (1987) Chapman and Hall, New York

2   The Mechanical Properties of Materials as They Relate to Adhesives

2.1   Introduction

It has been emphasized that adhesives are engineering materials. To understand how adhesives work, it is necessary to understand their mechanical properties and the chemistry used to create those properties. In this Chapter, the fundamental properties of materials is discussed. In later chapters, we see how these properties are used to analyze stresses in adhesive bonds and how certain adhesive bonds can be used to determine these properties.

Many of the topics in this chapter form the basis for *rheology,* the study of the deformation and flow of materials. In its most detailed form, rheology is highly mathematical. In this book, rheological phenomena and measurements are described in terms of "what happens" and mathematical descriptions used only when necessary.

It is the objective of this chapter to develop an understanding of the basic mechanical properties of materials. In particular, it is important to become familiar with the concepts of modulus, elongation, fracture resistance and the ways stress can be applied to an adhesive bond. The response of a polymeric material to a sinusoidal stress is also analyzed. Finally, materials parameters are used in an analysis of the bending of beams.

2.2   Definition of Mechanical Stresses for Materials Testing

There are three types of forces which can be applied to an adhesive (or to any material, for that matter). These forces are shown schematically in Fig. 2.1, 2.2 and 2.3. The first fundamental measurement is the *tensile* measurement (Fig. 2.1). In this test, a bar of material of known dimension is firmly clamped into a tensile testing machine and a force is applied to the axial dimension of the sample.

In a second measurement shown in Fig. 2.2, a sample of known dimension is subjected to a force, *F*, on its faces in such a way that the forces oppose one another. This force is known as a *shearing* force and is of great importance in the testing and performance of adhesive bonds. Most adhesive bonds are designed to subject the adhesive to shear, rather than tension or cleavage forces.

The final measurement used to characterize an adhesive is shown in Fig. 2.3. Here, we see that the force is applied in a tensile fashion but the material has

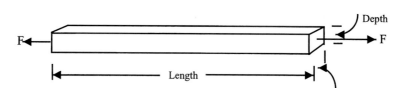

Figure 2.1   A bar of material to which a tensile force, *F*, is being applied. Note that for proper characterization of the physical properties of the material from which the bar is made, the dimensions of the bar must be known well

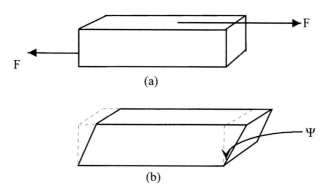

Figure 2.2   This figure shows the application of a tangential force to a rectangularly shaped material. Figure 2.2(a) shows the undeformed body with the tangential forces applied to two surfaces of the material. Even though the force is shown as being applied at a point on those surfaces, the force is actually applied over the entire surface. Figure 2.2(b) shows the bar after it has been deformed by the tangential forces. The sides of the body assume a trapezoidal shape. The degree of deformation is described by the angle Ψ shown in the figure. The dashed lines show the original shape of the bar. The figure portrays a "shearing" force

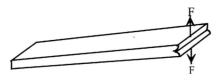

Figure 2.3   If a material has a pre-existing crack along one of its edges and if a force is applied in a tensile fashion perpendicular to the crack, the material is said to be placed in "cleavage." Later in this book, we call this way a load is applied "Mode I Cleavage"

a pre-existing crack in one of its faces. The force to which the sample is subjected is known as a *cleavage* force. This test is also very important for many adhesive materials because it measures the property which is most weak in most adhesives. Much of the rest of this chapter and the next deals with test methods that use these basic measurements to further characterize the properties of adhesive materials.

2.3   Stress–Strain Plots and the Definition of Materials Property Parameters

2.3.1   Tensile Forces

In the tensile test described in the previous section, if the sample has a known cross sectional area, A, and F is the force applied by the tensile testing machine, then we define the *tensile stress, σ,* as

$$\sigma = \frac{F}{A}$$

The tensile stress is an important engineering concept in that the force, F, is applied over a specific cross sectional area of sample. Many different materials could have the same elongation with applied force F if the cross sectional area of the sample was the appropriate size. Elongation is the change in the length of the sample as the result of tensile forces. The elongation of the sample is defined in terms of the original dimensions of the specimen. Thus, if the original length of the sample is l_0 and the length (displacement) of the sample after a certain amount of tensile stress was applied is l, then we can define the term ε as follows

$$\varepsilon = (l - l_0)/l_0$$

where ε is known as the *engineering tensile strain*. It is important to note that the engineering tensile strain is a dimensionless number and is usually reported as a fraction or multiplied by 100 to obtain a percentage. This figure is also sometimes reported as *elongation* in the industry.

A *stress–strain plot* can be generated using a tensile testing machine. A specimen of known cross-sectional area is subjected to a tensile force and the elongation is measured, as shown in Fig. 2.4. The tensile stress is plotted on the y axis and the engineering tensile strain is plotted on the x axis. At some temperature of test, many materials have stress–strain plots similar to that shown in Fig. 2.4. Stress-strain plots for individual materials differ in the initial slope, in the position of the knee, the length of the plateau portion of the curve, and the *elongation at break*, which is indicated by the X in the plot.

The slope of the initial part of the stress–strain plot is exceedingly important in both engineering and materials science. For most materials, the initial part of the

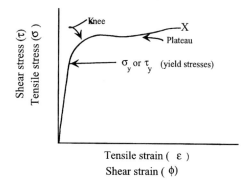

Figure 2.4   Schematic stress–strain curve. The engineering strain is plotted on the *x* axis while the stress is plotted on the *y* axis. The axes are labelled for either tensile or shear stress and strain. Similar curves but with different actual values will be measured under both types of application of force. The yield stress is shown as well as the failure at break (indicated by the "X")

stress–strain plot is linear thus, the relationship of stress and strain is as follows:

$$\sigma = E\varepsilon \tag{2.1}$$

where σ is the tensile stress, ε is the engineering tensile strain and E is a constant.

This relationship should be familiar. It is just a restatement of *Hooke's Law for Springs*, that the stress and the strain are proportional. The force applied to a spring and the resultant elongation are directly proportional. The proportionality constant is called the *spring constant, E*.

A spring is usually used as a model for materials which behave according to this equation. Materials which obey Hooke's law are known as *linear elastic* materials. The response is *linear* with increasing force. If the force is removed, the material returns *elastically* to its original state. The factor E is known as the *tensile modulus* or *Young's modulus* of the material in test. Since the engineering tensile strain is dimensionless, the Young's modulus has the units of stress, MegaPascal (MPa) in SI units and pounds per square inch (psi) in English units. Since the above equation, $\sigma = E\varepsilon$ expresses the relation between the stress and strain rather than force and displacement, Young's modulus is a materials parameter describing how a material reacts to a given tensile force. If the slope of the stress–strain plot is steep, then Young's modulus is high and a large tensile load must be applied to the sample to get a small elongation of the material. Materials that have a high Young's modulus are described as "stiff." Materials that have a low Young's modulus are described as "flexible." Table 2.1 provides a short list of well-known materials and a comparison of their Young's moduli.

As shown in Fig. 2.4, the stress point at which the stress–strain curve exhibits a "knee" is known as the *yield stress* of the material. This parameter plays an important role in our understanding of resistance to crack propagation as well as one of the parameters necessary for the proper design of adhesive bonds. The tensile yield stress is given the symbol σ_y and it marks the stress or strain at which the

Table 2.1   Young's Moduli and Poisson's Ratio for Some Well-Known Materials

Material	Young's modulus Pascal = N/m^2	Poisson's ratio
Aluminum	7×10^{10}	0.33
Mild steel	2.2×10^{11}	0.28
Silicon	6.9×10^{10}	
Glass	6×10^{10}	0.23
Poly(methylmethacrylate)	2.4×10^9	0.33
Polycarbonate	1.4×10^9	
Low density polyethylene	2.4×10^8	0.38
Natural rubber	2×10^6	0.49

material no longer follows Hooke's Law. After the yield stress is reached, the material is non-elastic and is said to have been *plastically deformed.* Plastic deformation is a sign that the material is absorbing energy.

Not all materials display the plateau region shown in Fig. 2.4. The plateau is seen in materials which "neck-in" or "draw down" as the sample elongates. Note that in the plateau region, the stress on the sample can actually decrease.

Eventually, the material can no longer sustain the stress and it breaks. The stress at this point is known as the *stress at break* while the strain at this point is known as the *strain at break* or the *elongation at break* of the material. The *ultimate tensile strength* of the material could be the stress at break. However, the ultimate tensile strength of the material could occur when the material begins to neck-in. All of these properties govern the potential uses for a material and also guide the adhesiologist in determining what type of adhesive could be made from the material.

When most materials are subjected to a tensile stress, they not only stretch but also become thinner in cross section in order to conserve volume. We can define a parameter which describes how much the material thins in response to a tensile stress in the following manner:

$$\nu = \frac{(r_0 - r)/r_0}{\varepsilon}$$

where r is the radius of a cylindrically shaped tensile specimen at a certain stress, r_0 is the original radius and ε is the tensile strain. The quantity ν is the ratio of the lateral strain to the tensile strain and is known as *Poisson's ratio.* This quantity is measured while the material is within its elastic region. For *isotropic materials*, i.e., materials which have the same properties in every direction, Poisson predicted that this ratio should be 0.25. In fact, many materials have a Poisson's ratio close to 0.25, as shown in Table 2.1.

The unit volume expansion, ΔV, of a material in tension can be calculated from the expression, $\Delta V = \varepsilon(1 - 2\nu)$. Most materials do not exhibit a decrease in volume when put into tensile stress. Therefore, ν has an upper value of 0.5.

Materials such as rubber have Poisson's ratio approaching 0.5. Steel has a Poisson's ratio of 0.26.

2.3.2 Shear Forces

Figure 2.2 shows the application of stress to the surfaces rather than the ends of a bar. We need to analyze this situation differently from tensile stress. Assume that we know the area over which the force is applied. The name *shear stress* is given to the force per unit area applied tangentially as shown in Fig. 2.2. The symbol τ denotes the shear stress and has the same units as the tensile stress.

   The response of the material to such a force is a deformation as shown in Fig. 2.2. The material deforms to form a parallelopiped where the angle between the original shape and the new shape is given by ψ. The shear strain is defined as the tangent of the angle ψ and is given the symbol ϕ. Similarly to the tensile test situation, $\tan \psi$ is dimensionless. A shear stress–strain experiment yields results similar to a tensile stress–strain experiment. There usually is a region in which the shear stress responds linearly to a shear strain, thus obeying Hooke's law. The following equation can be written:

$$\tau = G\phi \tag{2.2}$$

where G is known as the *shear modulus* of the material. G also has units of MegaPascal (MPa) or pounds per square inch (psi). Materials may also display a yield stress in shear and have many of the same features as those in the tensile stress–strain curve, as was shown in Fig. 2.4. It can also be shown that the shear modulus and the Young's modulus are related by the following formula:

$$G = \frac{E}{2(1 + \nu)}$$

where G is the shear modulus, E is the Young's modulus and ν is the Poisson's ratio.

2.3.3 Strain Energy Density

If we examine the stress–strain curve shown in Fig. 2.4, we can calculate the energy absorbed by the sample as a result of the deformation by finding the area under the curve. We define U, the *strain energy density*, as $U = \int \sigma \, d\varepsilon$.

   If a material is completely linear and elastic, the stress–strain curve is a straight line. Therefore, the area under the curve is just the area of a triangle. The ultimate strain energy density is exceedingly important in judging the usefulness of a material as an adhesive. For an adhesive to work, it must be able to absorb as much mechanical energy as possible. The ultimate strain energy density is the parameter describing how much mechanical energy a material can absorb. For most adhesive applications, we seek a material which is stiff enough to support the design load with as high an ultimate strain energy density as possible. Thus, when loads are applied, the mechanical energy can be dissipated in the adhesive without breaking the bond.

2.4   Introduction to Linear Elastic Fracture Mechanics

The deformation of a material also can be described in terms of a force and a displacement rather than a stress and strain. Needless to say, the resultant measurement is equally dependent upon the type of sample and its properties. That type of thinking is used for the analysis of the cleavage experiment shown in Fig. 2.3. In Chapter 1, we discussed a body with and without a hole and the resultant differences in stress concentration. Fracture mechanics describes the ability of a material to resist the effect of having a stress concentration internal to a body. The situation is generalized by utilizing a body of nondescript size and shape, but with known width as shown in Fig. 2.5.

Somewhere in this body there is a sharp crack (analogous to the sharp edge crack shown in Fig. 2.3 and the hole in Fig. 1.1). The crack has a length, a. If a force is applied to the body, a displacement results.

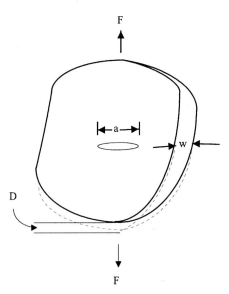

Figure 2.5 Diagram of a nondescript body used in the description of elementary linear-elastic fracture mechanics. The body has a non-specified shape but has a known width. Somewhere in the body, there exists a crack of length a. A force F can be applied to the body resulting in a displacement, D

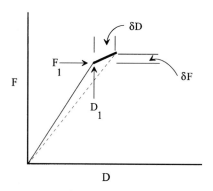

Figure 2.6   Stress–strain curve for the linear elastic body shown in Fig. 2.5. Note that the loading curve (thin solid line) and the unloading curve (dashed line) are both linear. The slopes differ because the stiffness of the body changes when the crack propagates. The thick section of line shows the change in slope of the loading curve after the crack propagates. The symbols are discussed in the text

If we assume that the body is linear and elastic, then the stress–strain curve is like the first portion of Fig. 2.6 (the thin solid line). A strain energy density is calculated for this situation. Using the symbols in Fig. 2.6: $U_1 = \frac{1}{2} F_1 D_1$.

This equation simply describes the area under the thin solid line in Fig. 2.6. At some point during the deformation of the body, the crack in the body grows. As this happens, the stiffness of the body changes and a new stress–strain curve results. The slope of the stress–strain curve changes because the stiffness of the body is different because it contains a larger crack. The strain energy density, U_2, in the body after the crack propagates is also calculated. This is the area under the thicker solid line. Since the material is linear and elastic, we calculate the strain energy density to be

$$U_2 = F_1 \delta D + \frac{1}{2} \delta F \delta D$$

The basis for this calculation is also simple. The area under the thicker solid line is divided into a small triangle whose area is $\frac{1}{2} \delta F \delta D$ and a parallelogram whose area is $F_1 \delta D$. The curve for unloading the sample would follow the dashed line portion of the curve. The strain energy density, U_3, for this portion of the curve is

$$U_3 = \frac{1}{2} (F_1 + \delta F)(D_1 + \delta D)$$

which is just the area of the triangle under the dashed portion of the curve. U_1 and U_2 describe the energy put into the sample in order to bring it to its final state. That state, however, is not the same as the initial state because the material has cracked. We take the difference between the energy put into the sample and the energy we could get out of the sample if we unloaded it. This is the energy used to propagate the crack, U_C

$$U_C = U_1 + U_2 - U_3 \qquad (2.3)$$

This analysis describes the energetics of crack propagation but it does not give us a criterion for the energy necessary to extend a crack. If a certain stress is applied to a linear elastic material, we know the strain. A materials parameter for crack propagation analogous to the Young's modulus for the tensile test is needed. Let us say that a crack propagates only if $U_C > U_{C,min}$. U_C and $U_{C,min}$ have units of energy and are not dependent on the size of the sample and the amount of crack growth that has taken place. The width of the sample, as shown in Fig. 2.5, is w. At the instant of crack growth, the infinitesimal change in the available energy with the change in the crack's length must exceed the minimum energy necessary for crack growth. If we divide by the width of the specimen, we describe the situation as follows:

$$\frac{1}{w} \frac{\delta}{\delta a} U_C \geq \frac{1}{w} \frac{\delta}{\delta a} U_{C,min}$$

Define a materials parameter, $\mathscr{G}_C$, as being the minimum change in the strain energy density with crack length necessary to cause the propagation of a crack. A criterion for crack propagation is as follows:

$$\frac{1}{w} \frac{\delta}{\delta a} U_c \geq \mathscr{G}_C \qquad (2.4)$$

This expression says that for a body of width w, the change in energy with a change in crack length has to be greater than or equal to the quantity $\mathscr{G}_C$, called the *strain energy release rate*. Note that the strain energy release rate has units of energy per unit area and is the rate of release of strain energy per unit area of crack growth. This equation forms the basis for *linear elastic fracture mechanics* and is used to describe the experimental results for samples of the form shown in Fig. 2.3. It is important to appreciate the elegance of this analysis. Using arguments based upon energetics, rather than stresses and strains, we are able to describe the propagation of a crack in a material of nondescript form and composition. Methods for determination of the strain energy release rate of adhesives are discussed in the next chapter.

The Young's modulus and the shear modulus are used to design structures to be loaded below the yield stress. The strain energy release rate allows us to decide which material should be used to generate a crack-resistant structure. All real materials contain flaws. If a material does not have resistance to the propagation of a flaw, the structure fails at loads smaller than a flaw-free structure would. Table 2.2

Table 2.2   Strain Energy Release Rates for Some Recognizable Materials

Material	$\mathscr{G}_{IC}$ (Joules/m^2)
Silicon	3
Steel	2000
Cured epoxy resin	700
Silica	20
Poly(methylmethacrylate)	400
Polycarbonate	2000

provides a list of strain energy release rates for a number of easily recognizable materials. This data provides insight as to why steel is used in construction of buildings and silicon is not. Silicon, even though it has a Young's modulus not substantially less than steel, propagates cracks when the strain energy release rate exceeds $3\,J/m^2$. Steel requires almost 1000 times more energy to propagate a crack than does silicon.

2.5   Introduction to Rheology of Liquids

The materials properties described above are for solids. Adhesives, however, often begin as liquids. A significant portion of a material's ability to perform as an adhesive depends upon its ability to "wet" a surface. Wetting of a surface does not depend just on interfacial characteristics (discussed in Chapter 4), but also depends on the ability of the material to flow on the surface with or without applied force. Thus, the characteristics of the adhesive as a liquid are important in the generation of adhesive bonds. Some adhesives are never fully solids but retain much of the character of liquids throughout their use. These materials are termed *viscoelastic*. Most polymeric materials have some degree of viscoelastic character. Certain adhesives, known as pressure sensitive adhesives, make great use of this characteristic.

Earlier in this chapter, a spring was used as a mechanical analogy for an elastic material. For a viscous material, we need a somewhat more complicated model, the dashpot. Figure 2.7 shows a dashpot which is a piston inside a liquid-containing cylinder. If we pull on the piston shaft slowly and steadily, the piston moves with

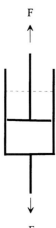

Figure 2.7   Drawing of a "dashpot." The dashed line is to indicate a liquid level. The inverted "T" is meant to indicate a piston. Application of a force causes the liquid to move past the piston

little applied force because liquids are infinitely deformable. If we pull rapidly on the piston shaft, however, the liquid cannot move fast enough past the edges of the piston and thus resists the motion of the piston. We have all seen dashpots in action. Part of the shock absorber in an automobile is a dashpot, as is part of the mechanism used to close doors automatically in buildings. If the material in Fig. 2.2 is a liquid and a shear stress is applied, we find that the liquid does not resist deformation when the shear stress is constant. Rather, the liquid shows a resistance to deformation when the *shear strain rate* is varied. Thus, if τ is the shear stress and $\delta\varepsilon/\delta t$ is the shear strain rate, the following relationship is found for many fluids:

$$\eta = \frac{\tau}{\delta\varepsilon/\delta t}$$

where η is defined as the *viscosity* of the fluid material. Rearranging this equation, we find:

$$\tau = \eta\dot{\varepsilon} \tag{2.5}$$

where $\dot{\varepsilon} = d\varepsilon/dt$. Equation (2.5) is analogous to Eq. (2.2) with viscosity replacing the shear modulus and the shear strain rate replacing the shear strain. Viscosity has units of poise or Stokes. Water has a viscosity of one centistoke at room temperature. All liquids have a viscosity often described as their "thickness." If the above equation describes the viscosity of the liquid for all shear rates, then the liquid is said to behave in a *Newtonian* fashion. A curve in Fig. 2.8 shows the shear stress-shear strain rate curve for a Newtonian fluid. Most liquids with low molecular weights behave in a Newtonian fashion at low to moderately high shear rates. Polymeric materials however, which form the basis for many adhesives, have high molecular weights and their response to shear rate can be non-Newtonian, which is somewhat more complicated.

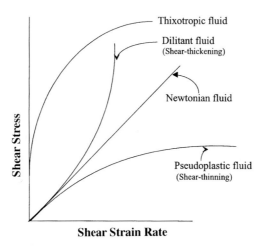

Figure 2.8   Plot of shear stress–shear strain rates for a number of different types of liquids

Figure 2.8 also shows flow phenomena observable for higher molecular weight liquids, colloids and suspensions. The *dilatant* liquid shows a nonlinear response of shear stress to shear strain rate in that the curve bends towards the abscissa (*y*-axis). A dilatant liquid is also known as a "shear thickening" liquid. The *pseudoplastic* liquid shows a curve which bends towards the ordinate (*x*-axis). A pseudoplastic liquid is also known as a "shear thinning" liquid. A primary example of a shear thinning material is a polymer melt. Polymers are high molecular weight molecules and their pseudoplasticity is caused by alignment of their long chains in the stress field. Other examples of pseudoplastic liquids are emulsions and suspensions.

Both dilatant and pseudoplastic liquids have a zero intercept on the shear stress axis at zero shear rate. Other liquids exhibit a non-zero intercept with the ordinate or at least what appears to be a non-zero intercept. A curve representing the behavior of such a liquid is also shown in Fig. 2.8. This liquid is said to display a "yield stress" analogous to the yield stress for solids. In other words, the material appears to act as a solid until the yield stress is reached, after which point it behaves as if it were a liquid. A *Bingham plastic* has a yield stress. After the yield stress has been applied, it displays Newtonian character. Liquid-like materials which display a yield stress are often called *thixotropic* materials. Ketchup, bearing grease, and cold cream are all examples of thixotropic liquids. The behavior of thixotropic liquids is very important for adhesive development. It is often necessary to have an adhesive which stays in place on a vertical surface, but must flow when adherends are mated.

2.6   Introduction to Linear Viscoelasticity

Many of the materials used as adhesives are polymers or they are monomers which become polymers during the cure or setting of the adhesive. Polymers belong to a class of materials which can be described as *viscoelastic*, i.e., they behave both as a viscous liquid as well as an elastic solid. The strength and performance of adhesives is heavily dependent upon the viscoelastic response of such polymers.

Consider the effect of a sinusoidal stress applied to a Hookean or elastic solid. The sinusoidal stress is described as:

$$\sigma(t) = \sigma_0 \sin(\omega t) \tag{2.6}$$

where $\sigma(t)$ is the time-dependent stress, t is the time and ω the angular frequency in radians per second of the applied stress. A graph of the sinusoidally applied stress is shown in Fig. 2.9.

σ_0 is the amplitude of the stress. Equation (2.6) is placed into Eq. (2.1) to discover the time dependent strain:

$$\frac{\sigma_0}{E} \sin(\omega t) = \varepsilon(t)$$

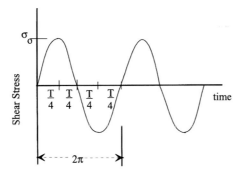

Figure 2.9   Graph showing a sinusoidal shear stress. The period is T (in time) and the amplitude given as σ_0

But

$$\varepsilon_0 = \frac{\sigma_0}{E}$$

so

$$\varepsilon_0 \sin(\omega t) = \varepsilon(t)$$

The amount of energy that is absorbed per cycle of the sinusoidal stress can be calculated by integrating the instantaneous rate of energy absorption over the entire cycle. The instantaneous rate of energy absorption, ξ, is given by the following expression:

$$\xi = \sigma \frac{\delta \varepsilon}{\delta t}$$

The calculation is done in a step-wise fashion to determine the energy absorbed in each portion of the cycle. The initial portion of the curve in Fig. 2.9 is divided into four time periods, $T/4$, where T is the period of the cycle. In angular frequency, a full period is 2π radians. The integrations are carried out as follows:

$$\Delta \Xi = \int_0^{T/4} \xi \, dt = \sigma_0 \varepsilon_0 \omega \int^{\pi/2\omega} \sin(\omega t) \cos(\omega t) \, dt$$

The maximum stored elastic energy in a material subjected to a sinusoidal stress is:

$$\Delta \Xi = \frac{E \varepsilon_0^2}{2}$$

Integration is carried out over all four parts of the cycle. Portions of the cycle which have an upward curvature provide a positive $E\varepsilon_0^2/2$, while portions of the cycle with negative curvature provide $-E\varepsilon_0^2/2$. Over the entire cycle, the total $\Delta \Xi$ is 0. For an elastic material, all of the energy put into the sample is returned upon unloading of the sample

Consider a Newtonian fluid which is modeled by the dashpot shown in Fig. 2.7. The situation changes substantially. The equation for the response of a Newtonian

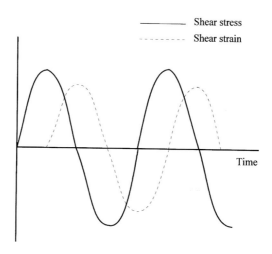

—————— Shear stress

- - - - - - - Shear strain

Time

Figure 2.10   Graph showing the difference between the shear stress and shear strain for a viscous liquid

fluid to stress is shown in Eq. (2.5). If the strain is a sinusoidal function, then we write:

$$\varepsilon(t) = \varepsilon_0 \sin(\omega t)$$

This relationship for the strain allows us to calculate a strain rate which we place into Eq. (2.5). Thus,

$$\frac{\delta \varepsilon}{\delta t} = \varepsilon_0 \omega \cos(\omega t)$$

and

$$\sigma(t) = \eta \varepsilon_0 \omega \cos(\omega t)$$

Figure 2.10 shows a plot of the stress and strain functions for a Newtonian fluid undergoing sinusoidal strain.

Note that the response of the Newtonian fluid is 90° out of phase with the excitation as would be expected for the derivative of a sine function. The calculation for the energy dissipated by the Newtonian fluid over one cycle of the excitation is repeated. This is done in the same fashion as described above for the elastic solid by dividing the period into four parts and integrating ξ over each segment. We find

$$\Delta\Xi = \int_0^{T/4} \sigma \frac{\delta \varepsilon}{\delta t}\, dt = \eta \omega^2 \varepsilon_0^2 \int_0^{\pi/2\omega} \cos^2(\omega t)\, dt$$

Carrying out this integration we find that

$$\Delta\Xi = \left(\frac{\pi}{4}\right) \eta \omega \varepsilon_0^2$$

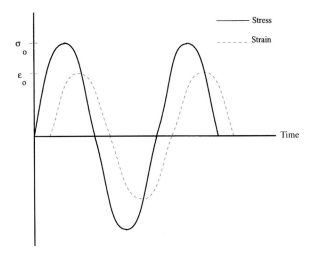

Figure 2.11 Stress and strain response functions for a viscoelastic material. Note that the stress and the strain are out of phase and the phase angle is less than 90°

for 1/4 of the period and for the full period,

$$\Delta\Xi_{tot} = \pi\varepsilon_0^2\eta\omega$$

That is, a Newtonian fluid dissipates energy for each cycle, in contrast to a Hookean material (a spring) which stores energy and returns it during each cycle. The strain in an elastic solid is in phase with the stress while the strain and the stress are 90° out of phase for a viscous liquid.

From the above analysis, it might be surmised that a *viscoelastic* material has a response in which the stress and the stress are out of phase but that the difference is less than 90°. Such a situation is depicted in Fig. 2.11. The following is the function for the strain:

$$\varepsilon = \varepsilon_0 \sin(\omega t)$$

The corresponding stress is out of phase with the strain by the phase angle δ, thus:

$$\sigma = \sigma_0 \sin(\omega t + \delta)$$

Using the trigonometric equality

$$\sin(\alpha + \beta) = \sin(\alpha)\cos(\beta) + \cos(\alpha)\sin(\beta) \tag{2.7}$$

and multiplying through by the identity $\varepsilon_0/\varepsilon_0$, we have the following relationship:

$$\sigma = \frac{\sigma_0}{\varepsilon_0}\cos(\delta)\varepsilon_0 \sin(\omega t) + \frac{\sigma_0}{\varepsilon_0}\sin(\delta)\varepsilon_0 \cos(\omega t)$$

The first term in the above equation contains a sine of the angular frequency. It describes the contribution which is in phase with the strain. The second term in the above equation contains a cosine of the angular frequency and it describes the contribution which is 90° out of phase with the strain. Each term in the above equation also has the term $(\sigma_0/\varepsilon_0)\cos\delta$. From Eq. (2.1), we know that this is just a modulus multiplied by a number. The following moduli:

$$E' = \frac{\sigma_0}{\varepsilon_0}\cos\delta \qquad (2.8)$$

and

$$E'' = \frac{\sigma_0}{\varepsilon_0}\sin\delta \qquad (2.9)$$

can then be defined. The first of these might be termed the "in-phase" modulus while the other may be termed the "out-of-phase" modulus. Note that we have given these moduli the symbol "E" which indicates that the experiment has been done in tension. A similar set of moduli can be defined for an experiment carried out in shear. In that case, the moduli would be given the symbols G' and G''. In this text, we normally use shear moduli when discussing viscoelastic properties.

The energy stored or dissipated during a cycle for either an elastic solid or a Newtonian fluid was derived above. We now do the same for a viscoelastic material:

$$\Delta\Xi_{tot} = \oint \sigma\, d\varepsilon = \oint \sigma \frac{d\varepsilon}{dt}\, dt = \int_0^{\frac{2\pi}{\omega}} \sigma_0\varepsilon_0\omega\sin(\omega t + \delta)\cos(\omega t)\, dt$$

We use the trigonometric substitution shown as Eq. (2.7) and carry out the integration to find:

$$\Delta\Xi_{tot} = \sigma_0\varepsilon_0\pi\sin\delta$$

Multiplying this relationship by the identity, $\varepsilon_0/\varepsilon_0$, and using the definition found in Eq. (2.9), we find that

$$\Delta\Xi_{tot} = \varepsilon_0^2\pi E''$$

This is the total energy lost during a cycle of excitation. This relationship is the basis for why E'' is called the *loss modulus* of the material. E' is related to the in-phase (elastic) response in which energy is *stored* in one portion of the cycle and released in another. E' is the *storage modulus* of the viscoelastic material.

Another important quantity is the ratio of the storage and loss moduli. The tan δ is defined:

$$\tan\delta = \frac{\sin\delta}{\cos\delta}$$

Equations (2.8) and (2.9) state that $\sin\delta = \varepsilon_0 E''/\sigma_0$ and $\cos\delta = \varepsilon_0 E'/\sigma_0$. Making these substitutions,

$$\tan\delta = \frac{E''}{E'}$$

We can also show from the energetic basis for our derivation of E' and E'', that the following is true:

$$\tan\delta = \frac{1}{2\pi}\frac{\Delta\Xi_{tot}}{\Delta\Xi_{stored}}$$

Thus, $\tan \delta$ is the ratio of the total energy lost during a cycle (related to the loss modulus) to the energy stored during $1/4$ of a cycle (related to the storage modulus). In future chapters it will be seen that all of these quantities have significant bearing on the use of polymers relate in adhesives.

The above description of the viscoelastic properties of materials as they are affected by a sinusoidal stress or strain should be very familiar to mechanical and electrical engineers. The description is entirely analogous to the damped oscillator problem in mechanics and the RC circuit in electronics. The phase angles have the same meaning and $\tan \delta$ has a meaning analogous to the "Q" of a circuit.

2.7   An Application of Materials Properties and Mechanics: The Bending of Beams

Adhesive bonds are made of one or more adherends and an adhesive. When an adherend is removed from an adhesive or an adhesive bond is subjected to a force, the adherend often acts as though it is a bending beam. A number of the adhesive test specimens which are discussed in the next chapter have been analyzed as though the adherends are bending beams or as if they are beams on an elastic foundation. It is therefore appropriate to discuss the basic theory of the bending of beams here. Much of the discussion in this section is taken from *The Strength of Materials* by Timoshenko.

The discussion of the bending of beams begins with Newton's Laws of Motion as they are applied to objects in equilibrium. Simply stated, an object which is in equilibrium is static and the sum of the forces acting on that body must add to zero and the sum of the torques (or moments) acting on that body must sum to zero. Mathematically this is stated: $\sum F_{ext} = 0$ and $\sum M_{ext} = 0$, where F_{ext} are the vector forces acting on the body externally and M_{ext} are the torques or moments acting on the body externally. Each of these equations, since they are vectors, can be written as a series of equations for any coordinate system. For example, for the external forces we can write: $\sum F_x = 0$, $\sum F_y = 0$ and $\sum F_z = 0$ for a Cartesian coordinate system. A similar set of equations can be written for the moments.

To understand the application of these equations to the theory of the bending of beams, we examine the simply supported beam shown in Fig. 2.12. The F_i are acting in a plane and the F_{R_i} are the reaction forces. In the investigation of the statics of this beam, we divide the beam into two parts at the line a–b. Consider the action of the left side of the beam on the right side of the beam, divided at a–b. The study of statics has shown that any system of parallel forces can be replaced by a force and a torque. So, we write for the right hand side of the beam that

$$V = F_{R_1} - F_1 - F_2$$

and

$$M = F_{R_1}x - F_1(x - p) - F_2(x - q)$$

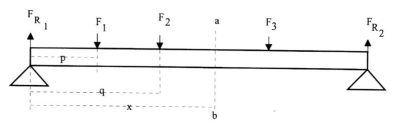

Figure 2.12   A simply supported beam acted upon by three forces. An imaginary plane is drawn through the beam at a–b

The force V acts on the a–b line. For the beam to be stable, the forces in the right hand side of the beam must balance V and M. Imagine an infinitesimal element in the region of a–b. The forces and moments act in the manner shown in Fig. 2.13.

Figure 2.2 shows a situation in which the forces are very similar to those shown for the element in Fig. 2.13. That is, a shearing force is being exerted across the element. In the absence of any external forces on this element, the magnitude of the shearing force on the left hand side of the element must be counterbalanced by the shearing force on the right hand side of the element. However, the magnitude of the moment on both sides cannot be the same since the force is now being exerted over a distance that is longer by dx. The increase in the moment M must be equal to the force exerted on the element multiplied by the lever arm length, thus $dM = V\,dx$ which can be rearranged to say

$$\frac{dM}{dx} = V \qquad\qquad (2.10)$$

Simply stated, the rate of change of the moment along the beam is equal to the shear force.

Suppose a distributed force is placed all along the beam such that the force f is applied uniformly per unit length dx. Figure 2.12 would have to be changed to show that force. The shearing force must increase from the left hand side of the element to

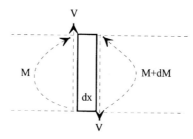

Figure 2.13   The infinitesimal section of the beam dx in the region of the line a–b. The forces on one side of the beam must be counterbalanced by the forces on the other side of the beam. However, because of the distance dx, the moment changes by dM

the right hand side of the element by an amount f. Therefore, we write $\mathrm{d}V = -f\,\mathrm{d}x$ which can be rearranged to give

$$\frac{\mathrm{d}V}{\mathrm{d}x} = -f \tag{2.11}$$

This equation says that in the case of a force distributed uniformly along a beam, the rate of change of the shearing force with distance is equal to the magnitude of the force per unit length. Equations (2.10) and (2.11) form much of the basis for the theory of the bending of beams.

Two topics remain for our consideration in this chapter: the definition of the moment of inertia of a beam and the equations for the deflection of a beam. These equations play a central role in the discussions concerning the bending of adherends in adhesive bonds. Two examples are discussed in the next chapter.

Examine Fig. 2.14. A beam that is not subjected to any forces is not deflected. Draw imaginary lines down the length of the beam. Draw lines perpendicular to the length of the beam. Apply forces to the beam, whether they be distributed forces or point forces. The beam assumes a shape where the imaginary lines described above change in shape or orientation. As shown in Fig. 2.14, the imaginary lines drawn perpendicular to the beam length turn in towards the side to which the force is applied. The imaginary lines drawn parallel to the length of the beam stay parallel to the sides of the beam for small increments down the length of the beam. However, the lines assume the same radius of curvature that the beam assumes under the applied force. The length of the parallel lines changes. At the center of the beam is a line which does not change in length. This is called the *neutral axis*. Above the neutral axis, the lines shorten in length (they are in compression) while below the neutral

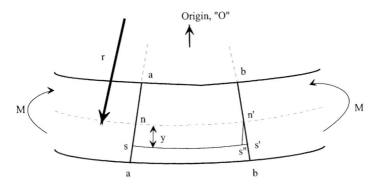

Figure 2.14   Diagram of a uniform rectangular beam in a pure bending situation. The beam has been subjected to a force or a system of forces which gives rise to the moment, M. The lines a–a and b–b were, before the application of the force, both perpendicular to the axis of the beam as well as parallel to each other. After the force was applied, the lines remain perpendicular to the neutral axis of the beam but are now no longer parallel to each other. On the upper side of the beam, the material is in compression while the lower side of the beam is in tension. The neutral axis n–n' suffers no change in length s–s' denotes a line of material in the lower half of the beam which is in tension and has elongated. Remote from the beam is the origin, "O," and the bent beam has a radius of curvature r. (Redrawn from Timoshenko with permission of Wadsworth Publishing Co.)

axis, the lines become longer (they are in tension). Even though Fig. 2.14 is idealized, this same situation is found in any beam problem. We can now analyze the state of strain in the beam using the mechanical properties discussed earlier in this chapter.

Geometry is used to determine the state of strain of the imaginary lines below the neutral axis (those in tension). This will be hard to visualize because the origin is distant from the imaginary lines with which we are dealing. Draw a line $n'-s''$, which is parallel to the line $a-a$. Taking the angle $\angle nOn'$, we find that the angle is similar to the angle $\angle s''n's'$, therefore:

$$\epsilon = \frac{s's''}{nn'} = \frac{y}{r}$$

where $s's''$ and nn' denote the line segments shown in Fig. 2.14, y is the distance from the neutral axis of the imaginary line in question, and r is the radius of curvature of the deflection of the beam. Assuming that the material used to form the beam follows Hooke's law (Eq. (2.1)), we write that the stresses along the length of the beam below the neutral axis are:

$$\sigma = E\frac{y}{r}$$

For any plane drawn through the beam, there will be a moment formed around the neutral axis. Figure 2.15 shows a diagram of the situation. With respect to the neutral axis, the value of that moment must be zero since the beam is in equilibrium. Thus, the force on the infinitesimal area dA is $(Ey/r)\,dA$ and the total moment over that cross section of the beam in the x direction must be:

$$\int \frac{Ey}{r}\,dA = \frac{E}{r}\int y\,dA = 0$$

The moment of the force acting on the area dA in the y direction, with respect to the neutral axis is $(Ey/r)y\,dA$ since the lever arm for the moment is the distance y from the neutral axis. The sum of these forces must be such to counterbalance the applied forces or the external moment. Therefore:

$$\int \frac{E}{r}y^2\,dA = \frac{E}{r}\int y^2\,dA = M = \frac{EI_z}{r} \tag{2.12}$$

where I_z is the integral of y^2 over all of the infinitesimal areas and it is known as the *moment of inertia* of the beam. The product EI_z is known as the *flexural rigidity* of the beam.

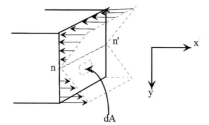

Figure 2.15 Diagram showing the stresses around neutral axis nn'. The infinitesimal area dA is a distance y from the neutral axis. (Redrawn from Timoshenko with permission of Wadsworth Publishing Co.)

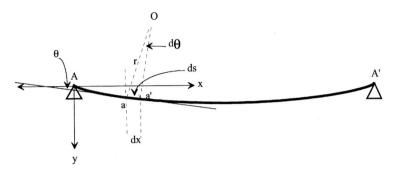

Figure 2.16   Diagram used in the derivation of the equations for the deflection of a beam. The beam A–A' is in pure bending. We geometrically examine the small length along the line segment a–a' with respect to the x and y axes which are defined in the diagram. (Redrawn from Timoshenko with permission of Wadsworth Publishing Co.)

The remaining task in this chapter is to describe the equations for the deflection of a beam under load. Some of that has been done in the paragraph above but now we analyze the beam more globally. Figure 2.16 provides a diagram of the situation.

In order to determine the deflection curve for this beam, we must first assume that the bending depends only upon the magnitude of the external bending moment M at the point of analysis. Use Eq. (2.12), i.e., $1/r = M/EI_z$. The curvature is examined geometrically. A small segment of the beam, a–a', is picked. A tangent is drawn from the segment a–a' back to the x axis. The tangent forms an angle θ with the x axis. Lines are drawn perpendicular to the points a and a'. At some point they intersect at O forming the angle $d\theta$. This defines the length of the radius of curvature, r. The length of the line segment is given as ds and we have $ds = r\,d\theta$ or $d\theta/ds = 1/r$. If the deflection of the beam is small (as it is for many adherends in actual adhesive bonds), then ds is similar to dx. θ is similar to $\tan\theta$ and $\tan\theta$ is similar to dy/dx, which is just the instantaneous slope of the deflection curve. These approximate values are placed into the above equations, thus

$$\frac{1}{r} = -\frac{d\theta}{ds} \Rightarrow \frac{1}{r} \approx -\frac{d}{ds}\frac{dy}{dx} = -\frac{d}{dx}\frac{dy}{dx} = -\frac{d^2 y}{dx^2}$$

The negative sign arises from the fact that the deflection is downward concave. Substitute Eq. (2.12) into the above equation and find:

$$EI_z\frac{d^2 y}{dx^2} = -M \qquad (2.13)$$

This differential equation can be integrated to find the deflection curve of a beam that is acted upon by an external moment, M. This equation can be further modified if we remember Eq. (2.10). Taking the derivative with respect to x of each side of Eq. (2.13), and substituting Eq. (2.10), we find that

$$EI_z\frac{d^3 y}{dx^3} = -V \qquad (2.14)$$

Finally, we can take another derivative of this Eq. (2.14) with respect to x and remembering Eq. (2.11), we find

$$EI_z \frac{\mathrm{d}^4 y}{\mathrm{d}x^4} = f \tag{2.15}$$

where f is the force per unit area in a situation of a uniformly distributed load on the beam.

In the next chapter, we see how Goland and Reissner as well as Kaelble and Dahlquist used these basic equations to analyze the mechanics of two types of adhesive bonds.

2.8   Summary

In this chapter, we have defined and examined many of the materials properties which are used as a basis for discussion in future chapters. In particular we defined important quantities such as the Young's and shear moduli, the Poisson's ratio, the strain energy and the critical strain energy release rate. The properties of liquids were also examined and the viscosity was defined. Descriptions were given of characteristics of liquids under varying shear rates. Important viscoelastic parameters were defined such as the storage and loss moduli. Finally, the bending of beams was analyzed according to the description given by Timoshenko. Inherent in the beam analysis was the use of the elongation, tensile modulus and shear and tensile Hooke's law properties which were described early in the chapter.

Bibliography

Barnes, H.A., Hutton, J.F. and Walters, K. *An Introduction into Rheology* (1989) Elsevier, Amsterdam

Ferry, J.D., *The Viscoelastic Properties of Polymers* (1980) John Wiley, New York

Hearle, J.W.S. *Polymers and their Properties*, Vol. 1 (1982) Ellis Horwood, Chichester, UK

Kinloch, A.J. and Young, R.J., *Fracture Behavior of Polymers* (1983) Elsevier, New York

Nielsen, L.E., *Mechanical Properties of Polymers* (1962) Reinhold Publishing Corp, Chapman and Hall, New York

Ruoff, A.L., *Materials Science* (1973) Prentice-Hall, Englewood Cliffs, NJ

Timoshenko, S., *The Strength of Materials*, Part I, Chapters 1–5 (1955) D. Van Nostrand, Princeton, NJ

3 Mechanical Tests of Adhesive Bond Performance

3.1 Introduction

The previous chapter gave us the basis for developing and understanding methods for testing the physical properties of adhesives and adhesive bonds. The primary ways of testing a material are tension, shear and cleavage. In this chapter, we discuss various specimens described in the literature on adhesive bond testing. The chapter is divided into sections dealing with each type of mechanical test. In each section, a general description of the test type is given along with suggestions for proper methodology for the test. With two test methods, the analysis of the bending of beams is used to examine the stress state in the adhesive as well as the adherend. The analysis shows that certain types of loading of adhesive bonds are to be avoided, if at all possible. It should be cautioned that this book is not a designer's guide. We hope to provide a useful discussion as to how adhesive bond specimens may be prepared and what fundamental information about the performance of adhesives can be gained. Considerable text is devoted to examination of adhesive bond tests described in the literature of the American Society for Testing and Materials (ASTM) [1]. The tests described in this chapter are used for structural adhesives, rubber based adhesives, wood construction adhesives, hot melt adhesives, and other types. There are, however, a series of tests particularly important for pressure sensitive adhesives which are described in Chapter 9.

There are several objectives for this chapter:

- to develop an appreciation for the three main types of adhesive bond tests
- to become familiar with what can and cannot be learned from each of the tests
- to develop an appreciation for the use of beam theory in understanding the stress state in adhesives bonds
- to gain practical knowledge about useful bond preparation procedures for a number of specimens.

3.2 Failure Modes and the Definition of Practical Adhesion

During the discussion in this book, we use the term "*mode of failure*." By this we mean the locus in the adhesive bond through which the failure propagates. If we can visually see adhesive on both sides of the specimen, we use the term *"failure in cohesion."* If we visually inspect the adhesive bond and find what appears to be adhesive on one adherend and adherend surface on the other adherend, we describe the failure as *"apparent failure in adhesion."* Note that the word "apparent" is used. Failures which are visually in adhesion may not necessarily be failures in adhesion. A thin cohesive failure near the adherend surface could have occurred. Such a failure can be detected by modern surface analysis techniques or proper application of older techniques such as staining or contact angle measurements. Sophisticated users of adhesives not only specify the strength of an adhesive used in a certain bonding situation but also specify the mode of failure which is observed when that bond is tested. Failure in cohesion is the preferred mode of failure because this type of failure provides assurance to the adhesive user that the adhesive has indeed "stuck." Therefore, the strength of the bond was limited by the physical properties of the adhesive and not adhesion.

The actual measured strength of an adhesive bond is termed *practical adhesion*. This term was coined by Mittal [2] who rightly emphasized that *practical adhesion* must be differentiated from the term *adhesion* defined in Section 1.2. Practical adhesion must depend upon adhesion. If there were no adhesion between the adhesive and the adherend, stress could not be transmitted from the adherend into the adhesive and so on. Practical adhesion (stress necessary to break an adhesive bond) is primarily dependent upon the physical properties of the adhesive and the adherend.

3.3   Tensile Testing of Adhesive Bonds

A tensile test of an adhesive bond puts the adhesive is a state of stress similar to Fig. 2.1. A listing of adhesive bond tensile test methods is given in Table 3.1. The table includes a number of "miscellaneous" test methods which are in some ways associated with tensile forces. For example, the "probe tack" test used for pressure-sensitive adhesives is listed here.

A typical specimen for evaluating the tensile properties of an adhesive is shown in Fig. 3.1. This specimen is similar to that used in ASTM Test Method D2095. Metal rods are generated to exacting specifications (described in ASTM Standard Practice D2094) and they are cleaned according to one of the methods described in Chapter 7 of this book. The metal rod ends must be polished so that the surfaces contain no burrs which could cross the adhesive gap and must be machined so that the surfaces can be parallel during assembly. Any cocking of the surfaces with respect to one another could force the test to be one of cleavage rather than tension. The metal rods are butted up to an adhesive which joins them, hence the term "butt tensile" test. After the adhesive cures or sets, the specimen is loaded in tension as depicted in Fig. 3.1. The specimen is loaded to failure. The tensile stress at break as well as the mode of failure is reported.

Table 3.1   A Selected Listing of ASTM Test Methods for Tensile and Miscellaneous Properties of Adhesive Bonds or Adhesives

Test number	Title of test	Short description of test
D897	Test method for tensile properties of adhesive bonds	Tensile loading to ultimate strength of button-like specimens of wood or metal
D950	Test method for impact strength of adhesive bonds	Determination of the level of pendulum impact force necessary to break a shear specimen
D1184	Test method for flexural strength of adhesive bonded laminated assemblies	Use of a three-point bend test to determine the level of force necessary to delaminate a laminate
D2095	Test method for tensile strength of adhesives by means of bar and rod specimens	Bars or rods are glued together at their ends and tested to ultimates strength in a tensile mode
D2556	Test method for the apparent viscosity of adhesives having shear-rate-dependent flow properties	Standard for the use of a Brookfield viscometer for adhesives having non-Newtonian character
D2979	Test method for determining tack of adhesives using an inverted probe machine	A special probe is brought into controlled light contact with an adhesive surface and the force to remove the probe is measured
D3121	Test method for tack of pressure sensitive adhesives by rolling ball	A steel ball is rolled down an incline and tack is measured by the distance the ball can move after it contacts an adhesive
D3808	Practice for qualitative determination of adhesion of adhesives to substrates by spot adhesion test method	A "spot" of adhesive is applied to a surface, allowed to set and an attempt is made to pry the spot from the surface. Very qualitative
D4688	Test method for evaluating structural adhesives for fingerjoining lumber	Fingerjointed wood (typically used in furniture manufacture) is tensile tested for ultimate strength

The major failing of this type of test is that even though an average stress at failure is reported, the actual stress distribution in the adhesive bond is not uniform throughout the adhesive. The stress distribution could be akin to that shown in Fig. 3.2. The adhesive at the edges of the butt tensile specimen is at a higher tensile stress than the adhesive in the center of the specimen. The average stress at failure is more likely due to these edge effects rather than the actual tensile strength of the adhesive. Butt tensile tests are not often used to evaluate adhesives because this mode of loading is not one that is normally used in adhesively bonded structures. The test has been used to good advantage in several fundamental studies, two of which we examine in Chapter 6.

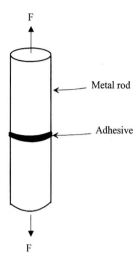

Figure 3.1   Diagram of a "butt tensile" specimen. Metal rods are used for the adherends. The surfaces of the metal rods must be smooth and parallel when the bond is made

A test method similar to D2095 is described in ASTM D897 in which studs are glued together and are pulled apart in a tensile fashion.

The stud pull-off test [3] is an interesting variation on the tensile test. In this test, a metal stud is adhered to a surface by means of a structural adhesive. The stud is machined in such a fashion that an actuator can be attached to the back of the stud so that a tensile force can be applied between the stud and the sample surface. This test could be used to determine a practical adhesion value to a particular surface. In addition, the test method can be modified such that the stud is bonded to a coated surface. If the adhesion between the adhesive used to bond the stud and the coating is good, then the test method can be used to obtain a figure of merit for the adhesion of the coating to the surface.

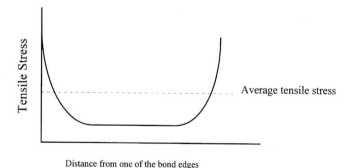

Figure 3.2   Stress state in a butt tensile specimen. The average tensile stress in the bond is not indicative of the actual state of stress in the bond since the adhesive at the edges of the specimen is at a higher state of stress than the adhesive in the interior

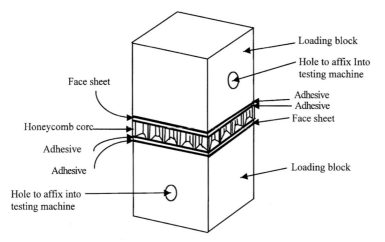

Figure 3.3 Diagram showing the construction of a flatwise tension specimen. The honeycomb core-face sheet sandwich is generated and it is post-bonded to the tensile testing blocks. Pins to affix the specimen in the tensile testing machine are placed through the holes shown in the diagram. The specimen is tested to failure

Another type of tensile test for adhesive bonds is the *flatwise tensile* test of bonded honeycomb core. Honeycomb core and structures made from it are a unique application of adhesives, generating a stiff but lightweight structure. It is important to know how well an adhesive can bond to the face sheet as well as to the honeycomb core. The flatwise tensile test, shown in Fig. 3.3, is used to determine the ability of *film adhesives* to wet the core and adhere to the facesheet. Film adhesives come in the form of self-supporting films. They are described in Chapter 8. To generate the flatwise tensile specimen, large blocks (usually made from aluminum) are cleaned by methods similar to those described in Chapter 7 as are the face sheets. The honeycomb core may be vapor-degreased, but may also be used as received from the manufacturer. Film adhesive is applied between the core and the face sheet as well as between the face sheet and the metal block. The entire assembly is cured under conditions which mimic those used to make honeycomb core sandwich panels. Sometimes the honeycomb core-face sheet sandwich is generated, cut to size and then post-bonded to make the specimen as shown in Fig. 3.3. After the assembly is generated, pins are placed through the holes in the aluminum blocks and fixtured in a tensile testing machine. The testing machine thus places a "flatwise" load on the core. When generating a honeycomb core containing adhesive bonds, the objective is to obtain good wetting of the core by the adhesive. This forces the failure to occur by the core ripping rather than extraction of the core from the adhesive. In general, those adhesives with appropriate flow and the ability to climb the walls of the core provide flatwise tensile bonds which fail the core. This test is used in aerospace and allied industries.

3.4   Shear Loading of Adhesive Bonds

In general, adhesives display their highest strength when loaded in shear. We have already described the loading conditions which place a material in shear in Chapter 2. If we look at Fig. 2.2, we can imagine adherends attached to each of the faces of the block and we can imagine the block in Fig. 2.2 to be the adhesive. The force is therefore applied to the adhesive through the adherends. There are many types of adhesive bond tests which place the adhesive in a state of shear such as those listed in Table 3.2. Indeed, most adhesive bonds used in actual structures are designed so that the adhesive is primarily in a state of shear. The reasons for this design choice become apparent as we begin to quote values of shear strength versus cleavage or peel strength for various adhesive types. Therefore, an understanding of shear loading is important. Much of this chapter is concerned with this type of adhesive bond.

Table 3.2   ASTM Test Methods Pertaining to Determination of the Shear Properties of Adhesive Bonds

Test number	Title of test	Short description of test
D905	Test method for strength properties of adhesive bonds in shear by compression loading	2″ × 4″ lumber is bonded and then tested by shearing the pieces in compression (the force is opposite to the sense shown in Fig. 3.4)
D1002	Test method for strength properties of adhesives in shear by tension loading	Most used test method for evaluating adhesives, shown in Fig. 3.4
D1780	Practice for conducting creep tests of metal-to-metal adhesives	D1002 shear specimens are subjected to a constant load and the movement of the adherends with respect to one another is determined
D2293	Test method for creep properties of adhesives in shear by compression loading (metal-to-metal)	A test similar to D1780 except that the constant load is in compression and is applied by a spring loaded device
D2294	Test method for creep properties of adhesives in shear by tension loading (metal-to-metal)	A test similar to D1780 except that the constant tensile load is applied by a spring-loaded device
D2295	Test method for strength of adhesives in shear by tension loading at elevated temperatures	A test similar to D1002 except that provisions are made for very high temperatures.

Table 3.2   Continued

Test number	Title of test	Short description of test
D2339	Test method for strength properties of adhesives in two-ply wood construction in shear by tension loading	A no-fillet test of plywood laminate shear strength. The plywood is made into a shear specimen by milling slots into the plywood
D2557	Test method for strength properties of adhesives in shear by tension loading in the temperature range of -267.8 to $-55°C$	A test similar to D1002 except that provision is made for very low temperatures
D3163	Test method for determining the strength of adhesively bonded rigid plastic lap shear joints in shear by tension loading	A test similar to D1002 except that provisions are made for the adherends to be rigid plastics
D3164	Test method for determining the strength of adhesively bonded plastic lap-shear sandwich joints in shear by tension loading	A special test similar to D1002 except that a plastic is "sandwiched" between adhesive layers which are bonded to metal adherends. This test measures the adhesion of the adhesive to the plastic
D3528	Test method for strength properties of double lap shear adhesive joints by tension loading	A lap shear test which attempts to correct for the non-linearity of the loading path for D1002 specimens by having two adherends instead of one on one end of the bond
D3983	Test method for measuring strength and shear modulus of nonrigid adhesives by the thick adherend tensile lap shear specimen	Instrumented thick adherend lap shear test in which stress-strain curves for the adhesive are generated
D4027	Test method for measuring shear properties of structural adhesives by the modified rail test	A complicated test for measuring the resistance of a wood/wood adhesive to combined tensile and shear loads or combined compression and shear loading
D4501	Test method for shear strength of adhesive bonds between rigid substrates by the block shear method	A small block is bonded to a large block. The specimen is fixtured to shear away the small block from the large block
D 4562	Test method for shear strength of adhesives using pin and collar specimen	A pin is bonded into a collar and the collar is sheared from the pin
D4896	Guide for use of adhesive bonded single lap joint results	A description of the "do's and don'ts" with respect to D1002 lap shear data.

3.4.1   The Standard Lap Shear Specimen

The standard test method for evaluating the shear strength of adhesive bonds is described in ASTM D1002. This test method is one of the most common, maligned and studied test methods for the evaluation of adhesive bonds. The specimen used in ASTM D1002 is shown in Fig. 3.4. The adherends are cleaned by an appropriate surface preparation method (see Chapter 7). The adhesive is applied to the region to be lapped. Paste adhesives (defined in Chapter 8), are usually applied to both adherends before mating. Film adhesives (defined in Chapter 8), are applied to only one of the adherends. In general, the adhesive is applied only in the region to be lapped. The lap length is 1/2 inch and the bond width is one inch. The thickness of the applied adhesive is determined by its intended use.

The bond is fixtured in some fashion. Fixturing can be as simple as the application of clips to the edges of the bond or as complicated as the vacuum bagging procedures used in the aerospace industry. The purpose of the fixturing device is to apply pressure to the adhesive bondline and to keep the adherends in place as the adhesive cures. Note that the adhesive is expected to flow out of the bonded area to form a "fillet" of adhesive extending beyond the range of the adherends. There are variations of this test specimen where the fillet is purposefully eliminated to evaluate the adhesive bond performance in its absence. Adams [4] has shown that the fillet can have a substantial effect on the measured strength of a lap shear specimen. The fillet nominally increases the length of the lap and minimizes the discontinuity of the properties at the end of the adherend.

The adhesive is cured or allowed to set. After cure, one possible test is to place the sample in a tensile testing machine and load the sample to failure. The direction of application of the load is shown in Fig. 3.4. Many lap shear specifications specify how much of the adherend should be clamped in the jaws of the tensile testing machine. It is certainly reasonable to believe that the bending of the specimen (and hence the real stress applied to the adhesive) is dependent upon the distance from the loading point to the lap region. The lap shear bond may also be placed in an adverse environment (such as exposure to elevated temperatures, solvents, or high humidity) before testing to failure. Specimens like that shown in

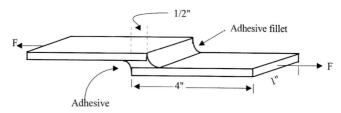

Figure 3.4   Diagram of the ASTM D1002 lap shear specimen. The adherends can be made from any material but the test is primarily used for rigid substrates such as metal, wood, and engineering plastics. The lap length and the specimen dimensions are those prescribed in ASTM D1002, but for special situations, could be any reasonable size that is agreed upon by the vendor and the buyer

Fig. 3.4 can also be used to determine fatigue life of adhesive bonds. The specimen is installed in a machine which applies a cyclic load and the number of cycles to failure is determined. With most modern structural adhesives, high frequency cyclic loading seldom leads to bond failure. However, low frequency cyclic loading, especially under adverse environmental conditions, can often show fatigue failure at loads lower than expected from the ultimate strength measured in a tensile testing machine.

Depending upon the type of adhesive, care must be taken to carefully monitor the conditions to which the adhesive bond is exposed before ultimate strength is determined. The reason for this concern is that the adhesive may exhibit post-cure or annealing as a result of such exposure. Such pre-test exposure could lead to anomolously high strengths not indicative of actual use conditions. This is discussed further in Chapter 8 when the chemistry of room temperature curing adhesives are described.

The lap shear specimen can be prepared in a number of ways including the single specimen ("finger specimen") and multiple specimen methods. In the single specimen method, the bonds are prepared individually as shown in Fig. 3.4. The bonds can then be tested. However, there are several potential pitfalls with the use of the single specimen method. First, care must be taken to keep the adherends aligned during cure, otherwise an extra torque on the bond could occur during test. Second, care must be taken that "flash" does not form on the sides of the bond. The adhesive "flash" would seal the bond in a manner not intended by the test. Third, it is important that the mating ends of the adherends be square and free of burrs. Burrs could dam up the adhesive and a lack of squareness would further complicate the already complicated stress field in this specimen.

In the multiple specimen method, large pieces of adherend are mated at one edge. Typically, adherends measuring $4'' \times 7''$ are bonded along their long edge. Once the adhesive is fixtured and cured, the large bonds can be cut or sawn into narrower strips, resulting in specimens like that shown in Fig. 3.4. One advantage of this method over the finger specimen method is that problems with adhesive flash are eliminated. There are also fewer chances that the adherends are cocked with respect to one another. However, the concerns about burrs and squareness of the adherend edge nearest the bond still remain. One other advantage of the multiple specimen method is that the lap shear strength is more reproducible than when the finger specimen method is used.

The ASTM D1002 lap shear test, when applied logically and realistically, can be used as a reasonable and easy comparison of the strength of adhesives. It can also be used as a quality control method when testing for consistency of adhesive bond strength. However, there are a number of reasons this test specimen is much maligned. The primary criticism is that D1002 does not accurately represent the actual way adhesive bonds are designed. Lap lengths and lap areas in engineering adhesive joints are far larger than those used in ASTM D1002. Another major criticism is that the shear state in this small specimen is not uniform. The non-uniformity of stress state forms the basis for numerous studies and has some interesting consequences in the formulation of adhesives (see Chapter 8).

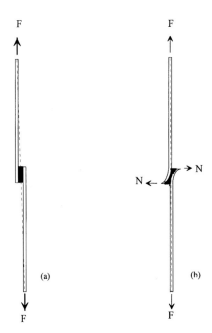

Figure 3.5 (a) The diagram shows a lap shear specimen at low levels of applied force, *F*. The dotted line
shows the line of force which the applied load wishes to
take. (b) The diagram shows the lap shear specimen
after a substantial load has been applied. The applied
force has attempted to be linear through the specimen.
The specimen attempts to comply with the necessity for
linearization of the line of force by bending at the lap
ends of the specimen

Figure 3.5(a) shows a D1002 shear specimen as force is applied. The line through
the specimen shows the direction of the loading force. It is easy to see that the
loading line (the dotted line) cannot possibly follow the adherends. Rather, the bond
must act as a hinge in the region of the lap. The center of the lap is the point
through which the force acts and it does not move during the test. However, the
ends of the lap region must move in order to "linearize" the stress (see Fig. 3.5(b)).
Note that the adherends have deflected at the ends of the lap. For the adherends to
deflect in such a manner, the adhesive cannot be in a state of pure shear. Rather,
there is a tensile (normal) force in the adhesive at the ends of the lap. The normal
load is shown as an "N" in Fig. 3.5. A simple mechanical experiment can demonstrate this effect. Visualize two stiff hinges joined with a nut and bolt. If the
combined hinges are pulled firmly at the unjoined ends, the ends of the joined parts
deflect in order to linearize the load.

The combination of shear load and normal loading of the adhesive forms the
basis for the major criticism of the D1002 lap shear specimen. This criticism, as
stated before, is somewhat unfounded if care is taken not to use the specimen as the
basis for the design of adhesive bonds. The state of stress in this specimen can be
quite useful because it places the adhesive in shear and in cleavage loading at the
same time. In fact, we can state that adhesives which do not have good resistance to
cleavage forces, as well as shear strength, will not exhibit high D1002 lap shear
strengths. Despite the stress state of the adhesive in this specimen and despite its
lack of realism, the D1002 lap shear specimen has been used to evaluate essentially

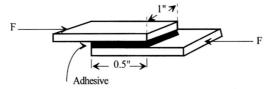

Figure 3.6   Compression lap shear specimen. Short adherends are used to minimize bending under the application of the compressive load

every adhesive. Because of its simplicity, this specimen will likely continue to be a used extensively in the evaluation of adhesives.

3.4.2   Variations on the Lap Shear Specimen

A specimen similar to the D1002 lap shear test can be used in compression rather than tension loading. The test method which describes this is ASTM D905, as applied to wood adherends. The loading state is theoretically the same as the D1002 specimen. However, practically, for the specimen to work, the adherends must be much shorter to minimize bending away from the lap. If metal adherends are used, the adherend length is usually slightly longer than the lap length itself. The compact size of this specimen makes it useful in those situations in which materials or facilities are limited. Figure 3.6 shows a compression lap shear specimen.

Krieger [6] and Hart-Smith [7] realized the limitations of the D1002 shear specimen. They also realized the importance of knowing the stress-strain properties of an adhesive in shear. ASTM D3983 describes a test similar to the test developed by Krieger and Hart-Smith, but for wood adherends. The specification for metal-to-metal bonds developed by Krieger and Hart-Smith is still under review in the ASTM as of this writing. The test specimen is shown in Fig. 3.7.

The test specimen in Fig. 3.7 is similar to the D1002 specimen with three very important exceptions. First, the adherends are much thicker. For aircraft aluminum,

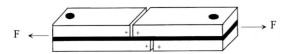

Figure 3.7   Thick adherend lap shear specimen. Adherends are thick enough so that bending at the ends of the lap is essentially eliminated. The force is applied by placing pins through the holes in the ends of the adherends. In tests used to determine the shear stress–strain properties of an adhesive, the specimen is fitted with an extensometer at the points indicated by crosses in the diagram. Thus, as the force is applied, the adherends move with respect to one another, and the adhesive is sheared. The assumption is that the compliance of the adhesive is much less than that of the adherends, so that all movement in the adherends causes equal movement in the adhesive

the adherends are 1/2 to 1″ thick. The increased thickness of the specimen is meant to eliminate any normal loads on the adhesive by not allowing the adherends to deflect. The specimen width is 1″ and the lap length is 1/2″. Second, fillets are eliminated which causes the adhesive to carry the load only in the bonded area and not outside it. Third, the specimen is instrumented to measure the deflection of the bondline. Instruments known as *extensometers* are mounted in positions shown approximately by the crosses in Fig. 3.7. The load is applied by a tensile testing machine and the deflection of the adherends is measured by the extensometers. A plot of shear stress (load divided by the lap area) versus the shear strain (determined by the adherend deflection) is measured. From this plot, the shear modulus of the adhesive, the shear yield stress, and the shear strain energy density can be determined. The shear strain energy density plays an important role in the bond design criteria devised by Hart-Smith [7]. This specimen and test are different from the D1002 also in that the data obtained are useful in bond design. Many adhesive manufacturers are now providing such data for their structural adhesives.

There are several other variations on lap shear specimens and lap shear tests. The primary variations attempt to linearize the loading path, increase the bonded area, or measure creep properties. Lap shear specimens which attempt to linearize the load are described in test methods such are ASTM D3528. Both of the bonds shown in Fig. 3.8 provide a more linear load path.The specimens in Fig. 3.8 form the basis for many adhesive bond designs. The problem with these specimens is that they are substantially more difficult to make than D1002 and thus are less useful as an adhesive product design or adhesive quality control tool. However, they are useful in actual engineering structures.

Generating specimens with increasing lap area is an instructive exercise. Several users of adhesive bonded structures have specifications which require lap shear strengths as a function of lap length with constant lap width. Figure 3.9 shows lap shear performance as a function of L/t for an epoxy structural adhesive on aircraft aluminum alloy. L is the lap length and t is the thickness of the adherend. Since the bond width is kept constant (usually 1″), the bonded area is increasing with increasing L/t. Note that the apparent shear strength seems to decrease as a function of increasing lap area. We would expect that as the lap area increased, the shear strength should remain the same, since we divide the force to break by the lap area. The apparent decrease comes primarily from the effect discussed above. It is also interesting to note that the lowest lap shear strength in the graph is that attained

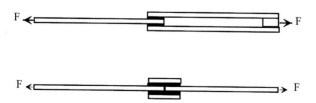

Figure 3.8   Two lap shear specimens which attempt to linearize the load path through the bond

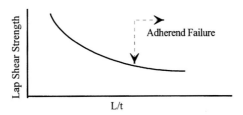

Figure 3.9   Plot of apparent lap shear versus L/t where L is the lap length and t is the adherend thickness. If the bond width is held constant, this is a plot of lap shear versus lap area. Note that after a certain lap area is achieved, the failure mode is in the adherend

with the highest lap area. It is also attained with failure in the adherend rather than the adhesive. The lap area at which the metal fails, rather than the adhesive, would normally be considered to be a design parameter. Structures using an L/t ratio providing adherend failure could be designed to withstand loads that are some factor lower than the breaking strength of this bond and the tensile strength of the adherend.

3.4.3   Specimen for Determining the True Shear Properties of an Adhesive

A truer state of shear is exhibited by the thick adherend lap shear specimen compared to the ASTM D1002 specimen. However, the adhesive is still not in a true state of shear even with the modified specimen since normal loading is minimized but not eliminated. To exhibit a true state of shear, the adhesive has to be fabricated into a special torsion specimen. The reason the torsion specimen provides a true state of shear is shown in Fig. 3.10. A cylinder in the non-torqued state is shown in Fig. 3.10(a). On the side of the cylinder is drawn an imaginary element of rectangular shape. If we twist the top and the bottom of the cylinder with respect to one another, this imaginary shape assumes the shape shown in Fig. 3.10(b).

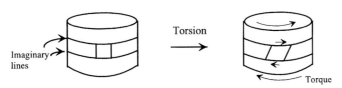

Figure 3.10   A cylindrically shaped body. The lines shown are imaginary or can be drawn on the body for the analysis. If the faces of the cylinder are torqued with respect to one another, the imaginary lines change to form the shape shown on the right. The change in shape is expected from a shear force applied to a rectangular element in the body

Compare the change in shape between these two figures and the change in shape in Fig. 2.2. The cylindrical specimen shown in Fig. 3.10(b) is in a state of pure shear. The ASTM tests do not provide for such a shear specimen, but one can be found in Benson [8]. In the Benson description, two cups are bonded together, lip to lip, so as to create a uniform bondline around the cups. The bonded cups are then placed in a torque machine designed to keep the cup faces parallel. Torque is applied to the bottom of one of the cups while the other is kept stationary. Instrumentation can be applied to the specimen or the cups are marked to show deflection with respect to one another. G, the true shear modulus of the adhesive can be measured. This test has interesting ramifications for the determination of the Poisson's ratio. Since E can be determined easily by tensile measurements of monolithic adhesives and G can be measured by this torsion method, one can easily calculate ν by Eq. (2.3). The determination of the Poisson's ratio by this method is probably easier than trying to test a material so that both lateral contraction as well as tensile elongation are determined simultaneously.

3.4.4   The Goland–Reissner Analysis of the Lap Shear Specimen

Some of the elements of beam theory were described in Section 2.7. Now, we shall see how these elements are used to describe the bending of the adherends in a lap shear specimen. The importance of this analysis lies in the description of the state of stress in the adhesive. The analysis begins with Eq. (2.10) through (2.15). The analysis for the lap shear specimen is somewhat different from the bending of beams analysis. It is actually an analysis of the bending of thin, cylindrically bent plates. However, the basic equations and their derivations are analogous to those discussed in the previous chapter.

The adhesive bond analyzed by Goland and Reissner is shown in Fig. 3.11. The problem is divided into two parts. First, the bending of the adherend away from the lap region is analyzed. This is the region of length l from the end a. Then the region of the lap is analyzed. This is shown as the length $2c$ in Fig. 3.11. Naturally, the solutions for the two sections must agree at the position where they meet. The problem is similar to deflections of beams, and we must consider moments and shearing forces. Figure 3.12 is a diagram of the coordinate systems and the way in which the moments and shear forces are depicted.

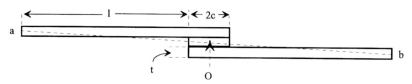

Figure 3.11   Schematic of the specimen analyzed by Goland and Reissner. The adherends have a length of $1 + 2c$. The lap length is $2c$. The loading line runs between points a and b and passes through the origin, O. The adherends have a thickness t

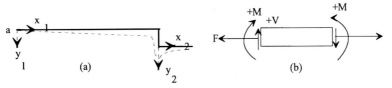

Figure 3.12   Diagram of the basis for the analysis of the lap shear specimen outside of the bonded area. Diagram (a) shows the neutral axis of the adherend and center of the bonded area before deflection (solid line) and after deflection (dotted line). Also shown are axes for the analysis; x_1 and y_1 are for the end of the adherend while x_2 and y_2 are for the end of the lap. Diagram (b) shows the bending moments for a small segment of the adherend, M, the shearing forces, V, and the applied load, F. The sign convention is given and is important for the complete analysis. (Redrawn from Goland and Reissner)

The analysis begins with the formulation of the equations for the bending moments at position 1 and 2. According to Goland and Reissner, those expressions are:

$$M_1 = F[\alpha x_1 - y_1]$$

and

$$M_2 = F\left[\alpha(l + x_2) - y_2 - \frac{t}{2}\right]$$

These equations come from geometric considerations of the neutral axis of the plate and the moments caused by the load, F. Note that F is not properly a force since Ft is the applied tensile stress. The angle α is the angle between the line of force (as shown in Figs. 3.11 and 3.12) and the x coordinates (x_1 or x_2). Equation (2.13) is invoked for each of these conditions and the following equations can be written.

$$R_1 \frac{d^2 y_1}{dx_1^2} = -M_1$$

and

$$R_2 \frac{d^2 y_2}{dx_2^2} = -M_2$$

In the above equations the R_i are known as the *flexural rigidity* of the plates (adherends) given by

$$R = \frac{Et^3}{12(1 - \nu^2)}$$

where E is the Young's modulus, t is the thickness and ν is the Poisson's ratio, all of the plate. The above four equations can be combined to give two coupled second order differential equations for which a trigonometric solution can be found. Note that two moments with the associated R are specified, one for the end of the adherend at point a (and coordinates x_1 and y_1) and one for the point nearest the bonded area (at coordinates x_2 and y_2).

After applying boundary conditions and some simplifying assumptions, such as the fact that R_1 is just $R_2/8$ since the lap region is almost twice as thick as the adherend, expressions of the following form are found for the moment and shearing force at the transition region between the adherend and the lap:

$$M_0 = k\frac{Ft}{2}$$

and

$$V_0 = kF\sqrt{\frac{3(1-\nu^2)Ft}{E}}$$

where k is

$$k = \frac{\cosh \Lambda}{\cosh \Lambda + 2\sqrt{2}\sinh \Lambda}$$

and Λ is

$$\Lambda = \sqrt{\frac{3(1-\nu^2)}{2}}\,\frac{c}{t}\,\sqrt{\frac{Ft}{E}}$$

These equations are used in the next discussion when the forces in the region of the adhesive bond are analyzed.

Let us now analyze the lap region, or the region defined by the length $2c$ in Fig. 3.11. The lap region is divided into two parts, an upper, u, and a lower, l. Figure 3.13 is a diagram of the situation.

An assumption is made that the deformation of the adherends is due completely to the longitudinal stress in the x direction in the adherend. As a result of this assumption, the adhesive then basically acts as a Hooke's Law solid between the two

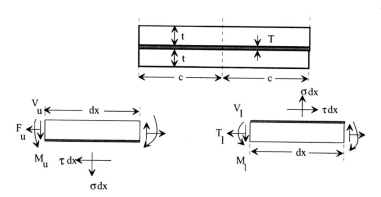

Figure 3.13   Diagram showing the elements of the analysis of the lap region of the lap shear joint. The symbols c and t are as defined in Fig. 3.11. T is the adhesive thickness. The lower diagrams show an element of length dx of the lap which has been divided into upper (u) and lower (l) portion. σ and τ are the tensile and shear forces, respectively. F is the force applied to the segment; V is the shear force applied to the segment, while M is the moment applied to the segment. (Redrawn from Goland and Reissner)

adherends. As shown in Fig. 3.13, the adhesive is divided down the middle. Shear stresses (τ) and normal stresses (σ) are defined for the adhesive. Also shown are the shearing forces for each element (dx) in the bonded area. These are denoted by V_u and V_l where the subscripts stand for the upper and lower segment, respectively. The moments (M) are defined in a similar way. In a manner entirely analogous to the way in which Timoshenko (see Bibliography) analyzed the beam problems described in the previous chapter, we write the conditions for equilibrium for both the upper and lower segments of the adhesive bond.

$$\frac{dV_u}{dx} - \sigma_0 = 0, \qquad \frac{dV_l}{dx} + \sigma_0 = 0 \tag{3.1}$$

are the conditions for vertical equilibrium.

$$\frac{dF_u}{dx} - \tau_0 = 0, \qquad \frac{dF_l}{dx} + \tau_0 = 0 \tag{3.2}$$

are the conditions for force equilibrium in direction of tension in the adherends.

$$\frac{dM_u}{dx} - V_u + \tau_0 \frac{t}{2} = 0, \qquad \frac{dM_l}{dx} - V_l + \tau_0 \frac{t}{2} = 0 \tag{3.3}$$

are the conditions for moment equilibrium in the adherends. Analogous to the situation encountered in Chapter 2 and using Eq. (2.13) we write the following for the vertical displacements of the upper and lower adherend:

$$\frac{d^2 v_u}{dx^2} = -\frac{M_u}{R}, \qquad \frac{d^2 v_l}{dx^2} = -\frac{M_l}{R} \tag{3.4}$$

where R is the flexural rigidity of the adherend as defined above. The next equations are for the longitudinal displacements of the adherends next to the adhesive:

$$\frac{du_u}{dx} = \frac{1}{E}\left(\frac{F_u}{t} - 6\frac{M_u}{t^2}\right), \qquad \frac{du_l}{dx} = \frac{1}{E}\left(\frac{T_l}{t} + 6\frac{M_l}{t^2}\right) \tag{3.5}$$

The final set of equations that Goland and Reissner needed to complete their analysis are the Hooke's Law stress-strain relationships for the adhesive:

$$\frac{\tau_0}{G_A} = \frac{u_u - u_l}{T}, \qquad \frac{\sigma_0}{E_A} = \frac{v_u - v_l}{T} \tag{3.6}$$

where G_A and E_A are the shear and tensile modulus of the adhesive, respectively. The manipulation of all of these expression begins with the substitution of Eq. (3.5) into the first of Eq. (3.6), differentiating twice with respect to x and taking into account Eqs. (3.2) and (3.3). We find:

$$\frac{d^3 \tau_0}{dx^3} - \frac{8G_A}{EtT}\frac{d\tau_0}{dx} = 0 \tag{3.7}$$

An equation for σ_0 can be found in a somewhat analogous way by using the second of Eqs. (3.6) , differentiating twice and substituting Eq. (3.4), thus:

$$\frac{1}{E_A}\frac{d^2\sigma_0}{dx^2} = \frac{1}{T}\frac{M_l - M_u}{R}$$

Differentiating again and using the equations for moment equilibrium, Eq. (3.3), and the conditions for shearing force equilibrium, Eq. (3.1), we find

$$\frac{1}{E_A}\frac{\mathrm{d}^4\sigma_0}{\mathrm{d}x^4} = -\frac{2}{TD}\sigma_0 \tag{3.8}$$

In order to solve any set of differential equations, the boundary conditions must be set and must agree with the physical reality of the problem being analyzed. To solve Eqs. (3.7) and (3.8), the boundary conditions are:

$$\text{at } x = c, \qquad M_u = T_u = V_u = 0, \quad M_l = M_0, \quad V_l = V_0, \quad F_l = F$$

$$\text{at } x = -c, \qquad M_l = T_l = V_l = 0, \quad M_u = -M_0, \quad V_u = V_0, \quad F_u = F$$

Note that the boundary conditions include the shearing force, V_0, and moment, M_0, which were determined for the adherend at the edge of the lap. These are combined with the equations in the above analysis to give the boundary conditions for the tensile force in the adhesive:

$$\text{at } x = \pm c, \qquad \frac{\mathrm{d}\tau_0}{\mathrm{d}x} = -\frac{G_A}{EtT}\left(F + 6\frac{M_0}{t}\right)$$

and

$$\int_{-c}^{c} \tau_0 \, \mathrm{d}x + F = 0$$

is the condition for equilibrium. Finally, the boundary conditions for the tensile forces can be set as being

$$\text{at } x = \pm c, \qquad \frac{\mathrm{d}^2\sigma_0}{\mathrm{d}x^2} = \frac{E_A}{TR}M_0$$

and

$$\frac{\mathrm{d}^3\sigma_0}{\mathrm{d}x^3} = \pm\frac{E_A}{TR}V_0$$

After applying the boundary conditions to the differential equations previously given, the shear stress in the adhesive is found to be:

$$\frac{\tau_0}{F}\frac{c}{t} = -\frac{1}{8}\left\{\frac{\beta c}{t}(1+3k)\frac{\cosh\dfrac{\beta c}{t}\dfrac{x}{c}}{\cosh\dfrac{\beta c}{t}} + 3(1-k)\right\}$$

where

$$\beta = \sqrt{8\frac{G_A}{E}\frac{t}{T}}$$

The term k was defined in the previous discussion on the stresses in the adherend away from the joint. The equation for the tensile stresses in the adhesive is much more complicated than that for the shear stresses and is written as follows:

$$\frac{\sigma_0}{Ft}\left(\frac{c}{t}\right)^2 = \frac{1}{\Delta}\left\{\left(K_2\lambda^2\frac{k}{2} + \lambda k' \cosh\lambda\cos\lambda\right)\cosh\lambda\frac{x}{c}\cos\lambda\frac{x}{c}\right.$$
$$\left. + \left(K_1\lambda^2\frac{k}{2} + \lambda k'\sinh\lambda\sin\lambda\right)\sinh\lambda\frac{x}{c}\sin\lambda\frac{x}{c}\right\}$$

This extremely complicated expression looks even more obtuse when we define the terms which are included, namely:

$$\lambda = \frac{c}{t}\left(6\frac{E_A}{E}\frac{t}{T}\right)^{1/4}$$

and

$$K_1 = \cosh\lambda\sin\lambda + \sinh\lambda\cos\lambda$$
$$K_2 = \sinh\lambda\cos\lambda - \cosh\lambda\sin\lambda$$
$$\Delta = \tfrac{1}{2}(\sinh 2\lambda + \sin 2\lambda)$$

and

$$k' = \frac{V_0 c}{Ft^3} = kF\sqrt{\frac{3(1-\nu^2)Ft}{E}}$$

The mathematics in the previous discussion are very complicated and lead to expressions not easily interpreted. However, it should be noted that many of the terms in the above equations are based on the concepts discussed in the previous chapter, i.e., moduli, Poisson's ratio, moments, shear forces, and the bending of beams. An appropriate way to understand the above expressions is to plot the shear and tensile stress in the adhesive as a function of the distance from the center of the joint. Such plots are shown schematically in Figs. 3.14 and 3.15.

Figure 3.14 shows that the shear stress in the joint is not at all uniform. Rather, at the center of the bond, the shear stress is less than the average shear stress of the

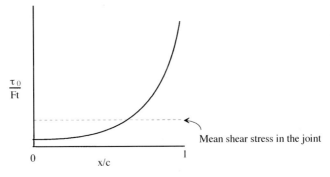

Figure 3.14 Schematic representation of the results of the Goland–Reissner analysis of the lap shear joint for the shear stresses in the joint (divided by the tensile stress applied to the adherend) as a function of the distance from the center of the joint

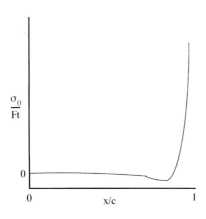

Figure 3.15   Schematic diagram showing the results of a plot of the tensile stresses in the adhesive (divided by the tensile load applied to the adherend) as a function of the distance from the center of the adhesive bond

bond while at the edge of the bond, the shear stress is much larger than the average shear stress of the bond.

A similar situation is encountered when the tensile stresses are calculated and plotted. Note that when we say tensile stresses in the adhesive, we mean stresses that are perpendicular (or "normal") to the primary tensile stress which has been applied to the adherend. That is, these stresses are perpendicular to the adhesive bondline. Figure 3.15 is such a plot.

In this figure, we see that the tensile stresses in the adhesive are zero at the center of the joint. This explains some of the phenomena observed when lap shear testing a structural adhesive. The center of the joint often displays cohesive failure even when the failure may be apparent adhesion failure away from the center. The normal stresses in the bond are maximized at the edges of the lap. This can be visualized by thinking about which part of the bond has to bend the most in order to linearize the load. One item that would not necessarily be obvious from the mathematical analysis is the compression region immediately before the rapid increase in the tensile stress. When applying a lever, there must be a fulcrum. The compression region from this analysis shows that the fulcrum for the lever formed by the adherend is just behind the maximum bend in towards the center of the bond. We encounter a situation similar to this later in this chapter. The existence of the compression zone and tensile stresses in this joint has important ramifications to be discussed in Chapter 8.

3.5   Cleavage Loading of Adhesive Bonds

In the previous chapter, we discussed what happens when a sharp crack propagates through a material. Using linear elastic fracture mechanics, we were able to define a materials parameter known as the strain energy release rate, $\mathscr{G}_C$. The strain energy release rate results from the balance of energies necessary to propagate a crack with the available strain energy. In this section, we discuss specimens called *cleavage specimens*, that allow us to measure this parameter. These methods are based on the fact that the adherends are not deformed significantly during the measurement. There are other adhesive evaluation specimens, called *peel specimens*, in which a crack is propagated but the adherends are measurably plastically deformed. Peel specimens are more widely used than cleavage specimens. The stress analysis of a type of peeling joint is also described in a following section. A listing of many of the ASTM test methods for cleavage loading and peel loading of adhesive bonds is given in Table 3.3.

3.5.1 Cleavage or Fracture Specimens

This section examines a few commonly used cleavage and fracture specimens. It is important to note that fracture processes can be initiated in a material or in an adhesive bond in a number of ways, known as *fracture modes*. The most common mode is cleavage and is called "Mode I." Cleavage has been depicted in Fig. 2.3 and is once again shown in Fig. 3.16. The next mode of fracture, called Mode II, is shearing and is similar to the shear force depicted in Fig. 2.2 but with the addition of a crack in the body. "Mode II" is also shown schematically in Fig. 3.16. The final mode of fracture is tearing. Tearing can be described as pushing the faces of the material above and below the crack in opposite directions from one another and is also depicted in Fig. 3.16. Roman numerals are used to designate these modes of fracture and they are usually given as a subscript to the strain energy release rate. It should be noted that the smallest strain energy release rates are almost always found for Mode I fracture. The specimens which we will discuss are only Mode I and the strain energy release rate is designated as $\mathscr{G}_{IC}$. When reading other literature on this topic, make sure the mode of fracture is specified.

3.5.1.1 Double Cantilever Beam Specimens

The simplest fracture mechanics specimen to generate and analyze is the uniform, double cantilever beam specimen. This specimen is shown schematically in Fig. 3.17 and described in ASTM D3433. In this specimen, the adherends are uniform in shape and profile. Their shape is usually square in cross section with dimensions of $1'' \times 1''$. Initially, an end crack is generated by driving a razor blade into the edge of the specimen. The blade is removed before testing. The load is applied at the end of the specimen in one of a number of ways. Most commonly, holes are drilled through the specimen as shown in Fig. 3.17 and the specimen is fixed in a tensile testing machine by means of these holes. As the load is applied, the initial crack propagates. One parameter measured is the displacement of the specimen determined by the crosshead movement of the tensile testing machine. The second parameter measured is the crack length as a function of load. This measurement is substantially more difficult and is made by either fast photography or by affixing instruments to

Table 3.3. ASTM Test Methods Pertaining to the Determination of Cleavage or Shear Properties of Adhesive Bonds

Test	Title of test	Short description of test
D903	Test method for peel or stripping strength of adhesive bonds	A thin adherend in bonded to a thick adherend. The thin adherend is stripped from the thick one at a 180° angle
D1062	Test method for cleavage strength of metal-to-metal adhesive bonds	Blocks of metal are bonded together and the specimen is loaded to make a cleavage load on the adhesive. Different from D903 in that neither adherend is flexible
D1781	Practice for climbing drum peel test for adhesives	A test method used primarily in the aerospace industry in which a thin adherend is stripped from a thicker adherend by having a drum "climb" the bond. Also used to measure the stripping force to remove a face sheet from a honeycomb sandwich bond
D1876	Test method for peel resistance of adhesives (T-peel test)	The most widely used peel test in which two equally thick, flexible adherends are bonded together and then peeled apart in a symetrical fashion such that the bond looks like a "T" while peeling
D3167	Test method for floating roller peel resistance of adhesives	A test method used mainly in the aerospace industry in which a thin adherend is peeled from a thick adherend over a 1″ diameter mandrel. The angle of the bond to the load is maintained constant
D3433	Practice for fracture strength in cleavage of adhesives in bonded joints	A double cantilever beam test used to measure $\mathscr{G}_I$ for adhesives. Thick adherends are used
D3762	Test method for adhesive-bonded surface durability of aluminum (wedge test)	A thin adherend fracture test in which surface-prepared metal is adhesively bonded and then a wedge is driven into the edge of the bond. The bond is exposed to an adverse environment and crack growth is measured
D3807	Test method for strength properties of adhesives in cleavage peel by tension loading (plastic-to-plastic)	A cross between D3433 and D1876 in which thick plastic samples are bonded and then pulled apart in mode similar to that of D3433
D5041	Test method for fracture strength in cleavage of adhesives in bonded joints	Thick adherends are bonded together with a bead of adhesive that is remote from the end of the test specimen. A specified wedge is driven into the end of the specimen and the energy to propogate a crack is measured

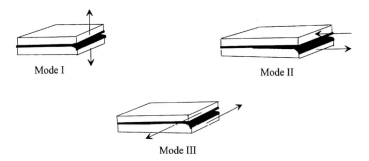

Figure 3.16   Schematic of the three modes of fracture. Mode I is known as cleavage. Mode II is known as shearing. Mode III is known as tearing. Note that Roman numerals are used to designate these modes of fracture

the adhesive bond. For example, one method is to paint the side of the bond with conductive paint at intervals and to measure the crack length by following the disruption of the conductive paths formed by the paint stripes.

3.5.1.2   Linear Elastic Fracture Mechanics Applied to the Double Cantilever Beam Specimen

Rewriting Eq. (2.3) in terms of differential forces and displacement, we have

$$U_C = F\delta D + \tfrac{1}{2}\delta F\delta D - \tfrac{1}{2}(F\delta D + D\delta F + \delta F\delta D)$$

This equation can be simplified to be:

$$U_C = \tfrac{1}{2}(F\delta D - D\delta F) \tag{3.9}$$

Substituting Eq. (3.9) into Eq. (2.4), we have

$$\frac{1}{w}\frac{\delta}{\delta a}U_C = \frac{1}{2w}\left(F\frac{\delta D}{\delta a} - D\frac{\delta F}{\delta a}\right) \geq \mathscr{G}_{\mathrm{IC}}$$

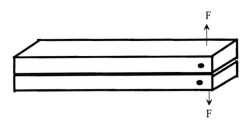

Figure 3.17   Double cantilever beam specimen

which provides an expression for the strain energy release rate in terms of measurable parameters, F, D, and their derivatives with respect to the crack length. We can make this equation an equality and by doing so, we make the measureables F and D into F_C and D_C, the critical force and displacement for crack growth. Thus,

$$\frac{1}{2w}\left(F_C \frac{\delta D}{\delta a} - D_C \frac{\delta F}{\delta a}\right) = \mathscr{G}_{\text{IC}} \tag{3.10}$$

Examination of Fig. 2.6 provides a way we can make Eq. (3.10) into an expression which measures one variable instead of two. If the axes of Fig. 2.6 were in terms of stress and strain, the slope of the line would be the modulus. However, since the axes are force and displacement, we may say only that the slope of the line is the *stiffness* of that particular specimen. The inverse of the stiffness is the pliability or the *compliance* of the specimen. $C = D/F$, because we are dealing with linear elastic materials, where C is the compliance. Using this expression we can simplify the equation for the critical force and displacement for crack growth:

$$\frac{D_C^2}{2w}\frac{1}{C^2}\frac{\delta C}{\delta a} = \frac{F_C^2}{2w}\frac{\delta C}{\delta a} = \mathscr{G}_{\text{IC}}$$

This last equation is important because the quantity $\delta C/\delta a$ can either be calculated or measured. For double cantilever beams, the quantity $\delta C/\delta a$ can be determined from beam theory. For a beam of uniform cross section, height h, width w, and modulus E, the change in compliance with crack length is found to be:

$$\frac{\delta C}{\delta a} = \frac{8}{Ew}\left(\frac{3a^2}{h^3} + \frac{1}{h}\right) \tag{3.11}$$

This equation says that we can make $\delta C/\delta a$ a constant if the quantity in the parentheses is a constant. This has been done and researchers have generated height-or width-tapered double cantilever beams. A height-tapered, double cantilever beam has been used in the examination of structural adhesives with aluminum adherends, while a width-tapered, double cantilever beam has been used to study adhesively bonded, carbon fiber-reinforced composites [9]. Depending on the Young's modulus of the adherends, different tapers are used to produce specimens of appropriate dimensions. The determination of $\mathscr{G}_{\text{IC}}$ is made more simple by using tapered beams because the critical strain energy release rate is directly related to the critical force for crack propagation. Figure 3.18 shows a comparison of F–D plots for the determination of $\mathscr{G}_{\text{IC}}$ for both uniform and tapered, double cantilever beam specimens.

Examination of the curves in the two sides of Fig. 3.18, demonstrates how the data from the two specimens differs. Figure 3.18(a) shows the data obtained for a uniform double cantilever beam. Each straight line section is associated with loading the specimen until a crack begins to propagate. When the specimen is reloaded, the compliance has changed (the length of the lever arm is longer) and the reloading curve is different. In each case, a different F_C is measured. These F_Cs correspond to the same $\mathscr{G}_{\text{IC}}$, which can be calculated from each measured F_C when the F_C is

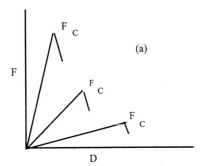
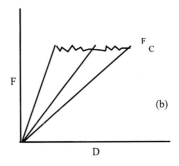

Figure 3.18   Schematic diagram of force-displacement curves measured for a double cantilever beam specimen. (a) Shows a result for a uniform, double cantilever beam. (b) Shows a result for a tapered, double cantilever beam. Note that the critical force for crack growth is easily determined from the force-displacement curve determined from a double cantilever beam

corrected for $\delta C/\delta a$. It is obvious from Fig. 3.18(b), that the tapered specimen provides a constant F_C no matter what the crack length was when it was measured. The tapered specimen provides a direct measure of $\mathscr{G}_{IC}$.

3.5.2   Blister Test

There are a number of other specimens used to determine the critical strain energy release rate of an adhesive. One method described by Dannenberg [10] is called the "blister test." It involves the use of a plate through which a hole has been drilled. A schematic of this apparatus is shown in Fig. 3.19. The hole is covered by Teflon[1] tape or other release material and the adhesive as well as another substrate are applied over the tape and the rest of the adherend. The hole is connected to a pressure source and the pressure is ramped from zero until it drops precipitously, indicating propagation of the crack. The critical strain energy release rate is then determined by the following equation:

$$\frac{F_C a}{E_a Q} = \mathscr{G}_{IC}$$

where E_a is the adhesive modulus, a is the initial crack length (the radius of the hole), F_C has been previously defined and Q is a geometry factor dependent upon the modulus of the upper adherend. This test is known as the blister test because of the shape of the adhesive/adherend combination when the crack is propagating. This test method has recently been modified to provide a *constrained blister test* in which a box is placed over the entire specimen [11]. This constrains the blister to grow only

---

[1] "Teflon" is a registered trademark of E.I. Dupont de Nemours and Co. Inc.

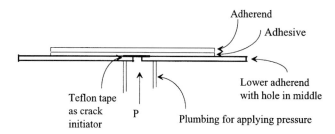

Figure 3.19   Schematic diagram of the blister crack propagation test. A hole is drilled through the lower adherend and fixtured with plumbing, allowing the application of pressure through the hole. Poly(tetrafluoroethylene) tape is applied over the hole. Adhesive and another adherend are then applied. Pressure is applied to the joint until measurable crack propagation occurs

to a certain vertical dimension and provides a method by which adhesive bonds having a more flexible top adherend can be evaluated.

3.5.3   Compact Tension Test

The compact tension specimen provides a means of determining the inherent fracture resistance of the adhesive because the entire specimen is made from the adhesive. This type of specimen is useful only for reasonably stiff adhesives. The test is not useful for rubbery materials. A diagram of the test specimen is shown in Fig. 3.20. A mold is prepared with the desired dimensions. Adhesive is placed in the mold and then appropriately cured. After the specimen is removed from the mold, a sharp crack is driven into its edge by a razor blade. The specimen is fixtured in a tensile testing device and the force-displacement curve is measured. This specimen has a number of advantages. Not much material is necessary and the test has been described in several places in the literature so comparisons can be drawn.

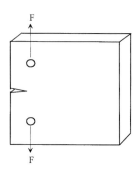

Figure 3.20   Compact tension specimen. Adhesive is cast and cured in a mold. Holes are drilled in the monolithic piece of adhesive. A crack is iniated by a sharp razor blade

Figure 3.21   Wedge test specimen. The adherends are usually thin (about 1/8″ thick for aluminum). The wedge is of a specified size and is usually driven in by a hammer. The bondline thickness is exaggerated in this diagram

3.5.4   Wedge Test

A popular fracture mechanics test for the study of the durability of structural adhesive bonds is the *wedge test*. Relatively thin adherends are surface-prepared (see Chapter 7) and then bonded. The bond is cut into 1″ wide strips and then a wedge is driven into the end the specimen. The specimen is shown schematically in Fig. 3.21.

The test is described in ASTM D3762. One side of the specimen is polished so that easily discernible marks can be inscribed. After the wedge is driven into the end of the specimen, the initial length of the crack is determined. In most cases, the specimen is then placed in a hostile environment. As we discuss in Chapter 7, hostile environments for structural adhesive bonds on aluminum include high temperatures and high humidities. The bonds are placed in such aggressive environments and the crack growth is measured as function of time of exposure. Boeing Corporation has shown that there is a strong correlation between the in-service durability of adhesive bonds and the extent of crack growth in the wedge test specimen [12]. In addition, the mode of failure can be an indicator of environmental durability. Thus, if one carries out a wedge test and the failure mode is apparently interfacial and the crack growth is long, the prediction is that the bond will not be durable in service. In contrast, a failure mode where the failure is cohesive in the adhesive and the crack growth is short is considered to be a predictor of good in-service bond durability.

3.6   Peel Tests

Peel tests are cleavage tests. However, at least one of the adherends is made from a flexible material which could be plastically deformed during the measurement. A typical peel test is shown in Fig. 3.22 and is known as the *T-peel test*, described in ASTM D1876. Two adherends of equal thickness are bonded with an adhesive. The ends or "tabs" of the specimen are placed in the jaws of a tensile testing machine and then separated at a chosen rate or rates.

The test can also be carried out below and above room temperature. If the adherends in this specimen are the same thickness and have the same bending modulus and yield strength, the peel is symmetrical and the crack front propagates down the center of the adhesive bondline. If one of the adherends has thickness or

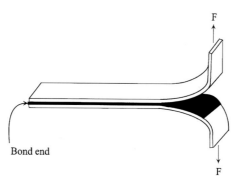

F

Bond end

F

Figure 3.22   T-peel test specimen. Two thin adherends are bonded with an adhesive. For aluminum, the adherend thickness is 0.020″ to 0.032″. The adherends will plastically deform during this test

bending properties substantially different from the other, the adhesive bond cocks so that the bond end bends towards the test fixture which is grasping the thinner adherend. The locus of failure also shifts towards the thinner adherend.

Another peel test is known as a "90° Peel Test" which involves bonding a flexible adherend to a rigid adherend. There is no specific test standard in the ASTM literature for this test. One can picture this test by looking at Fig. 3.22 and imagining that the lower flexible adherend is replaced by a thick, rigid adherend. The flexible adherend is peeled away from the rigid adherend at a fixed rate and so that the angle between the tab and the rigid adherend is kept at 90°. The rigid adherend must then be fixed to a trolley of some sort allowing the peel front to stay in a constant position under the testing machine crosshead as the bond is peeled. This test is described in more detail in Chapter 9 as it used with pressure-sensitive adhesives.

Another variation of the peel test is shown in Fig. 3.23 and is described in ASTM D903. The flexible adherend is bonded to a rigid adherend. The specimen is placed in a tensile testing machine so that the tab is pulled away parallel to the rigid adherend. The flexible adherend undergoes substantial bending to conform to the stress under which it is placed. This adherend must be flexible enough not to yield to failure by such a bend. This test is often used to examine the adhesion of films or sheets to an adhesive. It is also used to examine peel adhesion of very soft adhesives and the flexible adherend is often canvas in that case. A sealant or rubber based mastic is applied in a uniform manner to the rigid adherend. Before the adhesive is allowed to cure or the solvent is allowed to evaporate, the canvas is pressed into the adhesive. When the adhesive has cured, the canvas forms an ideal flexible adherend for this test.

Two other variations of peel tests are shown in Figs. 3.24 and 3.25. Both of these tests are fixed radius of curvature tests. In the 90° and 180° peel tests, the radius of curvature of the adherend in the region immediately adjacent to the peel front is controlled mainly by the bending stiffness of the adherend. Depending on the type of adhesive and the type of adherend, the crack could propagate through the

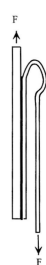

Figure 3.23 180° peel test. Adhesive is applied to a rigid adherend to which a very flexible adherend is attached. The thin adherend must be capable of extensive bending without yielding to failure. Canvas is often used as the thin adherend

adhesive or at some other locus (remember the discussion above regarding the T-peel test). In the *floating roller peel test* (Fig. 3.24) or the *climbing drum peel test* (Fig. 3.25), the radius of curvature near the peel front is controlled by the radius of the mandrel over which the flexible adherend is peeled. This system will also control the locus of the crack in the adhesive layer. For example, if a flexible adherend is peeled over a mandrel of small radius, the locus of crack propagation shifts close to the thin adherend. This becomes very useful if one is trying to examine the effect of surface preparations on adhesion. In the climbing drum peel test, the radius of curvature is much larger than in the floating roller peel test. This test is often used to determine the level of peel performance in honeycomb sandwich specimens. The floating

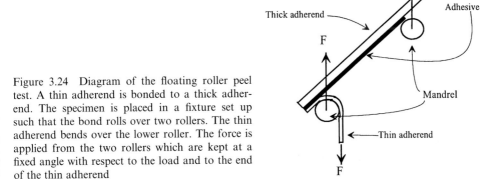

Figure 3.24 Diagram of the floating roller peel test. A thin adherend is bonded to a thick adherend. The specimen is placed in a fixture set up such that the bond rolls over two rollers. The thin adherend bends over the lower roller. The force is applied from the two rollers which are kept at a fixed angle with respect to the load and to the end of the thin adherend

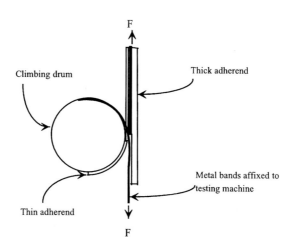

Figure 3.25   Schematic of the climbing drum peel test. A thin adherend is bonded to a thicker adherend. The end of the flexible member is affixed to a drum. The bonded end of the specimen is affixed firmly to the other crosshead by metal bands. As the test proceeds, the drum appears to climb the bond while wrapping the thin adherend around itself

roller peel is described in ASTM D3167 while the climbing drum peel is described in ASTM D1781.

In Fig. 3.24, we present an idealized version of the floating roller peel test. The mandrels shown are not free floating but are mounted in a fixture and roll over a race of ball bearings. In general, the fixture has the line between the centers of the mandrels at an angle of 45° with respect to the line of force. As the thin adherend is peeled around the lower mandrel, the thick adherend travels along the line formed by the mandrels. It is important to note that the radius of curvature of the mandrels plays a role in controlling the locus of failure in the bond. If the radius of the lower mandrel is small, it tends to force the failure near the thin adherend. If the radius of the lower mandrel is large, the failure is more towards center of bond. In this way, the floating roller peel specimen can be used to study surface preparations or primers. The floating roller peel test was developed originally to test the bond strength of components in a helicopter rotor blade construction.

The climbing drum peel test is in some sense similar to the floating roller peel test in that the bond is peeled over a mandrel and the radius of the mandrel controls the peel front. The tests appear physically to be quite different, however. A schematic of the climbing drum peel test is shown in Fig. 3.25.

The drum is affixed to the testing machine by means of metal bands, one on each end of the drum. The flexible adherend is affixed to the drum by some mechanical means so that the adherend does not slip during the test. The other end of the adhesive bond is fixed firmly into the testing machine. This test seems peculiar when it is observed because the drum seems to climb the adhesive bond as the crossheads of the testing machine are moved apart. The results are reported as torque rather than as force to propagate a crack. This test is used for the testing of the peel strength of metal honeycomb adhesive bond sandwiches as well as metal-to-metal adhesive bond peel strengths. The test was originally developed to determine the torque which an aerospace fuselage or wing surface skin could withstand before it peeled.

3.6.1   Stress Analysis in a Peel Specimen

In this section, we will analyze the state of stress in an adhesive bond which is tested in peel. Much of the discussion is similar to the discussion in Sections 2.7 and 3.4.4. The analysis of the mechanics of the peeling of an adhesive from a surface results primarily from the work of Kaelble [13]. Many of the concepts which we discussed previously concerning the Goland-Reissner theory of force balances and the bending of beams were used by Kaelble in his analysis. Most of Kaelble's work involved the analysis of peel of *pressure sensitive adhesives* from a rigid substrate. We discuss pressure sensitive adhesives in Chapter 9.

The analysis is based on the theory of bending of beams on an elastic foundation. Therefore, it is equally applicable to other adhesives, taking into account the assumptions that Kaelble made in order to make his analysis tractable. As with the previous analyses, Kaelble's work is based on that of Timoshenko.

A peel specimen which has a load applied at the end is examined. Such a situation is shown schematically in Fig. 3.26, which also contains many of the variables used in this analysis. Figure 3.26 shows that state of the adherend can be analyzed in two segments, bonded and unbonded. The analysis which we present is that of the bonded area. The analysis is based on work by Kaelble, as corrected by Dahlquist [14], who corrected the analysis for the bending of the adherend away from the peel front. We do not include that discussion in this section .

The derivation begins with Eq. (2.15) which describes the deflection of a beam under a distributed load:

$$EI_z \frac{d^4 y}{dx^4} = f$$

Remember that f is a distributed force along the length of the beam. This equation must be modified for the coordinate change shown in Fig. 3.26 and must also provide an expression for the distributed force. For an elastic beam on an elastic foundation, the distributed force on the unloaded portion of the beam is just the distributed reaction on the beam by the foundation. Taking this change in coordinates into account, we write

$$EI_z \frac{d^4 x}{dy^4} = -f$$

E is the Young's modulus of the beam (in this case the tape backing) and f is now written as a negative f because it is the reaction of the foundation. I_z, as defined in Chapter 2, i.e., the moment of inertia of the beam (backing).

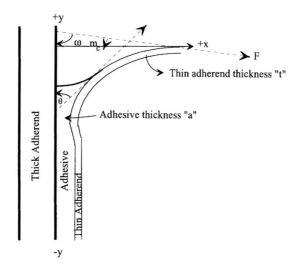

Figure 3.26 Schematic of the essential components of the Kaelble–Dahlquist stress analysis of peel. Important parameters include the peel angle, ω, the deflection angle at the peel boundary θ, and the cleavage moment arm, m_c. The identity of the remaining variables should be discernible from the diagram. (Redrawn from Dahlquist)

It is assumed that the adherend is elastic. In most cases, this assumption is reasonable, especially in comparison to the properties of pressure-sensitive adhesives. Another assumption is that the adhesive follows Hooke's Law for all displacements. Since pressure-sensitive adhesives are inherently rubber-like materials, the elongation of the adhesive can be many hundred per cent. Therefore, this assumption is somewhat dubious. It is gratifying and surprising that answers are obtained which are not far off from experimental results. For the specimen under consideration, a statement of Hooke's Law for the adhesive is:

$$\frac{1}{b}\frac{dF}{dy} = E_a \frac{x}{a}$$

where $b\,dy$ is the area over which the force F is applied (hence an infinitesimal stress), x/a is the strain in the adhesive and E_a is the Young's modulus of the adhesive. Rearranging this equation we find that

$$\frac{dF}{dy} = E_a \frac{b}{a} x$$

which is then substituted for the reaction of the beam to the adhesive layer.

$$EI_z \frac{d^4 y}{dx^4} = -E_a \frac{b}{a} x \tag{3.12}$$

The solution for Eq. (3.12) is similar to that found in the Goland–Reissner analysis for lap shear specimens:

$$x = e^{\beta y}(A \cos \beta y + B \sin \beta y)$$

where $\beta = [E_a b/4EI_z a]^{1/4}$. The constants in this equation can be determined by differentiating several times and applying the other equations for the bending of beams, appropriately modified for the situation shown in Fig. 3.26. The first boundary condition is that the cleavage moment at the bond boundary is equal to the bending moment in the backing. Applying these conditions and using Eq. (2.13), we have

$$EI_z \frac{d^2 x}{dy^2} = M_c = Fm_c$$

where M_c is the cleavage moment at the bond boundary and m_c is the normal to the line of action of the applied force, F. As shown in Fig. 3.26, it is the normal from the line of action of the force to the bond boundary. We also apply Eq. (2.14) for the shearing force perpendicular to the plane of the bond, thus

$$EI_z \frac{d^3 x}{dy^3} = -V = F \sin \omega$$

where ω is the angle shown in Fig. 3.26 and $F \sin \omega$ is the resolution of the force applied to the bond in the x direction. When these equation are used in the triply differentiated solution to the solution for the equation for the deflection curve of a beam, the following equation results:

$$x = \frac{e^{\beta y}}{2EI_z \beta^3} [(\beta M_c + f \sin \omega) \cos \beta y + \beta M_c \sin \beta y]$$

This equation describes a damped wave function with a period determined by β which is in turn determined by the physical constants of the adhesive and adherend.

Kaelble devised a rather unique apparatus called the bond stress analyzer [15] by which he was able to measure the stress normal to a peeling joint. His measurements were in surprisingly good agreement with the above analysis. The deflection equation also shows the same sort of compressive zone that was found from the Goland–Reissner analysis (see Fig. 3.15). This zone indicates that the adhesive is actually in compression in the region immediately behind the peel nip. This curious result is observable experimentally. The compression zone provides the rather interesting and useful phenomenon that pressure-sensitive tapes actually increase their practical adhesion to a substrate while they are being peeled away. This happens because the compressive force immediately behind the peel nip induces improved wetting of the substrate by the adhesive. The subject of wetting is discussed in more detail in the next Chapters 4 and 6.

3.7   Summary

In this chapter we have discussed a number of tests used to study the physical properties of adhesives and adhesive bonds. The tests were broadly separated into four categories: tensile, shear, cleavage, and peel. The tensile tests are typified by the tensile rod specimen in which the adhesive bond is found between two rod sections. The shear tests are typified by the standard lap shear test in which two adherends are lapped in a 1/2 square inch (3.21 cm^2) area. Fracture tests are typified by the uniform, double cantilever beam specimen. Peel tests are typified by the T-peel test. Many of the tests described in this chapter are found in the ASTM literature and a listing of some of those tests was presented. Various guidelines and hints for the preparation of the test specimens were presented throughout the chapter. More detailed mathematical analysis of the stresses in the lap shear and peel test specimens were given. The theory was based on the theory of the bending of beams.

Bibliography

Timoshenko, S., *Strength of Materials*, Vols. 1 and 2 (1955) D. Van Nostrand Company, Inc., Princeton, NJ

References

1. *1990 Annual Book of Standards*, Section 15, Volume 15.06, American Society for Testing and Materials, Philadelphia, PA
2. Mittal, K.L., in *Adhesion Science and Technology*, L.H. Lee (Ed.), vol. 9A (1975) Plenum Press, New York
3. Trade literature from SEMicro Co., Rockville, MD
4. Crocombe, A.D. and Adams, R.D., *J. Adhesion* (1981) 13, p. 141
5. Goland, M. and Reissner, E., *J. Appl. Mech., Trans Am. Soc. Engs.* (1944) 66, p. A17
6. Krieger, R.B., in *ASTM STP 981*, Johnson, W.S. (Ed.) (1988) American Society for Testing and Materials, Philadelphia, PA, pp. 264–275
7. Hart-Smith, L.J., NASA CR 112236 (1973).
8. Benson, N.K., in *Adhesion and Adhesives*, Houwinck and Salomon (Eds.) (1967) Elsevier, New York
9. Mostovoy, S. and Ripling, E. J. Progress Report for Contract # N00019-77-C-0256, September 15, 1978, prepared for Naval Air Systems Command
10. Dannenberg, H., *J. Appl. Polymer Sci.*, (1961) 5, p. 125
11. (a) Napolitano, M.J., Chudnovsky A., and Moet, A., *J. Adhesion Sci. Technol.* (1988) 2, p. 311. (b) Lai, Y.-H. and Dillard, D.A., *J. Adhesion* (1990) 31, p. 172
12. Marceau, J.A., Moji, Y. and McMillan, J.C., in *Proc. 21st SAMPE Symposium* (1976) 21
13. (a) Kaelble, D.H., *Trans. Soc. Rheol.* (1959) 3, p. 161. (b) Kaelble, D.H., *Trans. Soc. Rheol.* (1960) 4, p. 45
14. Dahlquist, C.A., in *Technical Seminar Proceedings, Pressure Sensitive Tape Council*, XI (1988), Pressure Sensitive Tape Council, Deerfield, IL, pp. 19–46
15. Kaelble, D.H., *Trans. Soc. Rheol.* (1965) 9, p. 135

4 The Basics of Intermolecular Forces and Surface Science

4.1 Introduction

In the previous chapters we have concerned ourselves with the mechanics of adhesive bonds. The discussion assumed that the interface or interphase of the adherend and adhesive was perfectly capable of transferring stress from the first to the second and so on. The phenomenon by which the adhesive takes up stress from the adherend is known as *adhesion*. Adhesion is a physical phenomenon resulting from the same attractive forces which bind atoms together to make molecules and molecules together to make liquids and solids. To understand adhesion, we must first understand the forces existing between atoms or molecules and then apply that knowledge to what occurs at surfaces and within interphases. In this chapter, we first discuss the forces binding atoms and molecules together. These concepts are familiar to those who have taken freshman chemistry and the mathematics employed are understandable to those who have taken college level physical chemistry. Enough explanatory material is provided so that understanding of the mathematics is not necessary to develop an understanding of the phenomena. After this discussion, observable surface chemical phenomena are described in terms of these basic physical forces. In Chapter 6, surface chemical phenomena are related to adhesion phenomena. Guidelines for good adhesion needed for the design of reliable adhesive bonds are given in Chapter 6, as well.

The objectives of this chapter are to develop or review information on the physical forces binding atoms or molecules together to make liquids and solids. This knowledge should naturally lead to an understanding of the physical basis for surface energy. Methods used to measure surface energy of materials as well as modern methods for determining their surface chemistry are discussed. In particular, contact angle measurements and how they play a role in surface science is emphasized. In addition, thermodynamics, force balances and the measurement of adhesion through the surface forces apparatus are discussed.

4.2 Fundamental Forces

A basic tenet of physics is that all natural phenomena can be described when all of the forces between bodies and their energy states are described. Physical forces in nature range from nuclear forces which bind protons and neutrons in an atom's nucleus to gravitational forces which control the motion of celestial bodies. Gravitational forces are for the most part, unimportant in the study of adhesion. Gravitational forces can play a role in the wetting of an adhesive or in the design of an adhesive bond. However, it is only those forces of a chemical nature that are important in understanding adhesion. The forces binding atoms to make molecules and molecules to make liquids and solids are most relevant in the study of adhesion. These topics are similar to the theory of solutions and the theories of the cohesive strength of materials.

There are several fundamental terms which need to be remembered or learned from basic physics before we can continue. The term *potential energy* has to do with the ability to do work. A rock sitting on a ledge has the *potential* to do work. *Work* is defined as a force times a distance. Thus, the work done by the rock falling off the ledge is the action of the gravitational force over the distance the rock falls. Once the rock has reached its final resting place, we say that the rock has a lower potential energy than it had before its fall and now it has less potential to do work. Mathematically,

$$W = Fd \tag{4.1}$$

where W is work, F is the force and d is the distance over which the force acts. The work done is the difference in potential energy between the starting and resting positions of the system. If Φ_1 is the potential energy of the starting state and Φ_2 is the potential energy of the final state of the system,

$$\Phi_2 - \Phi_1 = W \tag{4.2}$$

This important equation indicates the relationship between potential energy and work. Throughout the next section we discuss various mathematical functions describing the potential energy of various interactions between molecules and atoms. From Eq. (4.1) and Eq. (4.2), and assuming $\Phi_1 - \Phi_2$ is an infinitesimally small change such that it is equal to $\delta\Phi$ and F is constant, then

$$-\delta\Phi = \delta W = F\,\delta d$$

and

$$-\frac{\delta\Phi}{\delta d} = F$$

The force in a system can then be determined by differentiating the potential energy function by the distance over which the force acts. Similarly, the potential energy function can be determined by integrating a function describing the force with respect to the distance over which it acts. We use these simple physical concepts repeatedly in the next sections.

4.2.1   Electrostatic Forces

The electrostatic force occurs between atoms or molecules which bear a charge. This force is also known as the Coulombic force. Particles bearing like electrical charges repel each other while particles bearing opposite electrical charges attract each other. The potential energy of interaction between atoms or molecules having a charge is given by the following equation:

$$\Phi^{El} = \frac{q_1 q_2}{4\pi\varepsilon r}$$

where q_i are the charges on the atoms or molecules (the charges have a positive or negative sign), ε is the dielectric constant of the medium in which the charged particles are found, and r is the distance between the atoms or molecules. If the particles have like charges, the energy of interaction is positive or repulsive. If the particles carry unlike charges, the potential energy is negative or attractive. We can calculate the force of interaction by taking the derivative of the potential energy with respect to distance:

$$\frac{d\Phi^{El}}{dr} = \frac{q_1 q_2}{4\pi\varepsilon r^2}$$

The electrostatic force is the strongest force of interaction (other than covalent bonding) between atoms or molecules. This force has been studied as a potential contributor to adhesion phenomena. However, not all adhesion phenomena can be explained by electrostatics. Electrostatic forces play a primary role in the formation of *ionic* bonds and ionic crystals. In an ionic crystal, such as NaCl, an electron has been transferred from sodium to chlorine. The resulting ions attract each other in a manner described by Coulomb's Law which can be used to calculate the lattice energy of ionic crystals. The energy required to break an ionic bond is very large, usually on the order of 100 kcal/mole or more. This number is important for comparison to the other forces of attraction discussed below.

4.2.2   van der Waals Interactions

In standard freshman chemistry textbooks, the ideal gas is normally thoroughly discussed. The ideal gas law is stated as:

$$PV = nRT$$

where P is the pressure, V is the volume, n is the number of moles of gas, R is the gas constant, and T is the absolute temperature. It was noted early in the study of the physical properties of materials that most gases do not follow the perfect gas law exactly. One of the first attempts to describe the deviation of gases from the perfect gas law was the equation of state developed by J.D. van der Waals, a Dutch physicist who lived 1837–1923:

$$\left(P + \frac{an^2}{V^2}\right)(V - bn) = nRT$$

P, V, n, R and T are as described above while the constants a and b are meant to describe the attractive and repulsive forces between gas atoms or molecules which the perfect gas law neglects. All of the forces leading gases to deviate from the perfect gas law are considered to be "van der Waals forces." [1] We discuss each of these forces individually in the next sections.

4.2.2.1   Dipole–Dipole Interactions

Each element in the periodic table can be characterized by how well it attracts electrons. Thus, elements on the right hand side of the periodic table are said to be *electronegative* in comparison to the elements on the left hand side of the periodic table. When atoms are bound together to make molecules, the electronegativity of the individual atoms acts to draw electrons towards those that are the most electronegative. Thus, a molecule such as CF_3CH_3, with the very electronegative fluorine atoms on one end of the molecule, has more of the electrons in the molecule residing more on one side than on the other. One could say that there was a partial charge on either end of the molecule. The CF_3 side has a partial negative charge and correspondingly, the CH_3 end has a partial positive charge. In terms of quantum mechanics, the probability function for the electron is greater in the region around the fluorine atoms than it is around the hydrogen atoms. This type of molecule, with a partial separation of charge is known as a *dipole*.

The dipole is characterized by the magnitude of the virtual charge on the ends of the molecule as well as by the distance separating the virtual charges. It is usual to draw a dipole as a dumbbell. The charges reside in the "balls" of the dumbbell. The handle of the dumbbell is the length separating the charges. The dipole is able to act in a mechanical way. If an interaction occurs between a singly charged species and a dipole, the opposite charges attract and the similar charges repel according to Coulomb's Law. The line of action of this force is controlled by the "lever" holding the virtual charges together. A force acting on a lever in this way is a "moment" and for this situation, we can define a *dipole moment*, μ:

$$\mu = ql$$

where q is the magnitude of the virtual charge, and l is the molecular length separating the charges.

Two dipoles can interact. The oppositely charged ends of the dipole attract and the similarly charged ends of the dipoles repel, thus changing the spatial orientation of one with respect to the other. Figure 4.1 shows such a situation. The potential energy of interaction of two dipoles becomes a matter of trigonometric analysis of charges and moments acting upon one another. This dipole–dipole potential energy of interaction is written as follows:

$$\Phi^P = \frac{\mu_1 \mu_2}{r^3} \left(2 \cos \theta_1 \cos \theta_2 - \sin \theta_1 \sin \theta_2 \cos[\phi_1 - \phi_2] \right)$$

where μ_1 and μ_2 are the dipole moments and r is the distance of separation of the centroids of the two dipole moments [2]. The angles are all shown in Fig. 4.1.

An important advancement concerning the understanding of dipolar species came with the work of Keesom [3]. He surmised that dipoles in a liquid or gas did

Figure 4.1 Diagram showing the interaction between two dipoles. The interaction specified by the angles of orientation as well as by the dipole moments of the two molecules

not exist as species rigidly fixed with one another. Rather, if a liquid or a gas is at a temperature such that its thermal energy is greater than the rotational energy of the dipoles in that material, then the dipoles are free to rotate with respect to one another. The potential energy of interaction must be averaged over all values of θ and ϕ to provide a thermally averaged interaction. Keesom derived the following expression for the potential energy of interaction for rotating dipoles with an average thermal energy of kT, where k is Boltzmann's constant and T is the absolute temperature:

$$\Phi^{P,K} = \frac{-2\mu_1^2\mu_2^2}{3kTr^6}$$

Other constants in the equation were described previously. An adhesive, when applied, is almost always a liquid and may be described by a Keesom potential, although it is somewhat dubious for us to assume that the interactions occuring between a solid adherend and a liquid adhesive would best be described this way. However, the Keesom potential may prove to be a reasonable approximation in some cases.

4.2.2.2 Dipole–Induced Dipole

In another type of van der Waals interaction between molecules, greater attention is given to the interaction of the electron clouds surrounding molecules.When a molecule with a spherical, symmetrical charge distribution encounters a dipole, we might expect no interaction between these molecules. However, this is not the case. There is a measurable interaction between the two molecules, called the *dipole–induced dipole* interaction. This interaction occurs because of the nature of electron probability distributions around the nuclei in a molecule. We know from atomic theory that electrons move in molecular orbitals and these molecular orbitals can interact with other charges, changing the probability distribution of the electron in its orbital. Simply stated, the electrons in the spherical, symmetrical molecule see the dipole as two charges. The electrons are attracted to the positive end of the dipole and repelled by the negative end. This creates a dipole moment in the otherwise spherical, symmetrical molecule. We then have a dipole interacting with a dipole that was created by the first dipole's presence, hence the term *dipole–induced dipole interaction* [4]. The expression which describes the potential energy of the dipole–induced dipole interaction is as follows:

$$\Phi^I = -\frac{\mu_1^2 \alpha_2 + \mu_2^2 \alpha_1}{r^6} \tag{4.3}$$

in which the dipole moments, μ_i, are as previously described and α_i are the molecular polarizabilities. This expression is written as if each of the molecules interacting have dipole moments and these dipoles act upon each other to further increase the dipole strength of the other molecule. If one of the molecules did not have a permanent dipole moment, then the expression is written:

$$\Phi^I = -\frac{\mu_1^2 \alpha_2}{r^6}$$

The quantity, α, the polarizability, is a measure of how tightly the electrons are held by the atom or molecule and is roughly proportional to the molecular or atomic volume.

4.2.2.3   Dispersion Forces

The final energy of interaction is fundamental to the study of adhesion and to the study of polymeric materials. Let us consider a situation in which two atoms or molecules with spherical charge distributions are brought near one another. Noble gases and molecules such as methane have spherical, symmetrical charge distributions. We might think that because they do not have a charge or a virtual separation of charge, that there would be no interaction between these two species. There is, however, a measurable interaction and it is found in all materials. The source of this interaction stems naturally from the discussion on the dipole–induced dipole interaction. In a spherical, symmetrical charge distribution, there is the finite probability, at any one instant in time, that the electrons in an atom or molecule are all on one or the other side of the atom of molecule. If that is the case, then the atom or molecule has a partially unshielded nucleus or nuclei on one side and an excess of electrical charge on the other. This situation forms an *instantaneous dipole* which can induce an instantaneous dipole in the other atom or molecule with a spherical charge distribution. The result is a net potential energy of interaction which leads to an attraction between these two atoms or molecules. Because of the instantaneous nature of this interaction, its magnitude can be expected to be small. The expression which describes the potential energy of interaction between two atoms or molecules acting through *instantaneous dipole–induced instantaneous dipole* interaction is:

$$\Phi^D = -\frac{3}{4}\left(\frac{\alpha_1^2 C_1}{r^6}\right) \approx -\frac{3}{4}\left(\frac{\alpha_1^2 I_1}{r^6}\right)$$

and

$$\Phi_{12}^D = -\frac{3}{4}\frac{\alpha_1 \alpha_2}{r_{12}^6}\left(\frac{2 C_1 C_2}{C_1 + C_2}\right) \approx -\frac{3}{4}\frac{\alpha_1 \alpha_2}{r_{12}^6}\left(\frac{2 I_1 I_2}{I_1 + I_2}\right)$$

The first expression is for the interaction of like atoms or molecules, while the second expression is for unlike atoms or molecules. In the above expressions, the quantities α_i are the polarizabilities as described above, the C_i are molecular constants which can be approximated by the I_i, which are the ionization potentials for atom or molecule i. This potential energy of interaction is given the symbol Φ^D where D stands for dispersion force interaction. The name dispersion force comes from the relationship of this force to the dispersion of light in the visible and ultraviolet regions of the spectrum. Inherently, "dispersion force" does not accurately describe this phenomenon and may be misleading. However, the literature has adopted this name to describe the instantaneous dipole–induced dipole force extensively.

Upon examination of the equations for the dispersion force potential energy, we can see three things. First, the interaction is directly dependent upon the polarizability of each of the interacting species. Thus, atoms or molecules which have loosely held electrons (loosely held electrons are more easily displaced in an electric field) have large dispersion force interactions in comparison to those molecules which have tightly held electrons. Second, the dispersion force interaction is dependent upon the first ionization potential for the species. Third, the dispersion force interaction is inversely dependent upon the sixth power of the distance separating the two species. The interacting species must be close together for this potential energy of interaction to have any effect. This should be compared to the Coulombic potential energy of interaction which is dependent upon the inverse first power of distance. In charge–charge interactions, the action is over long distances.

The detailed description of the dispersion force interaction between surfaces is based on quantum electrodynamics which is outside of the scope of this book. The theory most often cited is that of Lifschitz [5]. The Lifschitz theory is somewhat difficult and the reader is referred to the useful explanation by Grimley [6]. Israelachvili [7] provides methodology to approximate the measurements needed to calculate the dispersion force interaction between two bodies.

4.2.3 Interactions through Electron Pair Sharing

The final interaction which can take place between two atoms or molecules is the formation of a chemical bond through the sharing of an electron pair. We call these "chemical bonds" to distinguish them from "physical bonds" formed by van der Waals interactions or ionic bonds formed by the interaction of two charged species. The types of chemical bonds formed by electron pair sharing fall into two broad categories: *covalent bonding* and *donor–acceptor interactions*. In covalent bonding, molecular species are formed by sharing of electron pairs. The electrons that were originally centered on one atom or were part of one molecule are now shared by the atoms in the new molecule. The description of the interaction of atoms or molecules to form new molecules is not a simple one. It requires a knowledge of quantum mechanics outside the scope of this book.

Covalent bonds are most often described in organic chemistry. Coordinate covalent bonding is a variation of covalent bonding in that a metal atom, usually an ion, acts as an *acceptor*, receiving electron pairs from ligands which are *donor* molecules. Reactions between transition metal ions and amines are examples of coordinate covalent bonding. This form of bonding can also be considered a subset of reactions known as *donor–acceptor* interactions, in which electron pairs are partially shared between atoms or between atoms and molecules.

Another particularly important subset of donor-acceptor interactions are *acid–base* interactions. These interactions include the well known Bronsted–Lowrey reactions in which a base (e.g., NaOH) reacts with an acid (e.g., H_2SO_4) to give a salt (e.g., Na_2SO_4).The reactions of Lewis acid–bases, such as antimony penta-fluoride (a Lewis acid) with ammonia (a Lewis Base), are also examples. The key feature of Lewis acid–base reactions is that Lewis acids are electron deficient and Lewis bases have an unbonded electron pair. Acid–base interactions have recently become very popular for describing observed adhesion phenomena. It should be clearly noted, however, that acid–base interactions are just one of a set of inter-actions which can take place between atoms and molecules and are not a funda-mental force of nature. We discuss each of these interactions and how they may play a role in the understanding of adhesion phenomena in ensuing sections.

4.2.4   Repulsive Forces

We have laid the groundwork describing the interactions between atoms or mole-cules through the interaction of their electron clouds and nuclei. However, remember that electrons are negatively charged particles. If two electron clouds come close enough together, the electrons see each other for what they are. When atoms or molecules come very near each other, there is a repulsion of their respective electron clouds and a resulting repulsion of the atoms or molecules. The equations described earlier all show potential energies of interaction which vary with the inverse power of distance to the sixth power or less. In comparison to repulsive forces, these are long range interactions. To describe repulsive forces, the inverse distance must be raised to a much higher power to signify just how short range these interactions are. One of the earliest and most famous potential energy expressions proposed to describe the interactions between atoms or molecules was developed by Lennard-Jones [8], specifically:

$$\Phi^{L-J} = -\frac{A}{r^6} + \frac{B}{r^{12}}$$

In this expression, A is a constant which scales the attractive interactions while B is a constant which scales the repulsive interactions. The attractive potential is written as the reciprocal sixth power of distance. If we compare this expression with those written above for the various van der Waals interactions, we find that all of them depend on distance to the reciprocal sixth power. The repulsive interaction is very short range in that the reciprocal is raised is the twelfth power of distance. This expression allows us to at least infer the effect of the various attractive constants on things having to do with surfaces. A Lennard-Jones force can also be calculated by taking the derivative of the potential with respect to distance as follows:

$$F^{L\text{-}J} = -\frac{d\Phi^{L\text{-}J}}{dr} = -\frac{6A}{r^7} + \frac{12B}{r^{13}} \tag{4.4}$$

This expression plays a role in our calculation of the interaction of two surfaces.

4.3   Surface Forces and Surface Energy

Surfaces abound in nature. Surfaces and interfaces are the demarcations between various states of matter, between different chemical entities, and between aggregates of those chemical entities, such as materials and living things. Materials, especially liquids, exhibit easily observable surface forces. If you attempt to slowly push a probe through the surface of a pure liquid such as water, you would encounter a resistance which is a manifestation of surface forces. In nature, surface forces allow insects to walk on water, for example. Interfacial forces induce the phenomenon of capillary rise which, when accompanied by transpiration, allows fluids to be transported from the roots to the tops of trees. The fact that liquids have a surface energy is also demonstrated by a simple experiment. We know, for example, that all things in nature tend to their lowest available energy state. A finely divided liquid, when suspended in another medium, assumes a spherical shape. Why?

Liquids have an energy associated with their surface. Spheres have the lowest possible surface area of any three dimensional object. Since all things tend to their lowest energy state, liquid droplets tend to be spherical (in the absence of gravitational distortion of shape) so that the energy associated with having a surface is minimized. Understanding surfaces and surface energetics is an important part of understanding adhesion and adhesives. It is the interfacial region which plays a crucial role not only in the forming of the adhesive bond, but also in the transfer of stress once the bond has formed.

Adamson [9] provides a simple molecular view of why liquids have an extra energy associated with their surface. Let us view the molecules in a liquid as a collection of balls interacting with each other by the set of forces described above. A molecule in the bulk of the liquid interacts with all of its nearest neighbors equally. However, a molecule which exists at a surface can interact only with molecules below and to the sides of it . This molecule has "unrequited valences." To counteract this imbalance of forces at the surface, the molecules tend to be further apart, thus increasing the force acting in the plane of the surface. This leads to the feel that a liquid has a "skin." In fact, it has been experimentally demonstrated that liquids (at their triple point) have lower density in the surface region [10]. Thus, we could explain the observed phenomena by saying that surface forces result from an imbalance in intermolecular forces for molecules which exist at a demarcation between phases and materials.

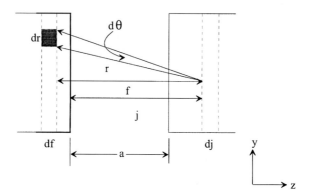

Figure 4.2   Diagram showing the basis of the calculation carried out by Fowler and Guggenheim. The diagram shows the indices over which the iterations are carried out. The basic idea is to sum all of the interactions between all elements on one side of the interface with all the elements on the other. (Redrawn from Fowler and Guggenheim)

One means of calculating the effect of molecular interactions between two surfaces is that described by Fowler and Guggenheim [11]. The type of calculation is similar to others found in the literature and its basis is shown in Fig. 4.2. Two important assumptions are used in this calculation. The first is that the density of the molecules is a constant throughout either side of the interacting surfaces. On a molecular scale, this is incorrect. However, qualitatively it provides a reasonable answer. The second assumption is that each point on either side of the interacting surfaces is acting by means of the Lennard-Jones force described earlier.

The entire integral used in the calculation is as follows:

$$F_T^{\text{L-J}} = 2\pi n^2 \int_{j=a}^{j=\infty} dj \int_{f=j}^{f=\infty} f \, df \int_{r=f}^{r=\infty} \left[-\frac{6A}{r^7} + \frac{12B}{r^{13}} \right] dr = \frac{2\pi n^2}{a^3} \left[\frac{A}{12} - \frac{B}{90a^6} \right] \tag{4.5}$$

In this expression, n is the density of molecules on either side of the two surfaces, a is the distance of separation of the two surfaces and A and B are the attractive and repulsive Lennard-Jones constants, respectively. The calculation starts by determining the number of molecules in an annulus at a distance r and varying the angle $d\theta$ and the interaction of all possible annuli on the leftmost surface on a point on the rightmost surface. The calculation then integrates over all possible points in the rightmost surface.

Now look at the total energy, ξ_T, necessary to separate these two surfaces to an infinite distance. We integrate the total force over all distances from the equilibrium distance, r_0, out to infinity:

$$\xi_T = \int_{a=r_0}^{a=\infty} F_T^{\text{L-J}} \, da \tag{4.6}$$

A force times a distance is energy. The term r_0 is the equilibrium distance between the two surfaces. Plugging the result of Eq. (4.5) into Eq. (4.6) gives us the total energy of interaction between these two surfaces:

$$\xi_T = \frac{\pi n^2}{12 r_0}\left(A - \frac{B}{30 r_0^6}\right)$$

Realizing that at r_0 (the equilibrium distance), the total force is zero, we have:

$$\frac{A}{12} = \frac{B}{90 r_0^6}$$

Substituting this equation into the expression for the total energy we have:

$$\xi_T = \frac{\pi n^2 A}{16 r_0^2} = 2\gamma \Rightarrow \gamma = \frac{\pi n^2 A}{32 r_0^2} \tag{4.7}$$

This is a crucial equation for this section of this book. Using the method of Fowler and Guggenheim, we have calculated the total energy of interaction existing between two surfaces whose molecules are interacting by means of a Lennard-Jones force. That interaction is found to depend upon the density of molecules in the surface, the equilibrium distance between the two surfaces (which could just as well be taken as an intermolecular spacing, making the assumption that the two surfaces were actually in contact at equilibrium), and the attractive constant A. The total energy due to the presence of two surfaces in contact is dependent upon the intermolecular forces that exist in the material and upon the intermolecular spacing. Equation (4.7) goes on to define a quantity γ which is one-half on the total energy of interaction. This quantity, γ, is the *surface energy* of the material. Note that γ depends upon the magnitude of intermolecular forces as demonstrated by its dependence on the constant A. The surface energy γ plays a crucial role in the understanding of adhesion phenomena. It is important to know that it is just as much a materials parameter as the tensile strength or other descriptors of materials properties. Table 4.1 provides a listing of the measured surface energy for a number of familiar liquids.

We can consider now how the surface energy and the stiffness of a material are related. The isothermal Young's modulus of a material can be shown to be [12]:

$$E = r_0\left(\frac{\partial \Phi^{\mathrm{L\text{-}J}}(r)}{\partial r}\right)_{T, r=r_0}$$

Table 4.1   Surface Energies of Familiar Liquids

Liquid	Surface energy (mJ/m^2) at 25°C
Water	72.0
Epoxy resin	43.0
Glycerol	63.4
Ethylene glycol	47.7
n-hexane	18.4
Benzene	28.9
Nitrobenzene	43.9

The subscripts indicate that the differential is taken at constant temperature and at $r = r_0$. The Lennard-Jones potential can be substituted into this expression and through algebra and the use of the equilibrium distance argument presented earlier, we find that

$$E = \frac{\pi n^2 A}{r_0^3}$$

Using Eq. (4.7), we can show that

$$E = \frac{32\gamma}{r_0}$$

This very interesting result shows that the isothermal Young's modulus is directly related to the surface energy of a material. We find that those materials with the highest stiffness are also those with the highest surface energies. Similar correlations can be drawn with other parameters related to the cohesive properties of materials.

4.4   Work of Cohesion and Adhesion

Consider the situation shown in Fig. 4.3. In this thought experiment, the brittle material of unit cross sectional area is subjected to a tensile force. The material breaks, creating two new surfaces. Since the material is completely brittle, the work done on the sample is dissipated only in creating the new surface. Under those assumptions, if both sides of the broken material are of the same composition, then we can say

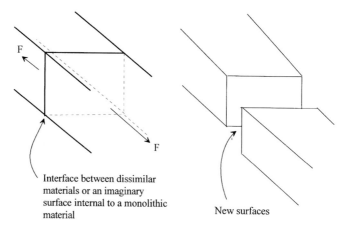

Interface between dissimilar materials or an imaginary surface internal to a monolithic material

New surfaces

Figure 4.3   Diagram showing the basis for the calculation of the work of cohesion and adhesion. A monolithic material is broken to create two surfaces of unit area. An interface between two materials is separated to create two different surfaces, each of unit area. The materials are assumed to be completely non-energy absorbing and non-energy dissipating, that is, entirely brittle

$$W_{\mathrm{coh}} = 2\gamma \tag{4.8}$$

where W_{coh} is defined as the *work of cohesion*. This equation has much the same sense as the result of the Fowler–Guggenheim analysis which resulted in Eq. (4.7). We can understand the origin of Eq. (4.8) if we just realize that the only thing which we have done by the application of work to the imaginary specimen is the creation of two new surfaces, each of unit area. If the new surfaces are each made of the same material, then the total energy expended must have been twice the surface energy of the material.

We have already discussed a similar situation when we discussed the definition of the strain energy release rate. The reader should examine Sections 2.4 and 3.5.1.2. When we derived the equation for the strain energy release rate, we discussed the effect of a crack propagating in a body. What happens when that crack propagates? *Two new surfaces are created!* Thus, in the case of a competely brittle material:

$$\frac{F^2}{2w}\frac{\delta C}{\delta a} \geq \mathcal{G}_{Ic} = W_{\mathrm{coh}} \tag{4.9}$$

In this equation, the lower case "c" stands for "critical" while the upper case "C" stands for the compliance of the material. The remainder of the symbols are defined in Chapters 2 and 3. This equation states that a crack grows in a completely brittle material, when the strain energy exceeds the surface energy of the material. This criterion is known as the Griffith fracture criterion [13] and was the first of its type. Griffith and his co-workers found that very few materials had a strain energy release rate as low as the work of cohesion, unsized glass fibers being one of those materials. It is found that most materials do not fail in a brittle manner, but absorb energy in a number of ways, including viscoelastically. Only a few materials behave according to the Griffith fracture criterion.

Imagine a situation in which two dissimilar materials are in intimate contact. Once again a tensile force splits the materials into two dissimilar materials. If the sample is of unit cross sectional area, then the energy expended should be the sum of the two surface energies. This is an incomplete description of this imaginary experiment. Because the two dissimilar materials were in contact, there were inter-molecular forces present which are now missing since the materials were separated. That is, an *interfacial energy* may have been present before the materials were split apart. As this energy is missing after the two surfaces are separated, we must subtract it from the energy done to create the two new surfaces:

$$W_{\mathrm{A}} = \gamma_1 + \gamma_2 - \gamma_{12} \tag{4.10}$$

where W_{A} is the *work of adhesion*, γ_i is the surface energy of the *i*th material and γ_{12} is the interfacial energy between the two materials in contact. This equation was postulated centuries ago and is known as the Dupre equation [14]. The interfacial energy can also be considered as the energy necessary to create a unit area of interface. The Dupre equation plays a central role in the study of adhesion. It is important to note that the work of adhesion is a thermodynamic parameter.

Therefore, it should not depend upon factors such as rate, thickness of adhesive, or other parameters which could affect the physical properties of the bulk adhesive. However, the work of adhesion is dependent upon temperature as well as the chemical constitution of the adhesive as would any chemical system.

4.5   Methods of Measurement of Surface Energy and Related Parameters

4.5.1   Surface Tension

If an attempt is made to push a probe through the surface of a liquid, the probe encounters a resistance to the deformation of the surface; known as the *surface tension*. Surface tension and surface energy are numerically identical for liquids. Surface energy is generally given in units of millijoules per meter squared (mJ/m^2) while surface tension is given in units of dynes/cm or Newtons per meter (N/m), i.e., the surface tension is given as a force per unit length. Techniques for the measurement of the surface tension of liquids have their basis in two types of measurements: probes and surface area increase. The probe methods generally involve the passage of a probe through the surface and the measurement of the force necessary to accomplish that passage. Such methods include the Wilhelmy plate [15] and the du Nuoy [16] ring.

Surface area increase can be used to measure the surface tension of liquids since the minimization of surface energy is a driving force in nature. We can measure surface area by suspending a drop of liquid on the tip of a syringe and then increasing the volume of the drop until it falls from the syringe under the action of gravity. The drop's shape depends upon the surface tension of the liquid. We could also place a clean capillary tube into a pool of liquid and observe the height to which the liquid travels up the tube under the influence of capillary pressure. The following sections include short descriptions of a few of these methods. When determining liquid surface tensions, the liquids must be in the purest possible state. A double distillation of the liquid in scrupulously clean glassware is recommended. Extremely small quantities of contaminants, especially those materials which are surface active, can cause very large changes in surface tension.

4.5.1.1   Drop Weight/Volume Method

The "Drop Weight/Drop Volume" [17] method is one of the easiest ways to determine both surface and interfacial tensions of liquids. The main piece of equipment necessary to perform this measurement is a hypodermic syringe equipped with a micrometer-driven plunger. A hypodermic needle with a highly polished tip and with known dimensions is applied to the end of the syringe. The liquid of interest is placed in the syringe which is then placed over a vessel. The micrometer is slowly driven until a drop falls from the tip of the needle. The number of drops are counted and their volume measured. Alternatively, the number of drops are counted and their weight is measured. The weight is converted to volume through knowledge of the density of the liquid. The average volume necessary to cause the drop the fall is used to calculate the surface tension of the liquid. Appropriate geometry factors are applied to arrive at the correct surface tension [18]. Interfacial tensions can be measured by placing the end of the hypodermic needle in another liquid in which the test liquid is not soluble. The liquid of higher density should be in the syringe. With a correction for buoyancy, the interfacial tension between the liquids can be measured.

4.5.1.2 Du Nuoy Tensiometer

Commercial instruments based upon the du Nuoy ring tensiometer [16] are available. The instrument consists of a sensitive force measuring device, such as a torsion wire, from which is suspended a lever arm. From the lever arm is suspended a harness and ring. The ring is usually made of platinum or another noble metal and is kept scrupulously clean. Normal cleaning procedures are usually followed by firing the ring with a propane torch.

The dimensions and shape of the ring are usually lumped into a "ring factor" supplied by its manufacturer. The shape of the ring is extremely important as any distortion results in incorrect measurements of the surface tension. The ring is placed under the surface of the test liquid. The liquid is slowly moved downward until the ring is near the surface. The force is repeatedly balanced by means of the torsion wire and eventually the ring breaks through the liquid surface. That force is recorded and by means of appropriate conversion factors, the surface tension of the liquid is calculated.

4.5.2   Surface Energy of Solids

The concept of surface tension is not applicable to solids. Even though it is likely that solid surfaces are under tension, it is not easy to conceive of a method to measure surface area increases or forces necessary to pass probes through the surface of a solid since both would irreparably damage the solid surface. Since the damage is irreversible, this would not be considered a thermodynamic measurement. However, the concept of a surface energy is certainly applicable to solid surfaces. Because a solid surface contains unrequited bonds, just as those between the molecules in the surface of a liquid do, a solid surface has a surface energy. Unfortunately, none of the methods even remotely similar to the ones we have described earlier are applicable to solids. For the most part, we have only indirect methods for estimating the surface energy of a solid. The easiest ways to estimate of the surface energy of a solid are based upon contact angle measurements. These measurements are so fundamental to the study of adhesives and adhesion, that it is appropriate to devote considerable space to their description. In the next section, we also describe a mechanical method for determining the surface energy of materials: the surface forces apparatus.

4.5.2.1 Contact Angle Methods

In a contact angle measurement, a drop of a liquid is placed upon the surface of a solid. The liquid is chosen so that it does not swell the surface of the solid nor does it react with the surface. The solid is assumed to be perfectly smooth and rigid. We can often find liquids which do not chemically interact with the solid, but it is difficult to find perfectly smooth solids. In addition, the forces which act at an interface are not only not negligible but in many cases, can distort the surface at a distance considerably remote from the area of contact. This can happen even in substrates which are nominally rigid. Thus, many of the suppositions necessary for the analysis of the contact angle measurement are difficult to achieve in reality. However, the simplicity of the technique, as well as its ability to provide useful data, tend to overshadow these shortcomings.

A diagram of the contact angle measurement is shown in Fig. 4.4.

The liquid is placed on the surface so that the effects of gravity to flatten the drop are negligible. Drop size is usually small (tens of microliters). The dispensing instrument is held very close to the surface and the drop of liquid is "laid" on the surface rather than "dropped." The drop is allowed to flow and equilibrate with the surface. Viscous liquids are allowed a longer time to equilibrate than low viscosity liquids. The measurement is usually done with a goniometer which is nothing more than a protractor mounted inside a telescope. The table upon which the solid rests should be precisely leveled and that level is used as the baseline of the protractor. Care must be taken to ensure that the cross hairs of the protractor are at the exact drop edge. This can be difficult when contact angles are either very high or very low. Several measurements are made on several drops which are placed in several locations on the surface. Accuracies of $\pm 1°$ are attainable with careful measurement.

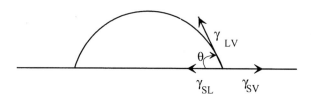

Figure 4.4 Schematic of the contact angle experiment. A drop of liquid is placed on a perfectly smooth, rigid solid. The angle of contact is measured at the three phase points between the solid, the liquid, and the vapor. The "interfacial tensions" between the phases used by Young to generate his equation are shown. Note the interfacial tension between the liquid and the solid is undefined

Contact angle measurements are dependent upon the direction in which the measurement is made. When a drop is laid down upon a surface and advances over the surface as it spreads, the contact angle in this situation is known as the *advancing contact angle.* If liquid is withdrawn from a drop that has already come into equilibrium with the surface, the contact angle is known as the *receding contact angle.* In general, the advancing angle is larger than the receding angle. The phenomenon of having a different contact angle under advancing and receding conditions is known as *contact angle hysteresis.* Johnson and Dettre [19] have described a number of reasons contact angle measurements are hysteretic, specifically: nonhomogeneous surface chemistry, surface roughness, and molecular rearrangement in the solid induced by the liquid and *vice versa.* The hysteretic character of contact angle measurements raises some doubts as to their character as equilibrium measurements of surface energetics.

The importance of the contact angle measurement was established by the analysis originally done by Young [20]. However, his analysis is inherently incorrect because solid surfaces do not have a well defined "surface tension." Additionally, the analysis did not take into account the potential distortion of the solid surface by the action of the surface tension of the liquid. Cherry [21] was able to show by thermodynamic arguments that the expression was correct, but not for the vectorial kind of argument originally provided by Young. The Young equation states:

$$\gamma_{LV} \cos \theta = \gamma_{SV} - \gamma_{SL} \qquad (4.11)$$

where θ is the contact angle (as shown in Fig. 4.4) and the γ_{ij} are the appropriate interfacial tensions between the "S" solid, the "L" liquid and the "V" vapor. It should be noted the γ_{SV} is the solid–vapor interfacial energy and not the true surface free energy of the solid. The surface free energy is related to γ_{SV} through the following relationship:

$$\gamma_{SV} = \gamma_S - \pi_e$$

where γ_S is the true surface free energy of the solid and π_e is a quantity known as the equilibrium spreading pressure. The term, π_e, is a measure of the energy released through adsorption of the vapor onto the surface of the solid, thus lowering its surface free energy. The equilibrium spreading pressure is important when the solid surface energy is high and the liquid surface energy is low.

An example of this situation is the wetting of a clean metal by a hydrocarbon. The equilibrium spreading pressure is manifested in the observation that the contact angle of the hydrocarbon on the clean metal surface is not zero even though the metal surface energy is much higher than that of the hydrocarbon. The equilibrium spreading pressure is not important when a high surface energy liquid wets a low surface energy material. Such a situation is exemplified by water on polyethylene. In most of this book, we will ignore π_e. Any quotation of γ_S which has been measured without consideration of the equilibrium spreading pressure should be considered suspect.

We know from our discussion of the Dupre equation that

$$W_A = \gamma_{LV} + \gamma_{SV} - \gamma_{SL}$$

Substitution of the Young Equation into the Dupre Equation results in the Young–Dupre Equation which states:

$$W_A = \gamma_{LV}(1 + \cos\theta) \tag{4.12}$$

This deceptively simple equation relates a thermodynamic parameter to two easily determinable quantities: the contact angle and the liquid–vapor interfacial tension. Examination of the data in Table 4.1 provides estimates of the prediction of the work of adhesion between a solid and a liquid. Suppose that an epoxy resin (surface tension of about 43 dynes/cm) completely wets the surface of an aluminum plate. The contact angle would be 0, $1 + \cos\theta$ would be 2 and the work of adhesion would be 86 mJ/m^2. This is an exceedingly small quantity. This energy is far lower than the amount needed to break all but the weakest of adhesive bonds. With the substantial difference between the work of adhesion and the actual amount of energy necessary to break an adhesive bond, one would assume that the work of adhesion plays an insignificant role on the practical work of adhesion. In Chapter 6, we find that this is not the case and discuss attempts to relate the thermodynamic work of adhesion to practical adhesion.

4.5.2.2   Direct Measurements of Solid Surface Energy

The above discussion indicates that the direct measurement of the surface energy of solids is a difficult task. In the modern examination of interactions at surfaces, a new technique allows us to probe directly the interactions between solid surfaces. The technique is the surface forces apparatus (SFA) [22] and the analysis of the experiment was done by Johnson, Kendall, and Roberts (JKR) [23]. Understanding the basis of the JKR theory and the measurement gives insight into many of the basic physical phenomena of adhesion. Energy balance, fracture mechanics, and mechanical properties of materials all play a role in the measurement as well as the analysis of the measurement.

Figure 4.5 shows a schematic of the meeting of two spheres. Hertz [24] was the first to analyze this situation and made the assumption that the spheres were

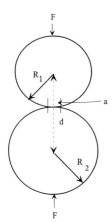

Figure 4.5   Diagram showing the basis for the Hertz analysis. Shown are two elastic spheres in contact. The radii of curvature are shown as well as the distance of separation of the two centers

perfectly elastic and exhibited no adhesion. Hertz was able to show that:

$$a^3 = \left(\frac{3\pi}{4}\right)(k_1 + k_2)\left(\frac{R_1 R_2}{R_1 + R_2}\right)F$$

where

$$k_i = \frac{1 - \nu_i^2}{\pi E_i}$$

The term, ν_i, is the Poisson's ratio of the ith material, E_i is its tensile modulus, R_i is the radius of curvature of the ith material, F is the force which is applied to the two materials, and a is the radius of contact between the two spheres. In addition, the Hertz theory demonstrated that the distance of approach of the centers of the two spheres, d, would be:

$$d^3 = \left(\frac{9\pi^2}{16}\right)(k_1 + k_2)^2\left(\frac{R_1 R_2}{R_1 + R_2}\right)^{-1}F^2 \tag{4.15}$$

Figure 4.6 shows the situation as analyzed by Johnson, Kendall and Roberts. These workers noted that the force necessary to separate two bodies in contact was not zero as assumed by Hertz and that the radius of contact of the two bodies was not well predicted by the Hertz equation written above. The distance of separation equation was also incorrect. Johnson, Kendall and Roberts made the correct supposition in stating that the deviation of the Hertz equations from experimental observations was due to the forces of adhesion.

The method for examining the contact mechanics of two spheres with forces of adhesion between their surfaces is very similar to the method we used to analyze linear elastic fracture mechanics in Chapters 2 and 3. It involves an *energy balance* approach. That is, the situation is not analyzed in terms of stresses and strains as it was in the case of the Goland–Reissner analysis of lap shear specimens, but rather in terms of energies. For the system shown in Fig. 4.6, we say that the total energy in the system, U_T, is made up of three parts: U_M, the mechanical potential energy, U_E, the elastic energy in the system, and U_S, the surface energy in the system. U_S is simply the work of adhesion in the case of spheres made of different materials in contact with one another and the work of cohesion in the case of similar materials

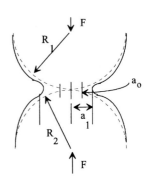

Figure 4.6   Schematic of the situation analyzed by JKR. The Hertz radius of contact is given by a_0 while the radius of contact for two bodies displaying adhesion is given by a_1. The radii of curvature are as described in Fig. 4.5. The dotted lines show the Hertz situation while the solid lines show the situation in which the two bodies display adhesion to one another

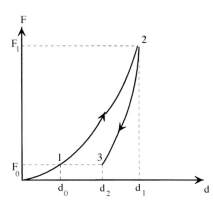

Figure 4.7   Force-displacement plot for the analysis of the contact mechanics of two spheres by means of the energy balance approach

in contact with one another. Let's look at the mechanical potential energy next. For this analysis, we need to examine Fig. 4.7.

We first calculate the mechanical potential energy in the system. If a force F_0 is applied to the two spheres and a resultant displacement (d_2) occurs, we can easily write the mechanical potential energy in the system as $F_0 d_2$ (position 3 in Fig. 4.7). We can calculate the elastic energy by first saying that the spheres are pushed into Hertzian contact by a force F_0, which results in a Hertz displacement of d_0. This situation ensues when no surface forces are present and corresponds with position 1 in Fig. 4.7 and with radius a_0 as shown in Fig. 4.6. We can now invoke the presence of surface forces by saying that this is equivalent to having an extra Hertz force applied to the two spheres. This is now the situation at position 2 with force F_1, displacement d_1 (Fig. 4.7) and radius a_1 (Fig. 4.6). Positions 1 and 2 are not real, but rather virtual situations which allow us to calculate the energy in the system. We now relax the system to get to the experimentally determined state at position 3 in Fig. 4.7. The total elastic energy in the system is now the amount of energy necessary to attain position 2 minus the energy required to attain position 3. The energy necessary to attain position 2 is easily determined, since we have assumed that the body follows Hertzian mechanics. Rearranging Eq. (4.15), we can find d and then integrate $d\,\mathrm{d}F$ from $F = 0$ to $F = F_1$:

$$U_2 = \frac{2}{3} \int_0^{F_1} \frac{F^{2/3}}{K^{2/3} R^{1/3}}\,\mathrm{d}F$$

where $R = (R_1 R_2)/(R_1 + R_2)$ and $K = (4/3\pi)(k_1 + k_2)$.

The calculation of U_3 can be equally straightforward if one knows the relationship between F and d for the "unloading" curve. The load-displacement curve for this situation was derived by Johnson [25] and it has the form:

$$d = \frac{2}{3} \frac{F}{K a_1}$$

which leads to:

$$U_3 = \int_{F_1}^{F_0} \frac{2}{3} \frac{F}{K a_1}\,\mathrm{d}F$$

Combining all of these relationships we have:

$$U_T = \frac{1}{K^{2/3}R^{1/3}}[\tfrac{1}{15}F_1^{2/3} + \tfrac{1}{3}F_0^2 F_1^{-1/3}] - \frac{1}{K^{2/3}R^{1/3}}[\tfrac{1}{3}F_0 F_1^{2/3} + \tfrac{2}{3}F_0^2 F_1^{-1/3}] - W_A \pi \frac{R^{2/3}F_1^{2/3}}{K^{2/3}}$$

This complicated algebraic expression can be used to find a relationship between F_1 and F_0 and more importantly, a relationship between F_0 and a_1. At equilibrium (here is the energy balance part):

$$\frac{dU_T}{dF_1} = 0$$

Applying this equilibrium condition to the equation for U_T we find

$$F_1 = F_0 + 3W_A \pi R + \sqrt{6W_A R F_0 + (3W_A \pi R)^2}$$

This equation shows that the apparent Hertz force is greater than the actual applied load and that the increase is due to the work of adhesion. This result can also be used to predict other aspects of the contact region when surface forces are taken into account. The radius of the contact area is found to be bigger than the Hertz contact area according to the following equation:

$$a^3 = \frac{R}{K}\left(F + 3W_A \pi R + \sqrt{6W_A \pi R F + (3W_A \pi R)^2}\right) \qquad (4.16)$$

Examination of this equation shows that at zero applied force, there is still a finite contact radius which is not predicted by the Hertz analysis and which is one of the possible experimental proofs of the JKR theory. Also, by examination of the equation for the contact radius, we find that if a tensile force is applied to the two spheres (i.e., a $-F$), the radius decreases until the point that

$$F_{JKR} = -\tfrac{3}{2}W_A \pi R \qquad (4.17)$$

One can form two elastic spheres and place them in intimate contact. A tensile load is applied until they spontaneously separate. A force can be measured and directly related to the work of adhesion. If the two materials in contact are the same material, then $W_A = W_C = 2\gamma_S$ and Eq. (4.17) can be used to measure directly the surface energy of a solid.

Two basic kinds of equipment are used to measure directly the surface energy of solids based on the JKR theory. The first one was described by JKR; a schematic of this apparatus is shown in Fig. 4.8.

The apparatus is remarkably simple. The sample must be optically clear and elastic under the loads of interest. The other half of the sample can also be a sphere but most often is flat and coated either with the same material as the hemisphere is made or another material of interest (a sphere in contact with a sphere is the same as a sphere in contact with a flat material according to the Derjaguin approximation [26] if the radius of curvature of the sphere is large). The hemisphere of sample is mounted on an optically clear, rigid support capable of vertical movement. The force is measured by means of an analytical balance and the radius of contact between the

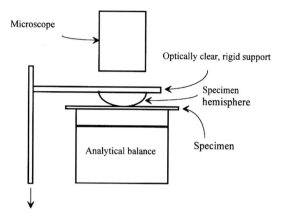

Figure 4.8   Schematic diagram of an apparatus useful for determining surface energy by means of the JKR theory

sphere and the flat is measured through the optical microscope. Equation (4.16) is used to determine the work of adhesion between the two materials.

The apparatus most often used for direct measurements of the forces of adhesion between solid surfaces is the surfaces forces apparatus (SFA) [22]. Originally described by Tabor [27], but extensively developed and used by Israelachvili [28] and co-workers, the SFA uses a direct mechanical means to measure the distances between surfaces down to the Angstrom level as well a mechanical means to measure the forces between those surfaces. Figure 4.9 shows a diagram of the surface forces apparatus.

The apparatus measures force by the deflection of a double cantilever of known force constant and the measurement of the distance of separation of the two surfaces through interferometry. The samples need to be almost atomically flat, thin (about 2–5 microns) and optically clear. The back of each sample is silvered to make it

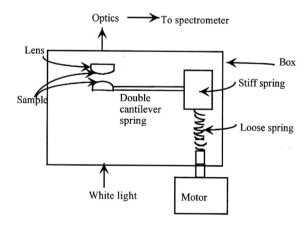

Figure 4.9   Schematic of the Israelachvili Surface Forces Apparatus (SFA)

partially reflective. The samples are then mounted on the lenses by means of an adhesive. The lenses are mounted into the apparatus so that the apexes of the lenses are crossed with respect to one another, resulting in essentially a point contact. The sample surfaces are brought close together by a motor. The distance separating the sample surfaces can be monitored by passing white light through the samples. As the samples near each other, interferometric fringes can be observed in the spectrometer. These are known as "Fringes of Equal Chromatic Order" or FECO. The distance between the fringes (as observed in the spectrometer) can be used to measure the distance between the surfaces. The shape of the fringes also corresponds to the shape of the lens' surfaces.

When the sample surface is not in contact, the FECO are roughly parabolic in shape. When the surfaces are in contact, the contact area is flat and the rest of the FECO mirrors the shape of the surfaces outside of the contact zone. The JKR theory predicts such a shape and experiments have shown it to be correct [29]. At some distance of separation, the forces of attraction between the surfaces overcome the restraining force of the spring, and the samples jump into contact. After contact, compressive force can be applied and Eq. (4.16) can be used to measure the work of adhesion between the two surfaces.

Alternatively, after the jump into contact is made, a tensile force can be applied and the force necessary to remove the samples from contact can be measured using Eq. (4.17). If possible, both measurements should be made and the results should agree. Results of measurements of this type and their implications to adhesion science are discussed in Chapter 6.

4.6 Surface Thermodynamics and Predictions of Surface and Interfacial Tensions

In the context of this book, the *understanding* of adhesion and adhesives, it is important to relate contact angle measurements to the basic forces between atoms and molecules. The seminal work in this area was done during the 1950s by Good and Girifalco [30]. To understand this work, we must first realize another important aspect of surface energy, its status as a thermodynamic parameter. If we examine Fig. 4.10, we see an imaginary situation with a section of surface drawn as a free body.

Imagine that we have a line (indicated by the dashed line) drawn somewhere in that body. We imagine a force acting across the line as shown in Fig. 4.10. We know from our earlier discussion that the surface tends to resist deformation. If the surface is a liquid, the amount of resistance is the "surface tension." If the surface is deformed, such as by increasing area, work is done on this system. Following Cherry [31], we can describe the internal energy of a system as follows:

$$d\xi = dq - dw + \sum_i \mu_i \, dN_i$$

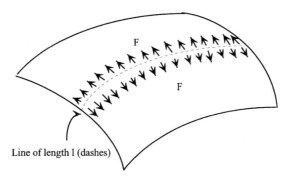

Line of length 1 (dashes)

Figure 4.10   A section of surface through which a dashed imaginary line has been drawn. The action of surface tension is to pull in two dimensions across this line. In a liquid, surface tension and surface energy have the same value as well as the same sense

where ξ is the internal energy of the system, q is heat, w is work, μ_i is the chemical potential of the ith constituent in the system and N_i is the number of moles of the ith component in the system. For the situation of importance to our discussion, the work in the system includes not only the normally considered pressure (P)-volume (V) work, but since the system contains a surface, it also can do work by expanding the surface area. Thus:

$$dw = d(PV) - \gamma \, d\Omega$$

where Ω is the surface area. The change in heat in the system is defined in terms of the entropy (S):

$$dq = T \, dS$$

Using the above equations and constraining the system to be at constant temperature, pressure and moles of materials, we can easily show that:

$$d\xi = T \, dS - P \, dV + \gamma \, d\Omega + \sum_i \mu_i \, dN_i$$

The Helmholtz free energy of a system is:

$$A = \xi - TS$$

and

$$dA = \gamma \, d\Omega - P \, dV - S \, dT + \sum_i \mu_i \, dN_i$$

which, if we define a system under constraints of constant volume, temperature, and moles of materials, gives:

$$\gamma = \left(\frac{\partial A}{\partial \Omega} \right)_{V, T, N_i}$$

The importance of this equation is simply stated in that the surface energy can be described as the change in a thermodynamic system free energy variable with a change in area. A similar derivation can be made for the Gibbs free energy of the system, G, in that situation:

$$\gamma = \left(\frac{\partial G}{\partial \Omega}\right)_{P,T,N_i}$$

The Gibbs free energy and the Helmholtz free energy are related as follows:

$$G = A + PV$$

The work of cohesion and adhesion that we have previously described are therefore also thermodynamic variables. This derivation and the definition of the surface energy as a free energy variable sets the stage for the Good-Girifalco derivation.

4.6.1   The Good–Girifalco Relationship

Good and Girifalco define a thermodynamic parameter, usually denoted ϕ, based upon the following ratio:

$$\phi = \frac{W_A}{\sqrt{W_{C,1}W_{C,2}}}$$

where ϕ is known as the *interaction parameter*, W_A is the work of adhesion and the $W_{C,i}$ are the works of cohesion of the two phases in contact. If we enter the equations for the definitions of the works of cohesion and adhesion, the Dupre equations, we find:

$$\phi = \frac{\gamma_1 + \gamma_2 - \gamma_{12}}{\sqrt{2\gamma_1 2\gamma_2}}$$

rearranging

$$\gamma_{12} = \gamma_1 + \gamma_2 - 2\phi\sqrt{\gamma_1\gamma_2} \tag{4.18}$$

This is an interesting equation. It shows that if we have a way to calculate or measure ϕ, we can get the value of γ_{12} by knowing the values of γ_1 and γ_2. We know from the thermodynamic derivation we performed above and from the calculations that we did in deriving the basis for the surface energy (Eq. 4.7), we find the following:

$$\phi = \frac{(\pi n_1 n_2 A_{12})/16r_{0,12}^2}{\sqrt{(\pi n_1^2 A_1/16r_{0,1}^2)(\pi n_2^2 A_2/16r_{0,2}^2)}}$$

Knowledge of the attractive constants of the materials allows us to calculate ϕ, which in turn allows us to calculate γ_{12}. The attractive constants for a number of liquids are known and thus ϕ can be calculated. Good and Elbing [32] used this relationship to predict interfacial energies of materials. An example is shown in Table 4.2.

The results of Good and Elbing are important for a number of reasons. First of all, it gives credence to the idea that molecules can act at interfaces in the same way they interact in their own bulk material. It also shows that we can calculate those

Table 4.2   A Sampling of the Results of Good & Elbing, showing the Relationship Between Measured and Calculated Interfacial Energies

Compound	Polarizability $(cm^3 \times 10^{-23})$	Dipole moment (Debye)	Ionization potential (eV)	Liquid surface tension (dynes/cm)	Interfacial tension with water (dynes/cm)	ϕ_{calc}	ϕ_{exp}
n-hexane	1.15	0.00	10.43	18.00	50.70	0.55	0.55
Chlorobenzene	1.23	1.58	10.50	33.60	37.40	0.69	0.67
Isovaleronitrile	0.99	3.53	10.00	43.90	25.70	0.97	0.97
Benzene	1.03	0.00	9.24	28.90	33.90	0.73	0.55
Carbon tetrachloride	1.06	0.00	11.10	26.95	45.00	0.61	0.55

energies in a manner familiar to anyone with some knowledge of physical chemistry. The Good and Girifalco relationship and the measurements of Good and Elbing provided the basis for further work which has added much to the understanding of adhesion. Finally, this work ties together adhesion science, contact angle measurements, and basic physical forces leading to further insight.

4.6.2   The Fowkes Hypothesis and Fractional Polarity

Fowkes [33] proposed a separation of the surface energy of a material into the potential energies of interaction that we described in the first part of this chapter. We know from quantum mechanics that the summation of potential energies is inherently incorrect in that many cross terms are neglected. The Fowkes hypothesis is a first order approximation which, simply stated, is that the surface energy of a material can be divided into component parts. Thus:

$$\gamma = \gamma^d + \gamma^p + \gamma^i + \cdots$$

where γ^p is the polar contribution to the surface energy, γ^i is the dipole induced dipole contribution to the surface energy and γ^d is the dispersion force contribution to the surface energy. Fowkes also made a fundamental hypothesis important to the study of interfaces and adhesion, namely that materials exhibiting only dispersion force interactions interact with other surfaces by only those interactions. It was also Fowkes' contention that polar force and dipole–induced dipole forces were insignificant when one of the two materials at an interface was non-polar. Mathematically this can be stated:

$$\gamma_{12} = \gamma_1 + \gamma_2 - 2\sqrt{\gamma_1^d \gamma_2^d} \tag{4.19}$$

where γ_1 and γ_2 are surface energies as we have previously defined them and γ_1^d and γ_2^d are the *dispersion force components* of the surface energy of materials 1 and 2, respectively. Examination of Eq. (4.19) and comparison to Eq. (4.18) shows that the Fowkes hypothesis states that in the case of dispersion force interactions, the interaction parameter is essentially 1.

Fowkes provided some ingenious experiments [34] which showed the validity of Eq. (4.19) in which he measured the interfacial energy between a series of liquids. One liquid was an n-alkane (which is purely dispersion force in nature) and the other liquid was mercury. The measured interfacial tensions were remarkably constant from hydrocarbon to hydrocarbon. From these measurements, he was able to calculate the dispersion force component of the surface energy of mercury. Other interfacial tension measurements with mercury then provided the dispersion force components for another series of liquids, including water, which was found to be $17\,mJ/m^2$, remarkably close to the value obtained from theoretical calculations [35]. Thus, the Fowkes measurements provide some credence for the equation as well as the separability of the surface energy of materials into their components. This subject is discussed again later in the section on acid–base interactions.

The success of the Fowkes hypothesis for dispersion force liquids prompted others to develop what is now called a theory of fractional polarity. That is, each liquid and solid was thought to have both dispersion force as well as polar force character. One such equation was developed by Owens and Wendt [36] who wrote:

$$W_A = 2\sqrt{\gamma_1^d \gamma_2^d} + 2\sqrt{\gamma_2^p \gamma_1^p}$$

This equation states that if one knows the polar force and dispersion components to the surface energy of a solid, then the work of adhesion can be determined from the sum of the square roots of their products. This equation has proven useful in the analysis of a number of experimental situations. However, the theory of fractional polarity cannot be taken to extremes. Erroneous results are obtained if the analysis is taken beyond the Owens and Wendt equation.

4.6.3   The Zisman Plot

Another fundamentally important work relating contact angles and estimation of the surface energy of solids was that of Zisman [37]. In an important series of papers, Zisman and his co-workers were able to show that contact angle measurements could be used to determine a criterion for wettability as well as a means for probing the chemistry of surfaces. In these experiments, a series of probe liquids of known surface energy were used to measure contact angles against a series of pure polymeric and non-polymeric solids. For a series of liquids, it was found that a linear or quasi-linear relationship existed between the cosine of the contact angle made by a liquid on a particular surface and the surface energy of that liquid. The linear relationship could be extrapolated to cosine $\theta = 1$ (or $\theta = 0$), thus predicting the liquid surface tension at which a liquid would spontaneously wet the solid surface. This liquid surface tension was given a special name, the *critical wetting tension of the solid surface* or γ_C.

The mathematical formulation of the Zisman relationship is as follows:

$$\cos \theta = 1 + b(\gamma_C - \gamma_{LV})$$

where θ is the contact angle, γ_{LV} is the interfacial tension between the probe liquid and air saturated with the vapor of the liquid, γ_C is the critical wetting tension and b is the slope of the line. In general, a linear relationship is obtained only for those liquids which form a homologous series (e.g., n-alkanes) on a non-wetting surface. However, quasi-linear relationships are determined for a wide range of liquids. Kitazaki and Hata [38] have shown that the γ_C, which is measured for a particular surface, is dependent upon the type of liquids used. Thus, these authors proposed that different γ_Cs be measured and quoted for different homologous series of liquids. Kitazaki and Hata would have measured and quoted a γ_C for a series of dispersion force liquids, a different γ_C for hydrogen bonding liquids, and a different γ_C for polar liquids. The fact that a different critical wetting tension is measured for each type of liquid indicates that γ_C cannot be considered a thermodynamic parameter and should not be confused with the true surface energy of a solid, which can only be approximated by contact angle methods. A method by which solid surface energies can be measured was described in a previous section (the surface forces apparatus). The non-thermodynamic character of the critical wetting tension does not diminish its utility, however In Chapter 6, we examine the critical wetting tension as the basis for a criterion for good adhesion.

The critical wetting tension of a solid surface can be used to characterize surface chemistry. Zisman and co-workers demonstrated the relationship between γ_C and the chemical structure of a series of polymers. They were able to show that a surface containing a preponderance of CH_2 groups had a higher critical wetting tension (31 dynes/cm) than a surface containing a preponderance of CH_3 groups (22 dynes/cm), and a similar relationship was found between CF_2 (18 dynes/cm) and CF_3 groups (15 dynes/cm). Similar relationships could be found for partially fluorinated hydrocarbons as well as partially chlorinated hydrocarbons. A list of the relationship between surface chemical functionality and critical wetting tension is shown in Table 4.3.

Table 4.3   The Relationship between Surface Chemical Composition and the Critical Wetting Tension of a Number of Solids

Polymer	Critical wetting tension (dynes/cm)
Polytetrafluoroethylene	18
Polydimethyl siloxane (silicone)	21
Polyethylene	31
Polystyrene	33
Polyvinyl chloride	39
Cured epoxy resin	43
Polyethylene terephthalate (PET)	43
Nylon-6,6	46

4.6.4   Modern Application of Contact Angle Measurements

Contact angle measurements are the most sensitive of surface characterization tools. Contact angle measurements probe even short range van der Waals forces. The typical "analysis depth" of contact angle measurements is on the order of only five Angstrom units. One example of this type of surface chemical probing is the recent work by Whitesides and his co-workers [39] on the unique class of materials known as self-assembling monolayers. These materials are long chain hydrocarbons with a surface reactive group at one end and another functionality at the other end. The reactive group provides chemisorption and the crystallizable hydrocarbon group provides the driving force for self-assembly. Whitesides performed a series of unique experiments; two are described here. In the first experiment, a series of mixtures of alkane thiol alcohols were chemisorbed and self-assembled on gold. The series of mixtures ranged from total C_{11} hydrocarbon with a hydroxyl terminus to a total C_{19} hydrocarbon with a hydroxyl terminus and several compositions in between. The contact angle of water was measured on this series of surfaces. A schematic representation of the data is shown in Fig. 4.11.

As can be seen, the contact angle varies from low at full coverage of C_{11}–OH groups to higher at mixed coverage to once again a low contact angle at complete C_{19}–OH coverage. Whitesides and his co-workers ascribed this variation to the change of the surface from one which was entirely covered with OH groups (the terminal group for this series of alkanes) to one in which the layer had folded over, exposing $-CH_2-$ groups. The surface covered with $-CH_2$ groups has lower surface energy than OH groups and would be expected to be more poorly wet by water than OH. At the right hand side of the graph the surface is again entirely covered with OH groups. In another experiment, the Whitesides group designed a self-assembling monolayer which was terminated with carboxyl groups [36b]. They did contact angle measurements on this surface using water of varying pH. They were able to titrate

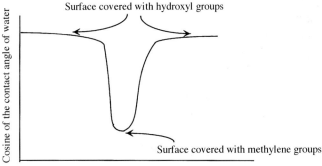

Figure 4.11   Measurements of the water contact angle on a series of surfaces in which the surface chemical concentration of $-CH_2$ groups was varied by application of varying concentration of C_{11} versus C_{19} self-assembling monolayers

the surface acidity and determine a pKa for the acid groups confined to the surface. This discussion not only amplifies the importance of contact angle measurements in surface and adhesion science, but it also describes a new area of investigation: self-assembling monolayers.

4.7   Modern Methods of Surface Analysis

Contact angle measurements provide an extremely sensitive tool by which the gross chemistry of a surface can be examined. The utility of contact angle measurements lies in their simplicity, rapidity of analysis, and economical equipment. Unfortunately, there are any number of surfaces which have equal surface energies and would thus exhibit similar critical wetting tensions. The contact angle measurement provides a "dull edge" to the knife that is cutting into the analysis of surfaces. For an adhesion scientist, it is of importance to know the chemistry of the surface where adhesion or abhesion occurs. In the past two decades, a significant number of new methods of surface analysis have been developed which now allow us to examine several features of surfaces of interest to adhesion scientists. A detailed description of these techniques is not within the scope of this book. Several references are given in the bibliography. These modern techniques yield either chemical or topological information. In the next section, we discuss techniques which probe the chemistry of surfaces.

4.7.1   Modern Methods for Analysis of the Chemistry of Surfaces

These techniques use an energetic probe to excite some physical process in a surface which results in the ejection of an energetic species which is analyzed. Table 4.4 provides a listing of some of these techniques, the species used to carry out the measurement, as well as the limitations and the capabilities of these techniques.

Table 4.4 does not list all of the techniques which have been used in surface science nor even in adhesion science. The techniques listed are the most commonly used by adhesion scientists. From the descriptions in Table 4.4, one can understand why several of these techniques are practiced in a "hard vacuum," that is, a vacuum of less than 5×10^{-7} Torr. Since the species analyzed are energetic particles, their mean free path is limited unless there are no other materials in the way. In fact, the surface analytical technique we are about to discuss is dependent upon the short mean free path of an electron in a solid.

Of the techniques listed in Table 4.4, **XPS** is by far the most widely practiced modern surface analysis technique, especially in adhesion science. The technique is based on the Einstein photoelectric effect. X-rays penetrate deeply into a material, usually to a depth of microns of more. For most atoms, the absorption of an X-ray

Table 4.4 Modern Surface Analysis Techniques, Capabilities and Limitations

Technique	Probe species	Species analyzed	Capabilities	Limitations
X-ray Photo electron Spectroscopy (XPS) or Electron Spectroscopy for Chemical Analysis (ESCA)	X-rays	Electrons (their energy and number)	Quantitative elemental analysis. Chemical information through line shape analysis. Depth profile information through angular dependent measurement. Useful for insulators and conductors. Widely used on polymers. Little spatial information.	Chemical information is limited. Depth profile information is limited. Sample can be damaged by too much X-ray exposure.
Secondary Ion Mass Spectrometry (SIMS)	Ions or neutrals	Ions (mass to charge ratio and their number)	Semi-quantitative elemental analysis. Excellent elemental depth profiling tool. Useful only for conductors or inorganic insulators.	Little chemical information. Sample is severely damaged.
Static Secondary Ion Mass Spectrometry (SSIMS)	Ions	Ions (mass to charge ratio and their number)	Non-quantitative tool for polymers. Extensive chemical information. Little sample damage. Excellent tool to use in combination with XPS.	Non-quantitative. Spectra are rich in information but are difficult to analyze for unknowns
Auger Electron Spectroscopy (AES)	Electrons	Electrons (their energy and their number)	Quantitative elemental analysis tool for semiconductors and conductors. Excellent profiling tool when used with ion milling. Excellent spatial resolution can be used for mapping.	Limited to non-insulators. Little chemical information.
Attenuated Total Reflectance Fourier Transform Infrared (ATR-FTIR) Spectroscopy	Infrared light	Infrared light	Detailed chemical information. Real specimens can be used. Non-vacuum method	Specimens must be very flat and capable of intimate contact with the necessary crystal. Depth of analysis is on the order of microns.
Infrared Reflectance Absorbance Spectroscopy (IRRAS)	Infrared light	Infrared light	Detailed chemical information. Depth of analysis on the order of 100–1000 Angstrom units. Non-vacuum method.	Need special specimens, e.g. coatings on a reflective surface.

emitted from aluminum or magnesium (material used in X-ray anode construction) is usually enough to ionize atoms. The electrons released, however, have a limited mean free path of about 50 Angstrom units and they are reabsorbed by the material except near the material's surface. Therefore, the only electrons which can escape the surface for analysis are those only a few tens of Angstrom units below the actual surface, hence the surface sensitivity of the technique.

The electrons emitted from an atom have a characteristic energy which can be analyzed by an electron spectrometer. Their number can also be counted. Knowing a set of conversion factors, one can determine the surface concentration of any element with the exception of hydrogen and helium. Using a high resolution electron spectrometer, one can also see a fine structure associated with each emission peak. The fine structure can be analyzed in terms of nearest neighbor effects. This is particularly true for the XPS peak associated with carbon. Thus, if carbon exists in a state bonded both to carbon as well as to oxygen, a small peak to the higher energy side of the main carbon peak can be detected. If carbon is also bonded to other higher electronegativity atoms such as fluorine, peaks at even higher energy are seen. This provides the basis for the limited chemical information available from XPS. We discuss some XPS experiments in the section on surface preparation of plastics in Chapter 7.

4.7.2   Topological Methods of Surface Analysis

We have already discussed the fact that contact angles can be affected by the presence of surface roughness (contact angle hysteresis). However, the analysis of this effect is not yet complete enough to use contact angles as a measure of surface topology. In Chapter 6, we find that adhesion is definitely affected by surface roughness. It is therefore important that we have methods to analyze the topology of surfaces.

The primary method for topological analysis used by adhesion scientists is electron microscopy. This technique requires a vacuum environment in which the sample surface is bombarded with electrons and either the transmission of those electrons is measured (Transmission Electron Microscopy, TEM), or the secondary emission of electrons is measured (Secondary Electron Microscopy or SEM). In the TEM technique, samples are thin-sectioned so that electrons can be transmitted through the sample. Contrast is found by means of the electron density of species in the sample. Higher atomic weight species provide dark areas. This technique provides the highest magnification (as high as 80,000 to 100,000×).

SEM analyzes the secondary electrons which are emitted from the sample. Contrast is also provided by means of atomic weights; in this case, high atomic weights appear lighter. SEM is easier to use and understand but is not capable of as high a magnification as TEM. SEM is typically limited to about 50,000×.

In recent years, new techniques known as *probe microscopies* have become available. In these techniques, fine mechanical probes are brought very close to a surface and the interaction of the tip of the probe with the surface is determined. If the sample is a conductor or semiconductor, the probe can be brought near to the sample surface and an electrical bias is applied. This causes electrons to tunnel from the probe tip to the sample surface. The tip can be rastered over the surface and either the current draw or the applied bias can be controlled through a feedback circuit. The level of feedback can be used as a measure of the surface morphology. The applied potential or current draw can be plotted as a function of the raster position and a topological picture can be developed. This technique can provide extremely high resolution pictures of the surface topology, down to atomic levels. This technique is known as Scanning Tunneling Microscopy or STM.

An important variation on the STM is the Atomic Force Microscope or AFM. In this scanning probe technique, a sharp tip, usually made from a ceramic insulator such as silicon nitride, is attached to a cantilever. The back of the cantilever is silvered and a laser is reflected from that mirror. The deflection of the cantilever is monitored by the deflection of the laser beam. If the tip is brought very close to a surface and if the force constant of the cantilever is small, the assembly can sense dispersion forces.

The sample is mounted on a piezoelectric crystal. A feedback circuit is employed to keep the tip at a constant displacement from the surface. A surface topology map can be obtained from the combination of the output of the feedback circuit and the voltages applied to the piezoelectric crystal. Atomic resolution is possible with the AFM on any type of insulator. This technique should prove extremely useful in the study of adhesion since it can probe any type of surface. An additional feature of both AFM and STM is that both techniques can be used under normal atmospheric conditions and even immersed in liquids.

4.8 Summary

In this chapter, the basics of surface science necessary for the understanding of the relationship between surface phenomena and adhesion have been described. The chapter began with a review of the fundamental forces between atoms and molecules which give rise not only to the cohesive strength of materials but also to forces at surfaces. A quantity known as the surface energy was derived and was described in a number of phenomenological as well as theoretical ways. The differences between solid surface energy and liquid surface tension (energy) were highlighted. Methods of measurement of solid and liquid surface energy were described. In particular, two measurements, the surface forces apparatus and the contact angle method were described in detail as a means to probe the surface energetics of solids. The JKR theory, which is used to describe the surface forces measurement, was described to exemplify the energy balance approach to adhesive interactions. Regarding contact angle measurements, the theories of Good and Girifalco as well as that of Fowkes were highlighted. The Zisman critical wetting tension measurement was also described and noted as being of particular importance in the science of adhesion.

Bibliography

Israelachvili, J., *Intermolecular and Surface Forces*, 2nd Edition (1991), Academic Press, London
Wu, S., *Polymer Interfaces and Adhesion*, Marcel Dekker (1982), New York
Patrick, R.L., (Ed.), *Treatise on Adhesion and Adhesives*, Volume 1: Theory (1969), Marcel Dekker, New York
Briggs, D. and Seah, M.P. (Eds.), *Practical Surface Analysis*, Vols. 1 and 2, 2nd Ed. (1990), Wiley, New York

References

1. Eggers, Jr., D.F., Gregory, N.W., Halsey Jr., G.D., and Rabinovitch, B.S., *Physical Chemistry* (1964), John Wiley and Sons, New York, pp. 168–173
2. Hirschfelder, O., Curtis, C.F., and Bird, R.B., *Molecular Theory of Gases and Liquids*, John Wiley (1954), New York
3. (a) Keesom, W.H., *Phys. Z.*, 22 (1921), p. 126. (b) Keesom, W.H., *Phys. Z.*, 23 (1922), p. 225
4. (a) Debye, P., *Phys. Zh.*, 21 (1920), p. 178. (b) Debye, P., *Phys. Zh.*, 22 (1921), p. 302
5. (a) Lifschitz, E.M., *Doklady Akademii Nauk. USSR*, 47, (1954), p. 643. (b) Dzyaloshinskii, I.E., Lifschitz, E.M., and Pitaevskii, L.P., *Advances in Physics*, vol. 10 (1961), p. 165
6. Israelachvili, J.N., *Intermolecular and Surface Forces*, 2nd Ed. (1991), Academic Press, London, Ch. 6
7. Grimley, T.B., in: *Aspects of Adhesion*, vol. 7 (1974), Transcripta Books, London, p. 11
8. Lennard-Jones, J.E., *Proc. Roy. Soc. London, Ser. A*, 196 (1924), p. 463
9. Adamson, A.W., *Physical Chemistry of Surfaces*, 4th Ed. (1982), Wiley-Interscience, New York
10. (a) Beaglehole, D., *Phys. Rev. Lett.*, 43, (1979), p. 2016. (b) Thomas, B.N., Barton, S.W., Novak, F., and Rice, S.A., *J. Chem. Phys.*, 86 (1987), p. 1036
11. Fowler, R., and Guggenheim, E.A., *Statistical Thermodynamics* (1952), Cambridge University Press, Cambridge, UK
12. Good, R.J., in *Treatise on Adhesion and Adhesives*, vol. 1, R.L. Patrick (Ed.) (1969), Marcel Dekker, New York, p. 50
13. Grifith, A.A., *Phil. Trans. Roy. Soc.*, A221 (1920), p. 163
14. Dupre, A., *Théorie Méchanique de la Chaleur*, Gauthier-Villars (1869), Paris, p. 369
15. Wilhelmy, L., *Ann. Phys.*, 119 (1863), p. 177
16. du Nuoy, P. Lecounte, *J. Gen. Physiol.*, 1 (1919), p. 521
17. (a) Harkins, W.D., and Brown, F.E., *J. Am. Chem. Soc.*, 41 (1919), p. 499. (b) Harkins, W.D., *Physical Chemistry of Surface Films*, (1952), Reinhold, New York
18. Andreas, J.M., Hauser, E.A., and Tucker, W.B., *J. Phys. Chem.*, 42 (1938), p. 1001
19. (a) Johnson, Jr., R.E., and Dettre, R.H., *J. Phys. Chem.*, 68 (1964), p. 1744. (b) Johnson, Jr., R.E., and Dettre, R.H., in *Surface and Colloid Science*, Vol. 2, E. Matijevic (Ed.) (1969), Wiley-Interscience, New York. (c) Wenzel, R.N., *Ind. Eng. Chem.*, 28 (1936), p. 988. (d) Cassie, A.B.D., and Baxter, S., *Trans. Far. Soc.*, 40 (1944), p. 546
20. Young, T., *Trans. Roy. Soc.*, 95 (1805), p. 65
21. Cherry, B.W., *Polymer Surfaces* (1981), Cambridge Univ. Press, Cambridge, pp. 24–25
22. Israelachvili, J.N., *Chemtracts: Anal Phys. Chem.*, 1 (1989), p. 1
23. Johnson, K.L., Kendall, K., and Roberts, A.D., *Proc. Roy. Soc. Ser. A.*, 324 (1971), p. 301
24. Hertz, H., *Miscellaneous Papers*, Jones and Schott (Eds.) (1896), Macmillan, London
25. Johnson, K.L., *Brit. J. Appl. Physics*, 9 (1958), p. 199
26. Derjaquin, B.V., *Kolloid Zh.*, 69 (1934), p. 155
27. Tabor, D., and Winterton, R.H.S., *Proc. Roy. Soc. Ser. A.*, 312 (1969), p. 435
28. (a) Israelachvili, J.N., and Tabor, D., *Proc. Roy. Soc. Ser. A.*, 331 (1972), p. 19. (b) Israelachvili, J.N., and Adams, G.E.J., *J. Chem Soc. Faraday Trans. I*, 74 (1978), p. 975

29. (a) Merrill, W.W., Pocius, A.V., Thakker, B.V., and Tirrell, M., *Langmuir*, 7 (1991), p. 1975.
    (b) Mangipudi, V., Tirrell, M., and Pocius, A.V., *J. Adhesion Sci. Technol.*, 8 (1994), p. 1.
    (c) Mangipudi, V., Tirrell, M., and Pocius, A.V., *Langmuir*, 11, (1995), p. 19. (d) Mangupudi,
    V., Tirrell, M., and Pocius, A.V., *Macromolecules*, submitted
30. (a) Girifalco, L.A., and Good, R.J., *J. Phys Chem.*, 61 (1957), p. 904. (b) Good, R.J., *J. Phys.
    Chem.*, 62 (1958), p. 1418. (c) Good, R.J., and Girifalco, L.A., *J. Phys. Chem.*, 64 (1960), p. 561.
    (d) Good, R.J. and Hope, C.J., *J. Coll. Interface Science*, 35 (1971), p. 171
31. Cherry, B.W., *Polymer Surfaces*, (1981) Cambridge University Press, Cambridge UK, pp. 2–4.
32. Good, R.J., and Elbing, E., *Ind. Eng. Chem.*, 62(3) (1970), p. 54
33. (a) Fowkes, F.M., *J. Phys. Chem.*, 66 (1962), p. 382. (b) Fowkes, F.M., *J. Phys. Chem.*, 67
    (1963), p. 2538
34. Fowkes, F.M., *Ind. Eng. Chem.*, 56(12) (1964), p. 40
35. Israelachvili, J.N., *J. Chem. Soc., Faraday Trans., II*, 45 (1973), p. 69
36. Owens, D.K., and Wendt, R.C., *J. Appl. Polymer Sci.*, 13 (1969), p. 1740
37. (a) Fox, H.W., and Zisman, W.A., *J. Colloid. Sci.*, 5 (1950), p. 514. (b) Fox, H.W., and
    Zisman, W.A., *J. Colloid. Sci.*, 7 (1952), p. 109. (c) Fox, H.W., and Zisman, W.A., *J. Colloid.
    Sci.*, 7 (1952), p. 428. (d) Zisman, W.A., in: *Advances in Chemistry Series,* No. 43, R.F. Gould
    (Ed.) (1964), American Chemical Society, Washington, DC, pp. 1–51. (e) Zisman, W.A., in:
    Polymer Science and Technology, Vol. 9A, L.H. Lee (Ed.) (1975), Plenum Press, New York,
    pp. 55–91
38. Kitazaki, Y., and Hata, T., *J. Adhesion*, 4 (1972), p. 123
39. (a) Whitesides, G. M., and Ferguson, G. S., *Chemtracts – Organic Chemistry*, 1 (1988), pp. 171–
    187. (b) Bain, C.D., and Whitesides, G.M., *Langmuir*, 5 (1989), p. 1370. (c) Bain, C.D., and
    Whitesides, G.M., *Science*, 240 (1988), p. 62

5 Basic Physico/Chemical Properties of Polymers

5.1 Introduction

In Chapter 2, we discussed fundamental properties of all materials. The tensile, shear, and fracture properties of materials were described. In Chapter 3, we discussed test methods which probed these properties for adhesives. The adhesives of interest are based upon organic materials. In particular, we are concerned with those materials that are polymeric or become polymeric in nature during the formation of an adhesive bond. It is important to discuss and to develop at least a basic understanding of the physico/chemical properties of polymers and how these properties affect the polymers' performance in an adhesive bond. In this chapter, we describe those physico/chemical characteristics causing a polymer to be different from non-polymeric materials. The parameters describing these differences are discussed. In addition, we discuss the materials properties particular to polymers. These properties include thermal transitions as well as the response of polymers to temperature and rate of application of stress. Linear viscoelasticity plays an important role in this chapter. Some discussion of methods for measuring these properties are given.

It is the goal of this chapter to lay the basis for relating surface science and polymer physical properties to the understanding of adhesion phenomena. Molecular weight and the thermal transitions of polymeric materials are discussed. Relations are made between graphs of dynamic mechanical properties and the chemical structures of polymers. A basic discussion of the time–temperature superposition principle as well as the meaning and use of the shift factor from the Williams–Landel–Ferry (WLF) equation are provided.

5.2 Basic Terminology

5.2.1 Monomers versus Polymers

Very fundamentally, the word *polymer* comes from the Greek "poly" meaning "many" and "mer" meaning part. Thus, polymers are made of many parts. The "mers" (or "monomers") are the individual units of molecules which have been linked together to form the polymer chain. In layman's terms, plastics are polymers, although it must be stated that not all polymers behave plastically under all conditions. It may be gathered from this discussion that the main differentiating feature of polymers from monomers is that they are long chains. One parameter characterizing these long chains is their molecular weight and that subject forms a portion of this discussion.

5.2.2   Basic Types of Polymeric Materials

Polymers can be classified according to their response to heat and also to the application and rate of application of stress. Polymers can be classified as either *thermoplastics* and *thermosets*. Thermoplastic materials melt upon heating and return to their original chemical state upon cooling. Thermoset materials become infusible and insoluble upon heating and after heating, do not return to their original chemical state upon cooling. Thermosets, in general, chemically degrade upon continued heating.

Thermoplastics can be further classified as *amorphous* or *semi-crystalline*. Amorphous thermoplastics have no long range order on the supermolecular level. Semi-crystalline thermoplastics have at least some portion of their bulk (and surface) in a state exhibiting long range order. If an amorphous thermoplastic is examined crystallographically, only amorphous halos are observed in the diffraction experiment. Semi-crystalline polymers exhibit both an amorphous halo as well as well-defined crystal patterns. The degree of crystallinity in a semi-crystalline polymer determines its physical properties to a great degree. Thermoset materials can be amorphous or semicrystalline. In general, thermoset materials are in the monomeric or *oligomeric* state when applied as an adhesive. An oligomer is a monomer which has been polymerized to only a low molecular weight.

We can also classify polymers according to their response to stress. Figure 5.1 shows tensile stress-strain curves for three distinct types of polymers. The curves should be examined according to two criteria. First, look at how much strain is induced in the material at a near ultimate stress. Second, examine the curves for their strain energy density. Curve 1 represents a polymer which has a high Young's modulus (stiffness) but a low elongation, resulting in a relatively small strain energy density at break. This type of polymer is called *brittle*. As discussed in the previous chapter, the term "brittle" means inability to absorb mechanical energy. Curve 3 represents a polymer which has a low Young's modulus and a very long strain to break. This type of polymer is classified as an *elastomer*. Note that the strain energy at break is moderately high for this type of polymer. Curve 2 corresponds to a "tough" or leathery type of polymer. Note that the stiffness is relatively high and the strain at break is at least intermediate between the other two types. A tough material is capable of a high strain energy density. Joining materials should have a high strain energy density capability as this indicates that the material can absorb a lot of energy before breaking. In later chapters, we discuss the chemistry of materials which enable the formulator to generate adhesives with a high strain energy density capability.

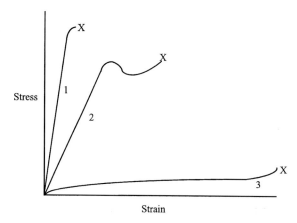

Figure 5.1   Stress–strain curves for three distinct types of polymers. The "X" marks the ultimate property of the polymer. Curve 1 corresponds to a brittle polymer, Curve 3 corresponds to an elastomeric polymer, while Curve 2 corresponds to a tough or leathery polymer

One of the unique features of polymeric materials is that a single high molecular weight polymer can exhibit all three of the stress strain curves shown in Fig. 5.1. However, a single high molecular weight polymer does not exhibit all of these characteristics at a single temperature or at a single rate of extension. A non-thermosetting, high molecular weight polymer is elastomeric at high temperatures, brittle at low temperatures, and can exhibit tough or leathery character at intermediate temperatures. In addition, at a single temperature and at high strain rates, polymers will behave as if they are at low temperatures, i.e., brittle. At a single temperature and low strain rates, a high molecular weight polymer behaves as if it were at high temperatures, i.e., elastomeric. This unique property of polymers is known as *time–temperature equivalency*, which forms the basis for much discussion in this and later chapters.

5.2.3   Molecular Weight

The primary characteristic which differentiates polymers from other materials is their chain-like structure. Essentially all of the processes used to manufacture polymers produce materials with a distribution of chain lengths and therefore, a distribution of molecular weights. With the exception of genetically engineered polymers, most polymers have a multitude of molecular weights, rather than a single molecular weight. As a result, *distributions*, rather than a single number, characterize the molecular weight of a polymer. Figure 5.2 shows a schematic molecular weight distribution curve for a polymer.

The molecular weight distribution shown in Fig. 5.2 could be considered either broad or narrow depending upon the range of the abscissa. Two average molecular weights are shown in Fig. 5.2. If N_i is the number of molecules at a certain

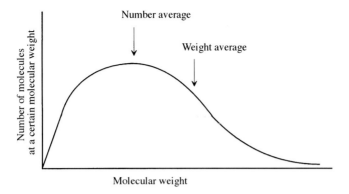

Figure 5.2   Schematic molecular weight distribution curve. The curve shows that a polymer has a wide range of molecular weights. Two average molecular weights are shown as well as their relative distribution on the molecular weight curve

molecular weight M_i, then

$$\bar{M}_n = \frac{\sum_i N_i M_i}{\sum_i N_i}$$

and

$$\bar{M}_w = \frac{\sum_i N_i M_i^2}{\sum_i N_i M_i}$$

The two average molecular weights are just the first and second moments of the molecular weight distribution. The number average molecular weight, $\bar{M}_n$, tends to be near the maximum in the molecular weight distribution curve. The weight average molecular weight, $\bar{M}_w$, tends toward the high molecular weight side of the distribution curve. A parameter for describing the breadth of the distribution is the *polydispersity* which is defined as

$$\text{polydispersity} = \frac{\bar{M}_w}{\bar{M}_n}$$

A high polydispersity means a broad molecular weight distribution while a small polydispersity denotes a narrow molecular weight distribution. The molecular weight of a polymer and its polydispersity control many of its properties, including its properties as an adhesive.

A particularly important molecular weight is known as the *entanglement molecular weight*. This parameter is determined by measuring the viscosity of a polymer as a function of average molecular weight. If one plots the log of the melt viscosity of a polymer as a function of the log of its weight average molecular weight, the curve shows an abrupt change in slope at a certain molecular weight. After the abrupt change, the slope is about 3.4. The point at which the slope changes is known as the entanglement molecular weight, M_e. As discussed above, polymers are long chain molecules. Below the entanglement molecular weight, the polymer chains are fairly free to move past each other. Above M_e, the molecular weight has become so high and the polymer chains have become so intertwined that one cannot pull on one chain without pulling on a substantial number of them. Thus, above M_e the polymer has substantially different flow characteristics than below M_e, and the polymer also has substantially different ability to absorb strain. M_e is normally a characteristic describing amorphous or semi-crystalline thermoplastics.

Thermoplastic materials are normally pictured as long chains which can move past each other to some degree. Thermoset materials are molecules of essentially infinite molecular weight and they do not flow when heated after they have set. The chemical basis for the thermosetting character of some adhesive materials is described in later chapters. At this point, we say that there are chemical means through which one can tie together many long molecular weight chains at various point along their lengths. If every chain is chemically linked to every other chain, the polymer is thought to have infinite molecular weight. The characteristic molecular weight of thermosets is M_c or the *molecular weight between crosslinks*. A crosslink is a tie point between two polymer chains. There are various chemical and physical means by which the molecular weight between crosslinks can be determined. Some of these are discussed below.

5.3   Thermal Transitions of Polymers

We are all familiar with the fact that low molecular weight materials undergo phase changes as a function of temperature. For example, water is a solid below 0°C and is a gas above 100°C. The temperatures which characterize water are thus the T_m or melt point (0°C) and the boiling point T_{bp} (100°C). In a similar manner, polymers have thermal transitions. Semi-crystalline thermoplastic polymers exhibit a T_m just as low molecular weight solids do. Amorphous thermoplastics do not exhibit a T_m. Thermoset polymers do not flow or melt and hence do not have a T_m. Because of their high molecular weight, no polymers exhibit a T_{bp}. However, some *oligomers* will exhibit a boiling point and can be distilled.

Polymers also exhibit a number of other thermal transitions which are not primary transitions such as those described above. In spite of their high molecular weight, polymer chain motion can take place at temperatures far below T_m. For example, the backbone of the polymer chain can vibrate and, in fact, can move in restricted crankshaft motions if enough thermal energy is available to the system. If a polymer chain has side groups, these can vibrate and rotate if enough thermal energy is available to them. If we take a polymer down to 0°K and warm it up, we find that the polymer goes through several transitions until its decomposition temperature is reached. These transitions are usually given Greek letters with the higher letters representing transitions at lower and lower temperatures. In addition to the melt temperature, the transition which is of most concern to adhesion scientists is the alpha transition or the *glass transition temperature*, T_g. The glass transition temperature is the temperature at which a polymer's physical properties change from that of a glass to that of a tough or leathery material. It is usually associated with the onset of long range motion in the polymer backbone.

5.3.1   Measurement of T_g

One of the more straightforward methods of measuring T_g which may be easily related to adhesive properties, is dynamic mechanical analysis. We discuss this method later. There are several other methods which can also be used. A simple method is differential scanning calorimetry (DSC). In this method, a small sample of polymer is placed in a sealed metal pan which is placed in a calorimeter capable of measuring small heat flows in the sample. The temperature is increased. At the glass transition temperature, the rate of heat flow into the sample increases, causing a change in slope as the thermal motions in the polymer are excited. The T_g is not a first order thermodynamic transition and is therefore rate dependent. It is important to know the rate at which the measurement is carried out. DSC is capable of measuring T_g at very slow rates. Another means of measuring T_g is through the determination of the refractive index as a function of temperature. The refractive index of a polymer decreases with temperature. The slope of such a plot exhibits a substantial change at the glass transition temperature.

The physical properties of a polymer also exhibit a rather substantial change at the glass transition temperature. Below the glass transition temperature, the polymer acts as though it is a glass and has a high stiffness. It is interesting to note that essentially all polymers have similar glassy moduli of about 3×10^9 Pascal. Above the glass transition temperature, the material first behaves tough or leathery and at higher temperatures, behaves as an elastomer. The modulus of the material decreases substantially above the T_g. Another way of determining the glass transition temperature of a polymer is to measure the stress-strain properties as a function of temperature. Although effective, this set of measurements is quite tedious to collect. For many adhesive materials, the maximizing of adhesive properties in the temperature range between T_g and T_m or the decomposition temperature of a thermoset is the goal of the adhesive formulator.

5.4   Dynamic Mechanical Measurements and Viscoelasticity

In Chapter 2, we defined the complex modulus of a viscoelastic material as well as the storage and loss moduli. That description provided the basis for linear viscoelasticity, but it did not provide a discussion of the means by which we measure these properties. In this section, methods through which these properties can be measured are described. The measurement of the viscoelastic properties of polymers by the application of a sinusoidal stress is known as *dynamic mechanical spectroscopy*.

5.4.1   Methods of Measurement of Dynamic Mechanical Properties

A schematic diagram of an instrument for the measurement of dynamic mechanical properties is shown in Fig. 5.3. The diagram is an extremely simple version of the many complicated devices of this type now available. A sample of polymer is firmly clamped between two pieces of metal which are much stiffer then the sample. One of clamps is connected to a sinusoidal driving device while the other is connected to a force transducer. The instrument should be capable of measuring both the frequency and the amplitude of the driven and transduced signals. The resulting data can then be analyzed as described in Chapter 2. An important feature (which was not emphasized in Chapter 2) is that dynamic mechanical measurements are done as a function of temperature (at a single frequency) or frequency (at a single temperature). The most versatile instruments of this type can carry out the measurement both of these ways. The reasons for the importance of this statement is made clear in this and later chapters.

The sample configuration shown in Fig. 5.3 is analogous to the lap shear specimen discussed in Chapter 3. The measurement done in this mode provides the shear storage and loss moduli. The measurement can be carried out so that the sample is suspended between the two clamps. The measurement is then in tension and the corresponding Young's moduli is determined. The sample must be stiff enough at the temperature and frequency range of interest, so that it does not slump or change shape during the measurement.

Another important means to make dynamic measurements is by a rotating or oscillating rheometer. A schematic of a sample configuration for such a rheometer is shown in Fig. 5.4. The sample is placed in a state of shear similar to the description in Fig. 3.9. The complex shear modulus can be determined by the application of an oscillating sinusoidal stress. This instrument is also useful for determining the viscosity of a materials as a function of shear rate, which is controlled by the rate of revolution of the upper spindle. Yield stresses of fluids can be measured as a function of temperature as well. This last measurement is important in the design of materials with non-sag characteristics.

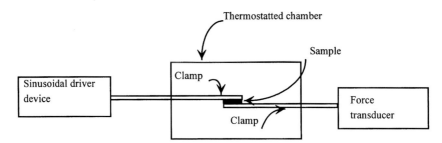

Figure 5.3   Diagram of a simple dynamic mechanical spectrometer used to measure the shear properties of a material. Note that a sinusoidal driver device is used. Frequency and temperature are controlled. The stiffness of the device must exceed that of the sample for the measurements to be valid

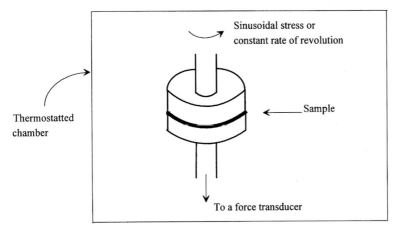

Figure 5.4 Simplistic diagram of the sensor head in a rotating viscometer. Note that in this configuration the sample is in pure shear

The last dynamic mechanical spectrometer discussed here is the torsion pendulum. This spectrometer was well researched by Gilham and his group at Princeton University [1]. A schematic of the apparatus is found in Fig. 5.5. The sample is held by a device which provides the spin. The spin is transmitted through the sample and the specimen rotates. When the spin is abruptly released (analogous to the wind-up and release of a mainspring), the response of the specimen to the initial perturbation is determined by watching the decay of the resulting oscillation.

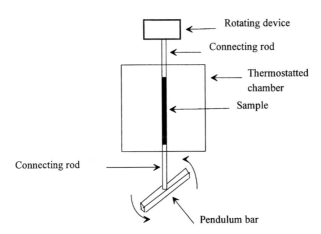

Figure 5.5 Schematic diagram of a torsion pendulum device used to measure dynamic mechanical properties of a polymer. If the sample is generated using a braid into which a thermoset polymer has been impregnated, the device can be used to measure the cure rate and the change in physical properties as a function of cure time

The oscillation can be observed in any one of a number of different ways. For example, on the bottom of the pendulum, a disk can be placed upon which is a digital code for position. The digital code can be read by a bank of lights and photodiodes. An exponentially damped sinusoidal curve results. The key features determined from this apparatus are the frequency and the decrease in amplitude between oscillations, not a direct measurement of modulus. The frequency of the oscillation is related to the stiffness of the material and the decrease in amplitude per cycle is related to the lossiness of the sample. The $\tan \delta$ can be determined from this measurement. If G' or G'' has been determined independently, the other can be determined with $\tan \delta$. The apparatus shown in Fig 5.5 has not found as much use as the other instruments described earlier because the actual Young's or shear moduli cannot be determined directly. The apparatus is, however, very useful for the study of the cure of thermosetting materials.

A glass braid can be impregnated with a thermosetting polymer. The braid is then placed in a thermostatted compartment in the torsion braid analyzer. The sample is heated and the stiffness of the sample is determined as a function of time. Gilham has made good use of this type of analysis in his description of T-T-T plots (Time-Temperature-Transformation plots) for thermosetting materials which we discuss later in this book [2].

5.4.2   Examples of Dynamic Mechanical Data for Polymers

In this section we do not differentiate between the Young and shear moduli but describe the parameters determined as the storage modulus, loss modulus, and $\tan \delta$. A typical dynamic mechanical spectrum for the storage modulus of a polymer is shown in Fig. 5.6. The absolute value of the temperature axis is not shown as this is a generic

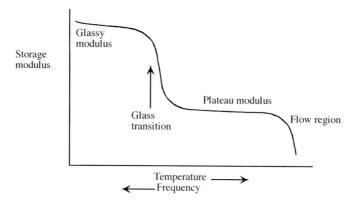

Figure 5.6   Generic dynamic mechanical spectrum for an amorphous thermoplastic. Note that the modulus drops sharply as the glass transition temperature is reached. Note that the abscissa can be either temperature or frequency. Similar curves are obtained for either variable, except that they act inversely to one another.

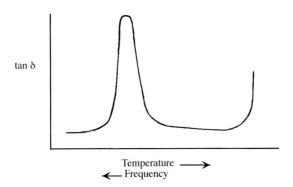

tan δ

Temperature ⟶
⟵ Frequency

Figure 5.7   Plot of the log of the loss modulus as a function of either frequency or temperature. Note that the frequency and the temperature are inversely related. The peak in the curve corresponds closely with the position of the glass transition

curve. It should be noted that a similarly shaped curve is obtained for all glassy polymeric materials, regardless of type. The curves shift along the temperature axis or vertically along the modulus axis, but the general features are very much like Fig. 5.6.

A plot of the loss modulus of this generic amorphous polymer has a shape similar to that of Fig. 5.6 except that the plot is inverted, i.e., the material has a higher loss modulus at those temperatures or frequencies when the storage modulus is low.

The plot for tan δ of the same generic glassy polymer looks similar to that shown in Fig. 5.7. Note that the tan δ curve displays a peak at about the same point that the storage modulus curve exhibits the maximum change in slope. Researchers have often designated the maximum in the tan δ curve as the glass transition temperature. It is important to note, however, that the position of the maximum change in slope or the position of the peak in the tan δ curve is not only dependent upon temperature, but also dependent upon frequency. Thus, if one determines dynamic mechanical spectra for a polymer at a single temperature but at various frequencies, a similar curve to that shown above is obtained, with the exception that the abscissa would be changing frequency instead of temperature. It is important to not only quote the glass transition temperature, but also the frequency at which the measurement was made when reporting such data. This property of viscoelastic materials is known as *time–temperature superposition*.

Figure 5.8 shows the dynamic mechanical spectra determined for a thermosetting polymer as a function of the degree of crosslinking. The degree of crosslinking usually is described by M_c, the molecular weight between crosslinks. As can easily be seen, the value as well as the extent of the plateau modulus is dependent upon M_c. Note that as M_c decreases, the flow region of the polymer begins to disappear. This behavior can be expected for a thermosetting material. Note also that the amount of decrease in the storage modulus decreases as the M_c decreases. This is also to be expected since an increase in crosslink density means a decrease in chain mobility.

We have described the effect of molecular weight on melt viscosity and the entanglement molecular weight, M_e. We would expect that the dynamic mechanical

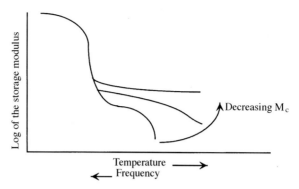

Figure 5.8   Plot of the log of the storage modulus as a function of frequency or temperature. The plot shows the effect of decreasing the molecular weight between crosslinks (i.e., increasing the number of crosslinks per unit weight) in the polymer

spectrum would also show some effect of the increase in molecular weight. Figure 5.9 shows that increasing the molecular weight of a polymer increases the temperature at which flow occurs. This has the effect of increasing the extent of the rubbery plateau. The features shown in the figures in this chapter are important in our discussion of structural adhesives, hot melt adhesives, and particularly pressure sensitive adhesives.

5.5   Time–Temperature Superposition

In Figs. 5.7, 5.8 and 5.9, the abscissa was labeled as increasing temperature or decreasing frequency. For polymers, the effect of changing these variables is identical.

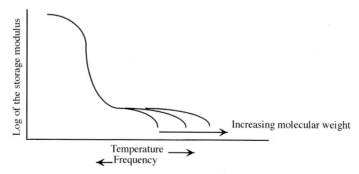

Figure 5.9   Plot of the log of the storage modulus as a function of either temperature or frequency. The plot also shows the effect of increasing the molecular weight of the polymer. For an amorphous polymer, this has the effect of increasing the extent of the plateau modulus

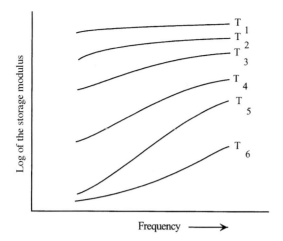

Figure 5.10   Plot of the log of the storage modulus measured as a function of frequency at six temperatures $T_1 < T_2 < T_3 \ldots$ etc.

A significant amount of the knowledge of the molecular basis for polymer properties has come from the experimental and theoretical study of the time–temperature superposition.

In any dynamic mechanical experiment, one typically varies either the temperature or the frequency over a specific range and measures the modulus of the material. The range of frequencies over which one can do experiments easily is limited, since extremely low frequencies are hard to maintain and are difficult to measure. If we measure the response of a polymer material to a small range of easily accessible frequencies (such as 0.1 to 100 Hz) and measure these responses over a wide range of temperatures (which are more easily variable, measurable, and maintainable) we can get the family of curves shown in Fig. 5.10. The temperatures are in the order $T_1 < T_2 < T_3 < T_4 < T_5 < T_6$. Examination of this generic data says that by shifting the curve for T_6 to the left and the curves for temperatures T_1 through T_4 to the right by some amount, then all of the curves would form a smooth curve in the shifted frequency space. This is found to be the case for most polymeric materials. The resultant *master curve* and the amount by which a curve is shifted is known as a *shift factor*. Thus, a master curve is a plot of the log of the storage modulus (or other modulus) as a function of a reduced rate variable. The reduced variable is obtained by multiplying the frequency by the shift factor. Thus, a set of curves such as that shown in Fig. 5.10 can be reduced to a single curve such as that shown in Fig. 5.11.

In Fig. 5.11, f is the frequency and a_T is the shift factor. The shift factors can be determined solely from overlapping the curves in each plot. Care must be taken that enough overlap is obtained with each curve, so that confidence in the measured a_T is high. One could also make a plot of a_T versus temperature which would lead to the determination of a_T values at intermediate temperatures.

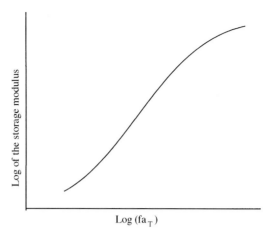

Figure 5.11   A "master curve" which could have been constructed from the data presented in schematic form in Fig. 5.10

A significant advance in the understanding of the viscoelastic properties of polymers occurred with the publication of the work of Williams, Landel and Ferry [3]. They were able to show that for a substantial number of polymers, the shift factors could be determined from a rather simple set of equations:

$$\log a_T = -\frac{8.86(T - T_S)}{101.6 + T - T_S}$$

is the Williams–Landel–Ferry (WLF) equation for the shift factor with respect to some standard temperature T_S. Alternatively, if the standard temperature is chosen to be the glass transition temperature, then

$$\log a_T = \frac{-17.5(T - T_g)}{51.6 + T - T_g}$$

The existence of such apparently useful universal equations for the shift factor has formed the basis for many experiments and theories regarding viscoelasticity of polymers.

5.6   Summary

In this chapter, we have defined a number of important parameters used to describe the characteristics of polymers. The definition of various molecular weights was presented. The entanglement molecular weight and the molecular weight between crosslinks are both important parameters for the understanding adhesives and adhesion. The thermal transitions of polymers were also discussed. Of primary importance here is the glass transition temperature and the melt temperature. The glass transition temperature marks the point at which the polymer changes from a glassy to a rubbery material. The inverse relationship between frequency and temperature was emphasized and related to the measurement of dynamic mechanical properties. Finally, the generation of master curves was described and the WLF equations were presented.

Bibliography

Barnes, H.A., Hutton, J.F., and Walters, K., *An Introduction to Rheology* (1980), Elsevier, Amsterdam

Nielsen, L.E., *Mechanical Properties of Polymers* (1962), Reinhold, New York

Boyer, R.F., *Polym. Sci. Eng.,* 8 (1968), p. 161

Boyer, R.F., *Polymer,* 17 (1976), p. 996

Ferry, J.D., *Viscoelastic Properties of Polymers,* 3rd Ed. (1980), Wiley, New York

Aklonis, J.L., and MacKnight, W.J., *Introduction to Polymer Viscoelasticity,* 2nd Ed. (1983), Wiley, New York

References

1. Gillham, J.K., *AIChE J.,* 20 (1974), p. 1066
2. Gillham, J.K., in *Developments in Polymer Characterization – 3,* J.V. Dawkins (Ed.) (1982), Applied Science, Essex, UK, pp. 159–227
3. Williams, M.L., Landel, R.F., and Ferry, J.D., *J. Am. Chem. Soc.,* 77 (1955), p. 3701

6 The Relationship of Surface Science and Adhesion Science

6.1 Introduction

In Chapter 4, some of the basic aspects of surface science were described, especially as they related to liquid surfaces and the interaction of liquids with solids. The interaction of liquids and solids forms the basis for the attachment of adhesives to adherends. In Chapter 5, some of the physico-chemical characteristics of polymeric materials forming the basis for most adhesives were described. In this chapter, we describe rationalizations of adhesion phenomena based upon some of the concepts in Chapters 4 and 5. This chapter is central to this book and to the understanding of adhesion phenomena.

The rationalizations used to explain observed adhesion phenomena and their relative importance in adhesion science are assessed in this chapter. An appreciation for the connection between surface science, polymer physics, and observed adhesion phenomena should be developed. Finally, guidelines for generating an adhesive bond to meet the expectations of the adhesive user are provided.

6.2 Rationalizations of Adhesion Phenomena

Normally, one would call this section "The Theory of Adhesion." Unfortunately, there is no unifying theory relating basic physico-chemical properties of materials to the actual physical strength of an adhesive bond. There are theories attempting to predict the strength of an adhesive bond, assuming that adhesion is perfect. There are also theories predicting the strength of interactions at interfaces. However, there are no theories making the complete connection among adhesion, the physical properties of the adhesive and adherend, and the practical strength of an adhesive bond. Rather, the literature on adhesion consists of many articles addressing specific areas of adhesion phenomena. A number of theories specifically related to those phenomena are used to explain them. In this chapter, we discuss some of the more prevalent rationalizations of adhesion phenomena along with experimental evidence for those rationalizations. It is reasonable to conclude that all of the rationalizations have merit. In fact, the physical bases for these rationalizations contribute to one degree or another to the strength of an adhesive bond. The goal of adhesion science is to predict adhesive bond strength from first principles. That goal is likely to be reached by the proper combination of the rationalizations of adhesion described below coupled with proper descriptions of how strain energy is dissipated in the adhesive and the adherend.

6.3   Electrostatic Theory of Adhesion

We know from elementary physical chemistry that all atoms have a property known as *electronegativity*, which is a measure of the strength of attraction between a certain atom and an electron. We have already discussed how electronegativity causes the formation of dipolar molecules. The periodic table is arranged in approximate order of electronegativity, with the more electronegative atoms to the right and the more electropositive atoms to the left. Thus, fluorine is very electronegative, while sodium is more electropositive. Assemblies of atoms can also have electronegative character. Solid surfaces also can be characterized as being electropositive or electronegative. In a familiar experiment, an amber rod is rubbed with fur and the rod accumulates a surface charge, which easily can be detected. A familiar child's birthday party trick is to take a latex rubber balloon and rub it on a wool sweater. The rubber balloon accumulates a surface charge and the balloon adheres to a number of non-conductive surfaces. In terms of recent adhesion science literature, one could say that surfaces electropositive in character are bases and surface electronegative in character are acids.

A primary proponent of the electrostatic theory of adhesion is Derjaguin [1] who proposed that essentially all adhesion phenomena could be explained by electrostatics. He generated a theory predicting the strength of adhesive bonds due to electrostatic forces and also attempted to prove the theory experimentally. Schematically, the basis for the theory is shown in Fig. 6.1, which shows an electropositive material donating charge to an electronegative material, thus creating an electrostatic bilayer at the interface. According to the Derjaguin theory, the strength of the adhesive bond comes from the force necessary to move the charged surfaces away from one another

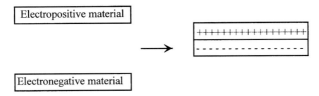

Figure 6.1   Schematic of the formation of an adhesive bond due to transfer of charge from an electropositive material to an electronegative material. The strength of the adhesive bond is thought to be due to the attraction between the charges on the opposite sides of the interface

overcoming Coulombic forces. The result of the Derjaguin theory is:

$$W_B = 2\pi\sigma_0^2 h_B \tag{6.1}$$

In this equation, W_B is the work to break the adhesive bond; σ_0 is the surface charge density; and h_B is the distance of separation at electrical breakdown in the air gap formed when the two materials are separated. Derjaguin and his co-workers used an ingenious method to determine the surface charge and separation distance required by this equation by incorporating Paschen's law for the breakdown of a gas under an electrical potential. Paschen's Law relates the breakdown potential of a gas to the ambient pressure and the distance of separation between two electrodes. Derjaguin and his co-workers assumed that the materials in contact acted as a capacitor and that the voltage across the capacitor was given by the following expression:

$$V^2 = \frac{8\pi E_C ph}{p}$$

where V is the voltage; p is the ambient gas pressure; E_C is the energy stored in the capacitor; and h is the distance of separation of the two planes of charge. As described by Huntsberger [2], the primary erroneous assumption these workers made was that $E_C = W_B$. Using this erroneous assumption, they measured the work to peel adhesive bonds away from glass. The measured W_B was equated with E_C, which was then used to plot $\log V$ versus $\log ph$ on a Paschen plot. From this plot they could calculate the charge density and separation distance described above by using the equation of the charge density in a capacitor. Unfortunately, their assumption was erroneous because it does not take into account energy dissipated in peeling that was not interfacial energy. Plastic deformation of the adhesive and the adherend was ignored. The only situation where the interfacial energy is the total energy to break an adhesive bond is when the adherends and adhesive are completely brittle. As a result of this erroneous assumption, the Derjaguin experiments and the electrostatic theory of adhesion have gone into disrepute. We see repeatedly in this chapter that much of the work to break an adhesive bond goes into plastic deformation of the adherend and the adhesive.

However, despite the shortcomings of the Derjaguin work, there are some recent examples indicating that the electrostatic component to adhesion cannot be ignored entirely. Dickinson and co-workers [3] at Washington State University have been studying *fracto-emission*. In these studies, adhesive bonds are placed in high vacuum under conditions where the emission of light, charged and neutral particles, as well as other electromagnetic emanations can be sensed. The adhesive bond is opened and the various emissions are measured. In the breakage of an epoxy/aluminum adhesive bond, for example, charged particles and light are emitted. If a pressure-sensitive adhesive tape is applied to a photographic emulsion and then stripped from that emulsion, development provides photographic evidence of light emitted in the debonding process. In an enlightening experiment, a piece of tape is applied to an AM transistor radio. When the tape is stripped off, the sound can be heard amplified through the radio, indicating the emission of radio frequency radiation during the debonding operation. All of these experiments indicate the possibility of the presence

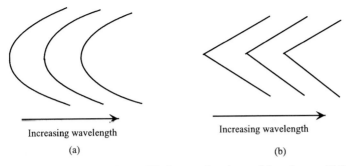

Figure 6.2   Schematic diagram of the FECO that can be observed in a "normal" SFA experiment (a) and that observed for mica–sapphire contact (b). The parabolic shape in the normal experiment is expected from the optics of the interferometer. The shape observed for mica–sapphire contact indicates extreme distortion of the surfaces of the samples when separated by large distances

of an electrostatic component to adhesion, since discharges are found. Dickinson makes no claim that his work supports or detracts from the electrostatic theory, but indicates that his findings could also be explained by breaking of covalent bonds.

Perhaps the most definitive work detecting the presence of an electrostatic component to adhesion is as reported by Smith and Horn [4]. These investigators used the surface forces apparatus (SFA) described in Section 4.5.2.2. The sample surfaces were glass and mica. The investigation was meant to provide JKR measurements of the interfacial energy. The means by which the interfacial distance is determined in the SFA is through interferometric fringes known as *Fringes of Equal Chromatic Order* or FECO [5]. Figure 6.2(a) shows schematically, how the FECO look in an SFA measurement between two normal surfaces as they are separated. Figure 6.2(b) shows Smith and Horn's observation for surfaces of mica and sapphire that had been brought into contact and then separated.

Much to the surprise of these investigators, the shape of the debonded spot, which is usually roughly parabolic in shape, was not parabolic at all. Rather, the contact spot was pointed and the forces seemed to extend over a long range of distance. In addition, the measured forces between the separated surfaces did not exhibit van der Waals behavior. Rather, the long range force seemed to change in a discontinuous fashion. Smith and Horn attached an electrometer to the samples and found that a charge had formed during contact. The discontinuous jumps corresponded to discharges from the surfaces, which was direct evidence of the presence of electrostatic forces in a direct adhesion experiment.

6.4   Diffusion Theory of Adhesion

The diffusion theory of adhesion is shown schematically in Fig. 6.3. Two materials, A and B, are brought into close contact. If the two materials are soluble in one another,

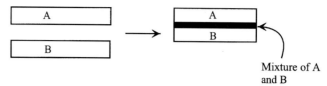

Mixture of A
and B

Figure 6.3   If material A and material B are at all soluble on one another, they dissolve in one another and form an interphase which is a solution of material A in material B and vice versa. This schematically shows diffusive bonding

they could form a solution. Even if the two materials met at an interface, in the case of diffusive bonding, we no longer have a true interface, but rather an interphase in which the properties of material A change gradually into the properties of material B. Diffusive bonding is the ultimate in adhesive bonding. In a "normal" adhesive bond, the adhesive and adherend are not soluble in one another and, at best, there is a microscopic morphology (see the next section) which "diffuses" the interphase. In this "normal" situation, there is usually a substantial mismatch between the properties of the adhesive and the adherend. As such, the contact between the adhesive and adherend acts as a discontinuity providing a stress concentration plane. The interphase formed in a diffusive adhesive bond does not lead to a stress concentration plane, as there is no discontinuity in physical properties.

Situations in which the adherend and adhesive are soluble in one another are relatively rare. Therefore, the diffusion theory of adhesion can be applied in only a limited number of cases. We can provide some simple criteria for the mutual solubility of materials based upon the theory of simple solutions developed by Hildebrand [6]. The basis of this theory is the *cohesive energy* of a material, E_{coh}, which is the amount of energy necessary to take all of the atoms or molecules in a mole of material and separate them to an infinite distance. The cohesive energy is, in itself, an important parameter since it provides a sense of how strongly the atoms or molecules in a solid or liquid are attracted to one another. The definition of E_{coh} is:

$$E_{coh} = \Delta H_{vap} - RT$$

where ΔH_{vap} is the enthalpy of vaporization; R is the gas constant; and T is the absolute temperature. We get a sense of the magnitude of intermolecular forces from the fact that the enthalpy change due to vaporization is the central factor in the equation for the cohesive energy. It takes a lot more energy to vaporize steel than it takes to vaporize acetone. Therefore, steel has a much higher cohesive energy than acetone. We define the cohesive energy density of a material as:

$$C.E.D. = \frac{E_{coh}}{V}$$

where C.E.D. is cohesive energy density and V is the molar volume. An important parameter in simple solubility theory is the solubility parameter, defined as:

$$\delta = \sqrt{\frac{E_{coh}}{V}}$$

where δ is the solubility parameter and δ^2 is the cohesive energy density. In a solution in which there are no specific chemical interactions, the enthalpy of solution is given by

$$\Delta H_{\text{soln}} = \phi_1\phi_2(\delta_1 - \delta_2)^2$$

where δ_i is the solubility parameter of component i and ϕ_i is the mole fraction of component i. This is an interesting equation since it predicts that there are no exothermic solutions and, in fact, the best one can do is to get no endotherm. There are many solutions which are exothermic, but remember that we had assumed a situation in which there were no specific chemical interactions. In that case, the solutions would have no exotherm. The criterion for the spontaneous formation of a solution is the sign and magnitude of the Gibbs free energy of mixing given by:

$$\Delta G_{\text{mix}} = \Delta H_{\text{mix}} - T\Delta S_{\text{mix}}$$

where ΔG_{mix} is the change in the Gibbs free energy of mixing, ΔH_{mix} is the enthalpy of solution; T is the absolute temperature; and ΔS_{mix} is the change in the entropy in the system. For a regular solution as defined by the equation above, the enthalpy of solution is either positive or zero. We rely on the entropy change to provide a negative Gibbs free energy of mixing. For low molecular weight materials, the change in entropy is always positive, and usually large, due to the increase in the disorder of a system when two materials are mixed. However, in polymeric materials, the entropy change is usually very small because the number of states in which a polymer can exist is limited by the high molecular weight. That is, all pieces of the polymer are connected to one another and the number of possible configurational states is limited. Since the entropy change is small and the enthalpy change is either 0 or positive, high molecular weight polymers are not likely to dissolve in one another. This is found to be the case in many, if not most, polymeric systems. Polymer pairs that are soluble in one another exhibit some enthalpy of mixing. For example, polymethyl methacrylate is soluble in polyvinylidene fluoride. This solubility is thought to be due to an exothermic acid–base reaction in which the basic methacrylate ester interacts with the acidic vinylidene fluoride group.

The above discussion leads us to one of the criteria for good adhesion. In a situation in which one polymer dissolves in another, there is ultimate adhesion. The criterion for obtaining solubility of one polymer in another is the solubility parameter. The most negative value of ΔH_{mix} that we can have is 0 or the point at which the solubility parameter of the two materials is the same. Thus, one criterion for good adhesion is that *the adhesive and adherend should have the same solubility parameter.*

There are numerous examples in which this concept has been put to use. Iyengar and Erickson [7] carried out a series of simple experiments in which a range of adhesives were used to make peel specimens between sheets of polyethylene terephthalate (PET). The solubility parameters of the adhesives were known. The solubility parameter of PET is about 10.3. Figure 6.4 is a drawing similar to that of Iyengar and Erickson in which the salient features of their data are presented.

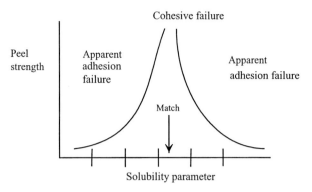

Figure 6.4   Diagram showing the features of the experiment of Iyengar and Erickson for PET bonded to PET by a variety of adhesives. The maximum in adhesive bond strength was found to be at the point when the solubility parameter of the adhesive is matched to the solubility parameter of PET. (Redrawn from Iyengar and Erickson)

Figure 6.4 shows a plot of peel strength versus the solubility parameter of the adhesive used. There is a strong dependence of practical adhesion on the solubility parameter of the adhesive. If the solubility parameter of the adhesive matches that of the substrate, the failure changes from apparent adhesion failure to cohesive failure in the substrate.

The concept of diffusion bonding is not new to those who have worked with adhesive bonding of plastics. For a number of plastics, bonding can be done by solvent welding. A solvent for the plastic is applied to both adherends and they are joined. While the solvent is present, the polymer molecules in the plastic parts can diffuse into one another. When the solvent has evaporated, an assembly which is inherently just the plastic remains. Plastics and solvents must be chosen carefully to avoid adverse effects, such as solvent-induced crazing on the bulk of the plastic. Plastics can be welded by melting the plastic part thermally or ultrasonically against another plastic part. In the melt state, the polymer molecules can intertwine and form the finished part. Once again, care must be taken since many plastic parts can distort dramatically when heated. Both of these examples of diffusive bonding are examples of *autohesion* in which a polymer adheres to itself.

Vinyl adhesives are typically a solution of polyvinyl chloride plus plasticizer in a solvent mixture of tetrahydrofuran and toluene. Tetrahydrofuran is an excellent solvent for vinyl and swells the vinyl surface to be bonded. While the solvent is still present, the vinyl in the adhesive diffuses into the adherends and forms the bond. Such adhesive bonds can even be formed under water.

6.4.1   Diffusive Adhesive Bonding and Block Copolymers at Interfaces

The desire to join dissimilar polymers by means of adhesives has led to a technology and portion of adhesion science concerning block copolymers at interfaces. *Block copolymers* are polymeric materials with at least two chemically distinct blocks of polymer which are chemically joined. Blocks of such a copolymer can be made so that they are each soluble in one of two mutually insoluble polymers to be joined. In this section, we review one study which addresses block copolymers at interfaces involving several concepts in this and previous chapters including fracture mechanics.

Polymers such as polymethyl methacrylate (PMMA) and polystyrene (PS) are not soluble in one another. Neither are polyisoprene (PI) and PS soluble in one another. If one melt presses PMMA against PS or PI against PS, one obtains a very poor adhesive bond. Application of a thin (on the order of nanometers) layer of a block copolymer of PS and PMMA between PS and PMMA leads to markedly better adhesion. Similarly, application of a thin layer of a block copolymer of PS and PI between PS and PI leads to a similar result. These studies, carried out by Brown *et al.* [8], have elucidated the polymer physics in these material combinations.

Brown and co-workers used a modification of the double cantilever beam test to study the effect of the presence of block copolymers at the interface. The double cantilever beam was asymmetric to account for the difference in materials properties between the PS and the PMMA. Block copolymers with varying lengths of the two blocks were applied at various thicknesses between PS and PMMA and then annealed. The level of adhesion increased only slightly with increasing thickness of the block copolymer. The major increase came with the increase of the molecular weight of the blocks at any single thickness of the block copolymer.

The level of adhesion was controlled by the entanglement molecular weight of the block on each side of the interface. When the M_e is exceeded for both sides of the interface, then the level of applied copolymer starts having an effect. A new quantity was defined which describes the amount of block copolymer at the interface, the *aerial chain density*, Σ. The situation is shown schematically in Fig. 6.5. Once M_e is exceeded for each block, the aerial chain density has an effect until the interface is saturated with the block copolymer. The physics of this separation process are governed by the phenomenon called *chain pull-out* which can be described by the

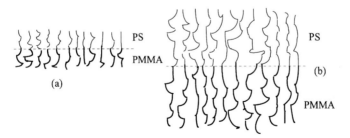

(a)

(b)

Figure 6.5 Schematic showing the difference between a block-copolymer with long or short arms across an interface. The dotted line shows the location of the interface. Thin lines show the PS block while the thicker lines show the PMMA block. When the lengths of the segments are short the block of the copolymer cannot intertwine with the polymer on either side of the interface (a). When the blocks are long (b) the blocks can intertwine with the polymer and increase the force necessary to separate the two sides of the interface from one another

reptation theory of polymer dynamics [9]. Reptation theory describes polymer motion as similar to that of a snake confined to a tube. If the snake is short, little energy required to move it down the tube. However, if the snake is long, its movement down a tube is convoluted and much energy is required to pull it out. The observations described above seem to follow the physics behind polymer reptation.

6.5   Mechanical Interlocking and Adhesion

The concepts in the previous section were directed towards adhesive bonding situations in which at least one of the adherends is a polymer. This provided an avenue by which a diffuse interphase could form at the junction between the adhesive and the adherend. We now examine a situation in which one or both of the adherends are impermeable to the adhesive. Suppose that the junction between the adhesive and the adherend is in a plane such as that shown in Fig. 6.6. The triangle at the edge of the bond is meant to indicate that a crack opening force is being exerted at the edge of the specimen. Several qualifications have to be expressed regarding such an adhesive bonding situation. Excursions of the crack opening force into the adhesive or the adherend is not necessitated by the force field since the interface acts as a stress concentrator and the crack propagates there.

Let us suppose that instead we have the interface shown in Fig. 6.7 in which the adherend is not smooth but rather has a roughness into which the adhesive can flow. If it can displace the air in the pockets on the surface, the two materials are in intimate contact along a tortuous path. If a wedge is driven into the edge of this bond, we can see no abrupt plane of stress transfer. Rather, for the crack to propagate across the bond, the lines of force have to take detours as shown by the series of arrows. Some of the detours go into the adhesive. In most cases, the adhesive can deform more than the adherend. If either the adhesive (or the adherend) plastically deforms during the debonding, energy is consumed and the strength of the adhesive bond appears to be higher.

Another reason surface roughness aids in adhesive bonding is the interlocking effect. In Fig. 6.7, a segment of the surface is indicated by arrows. In this segment, the adhesive has completely filled a pore on the surface. At this pore, the exit of the adhesive is partially blocked by part of the adherend. This place in the

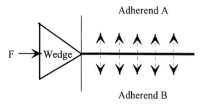

Figure 6.6   A wedge is driven into the edge of a sharp interface between adherends A and B. The loading is known as Mode I (see Chapter 2) and results in movement of the adherends as shown by the dotted lines in the figure. Little energy dissipation is required to separate the adherends and a clean separation of adherends is possible

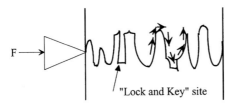

Figure 6.7   Schematic showing a tortuous interface between two adhering materials. When a Mode I loading is applied to this situation, the applied force cannot cleanly follow the path between the two adherends, but rather must make excursions. As excursions are made into either adherend, energy can be dissipated by plastic deformation. Note also the possibility of a "lock and key site" at which point the adhesive would have to physically pass through the material of the adherend in order for separation to take place

interphase may exhibit the so-called "lock and key" effect. A key, when turned into the tumblers of a lock, cannot be removed from the lock because of the physical impediment provided by the tumblers. In the same way, a solid adhesive in a pore such as that shown in Fig. 6.7, cannot move past the "overhang" of the pore without plastically deforming. Plastic deformation acts as an energy absorbing mechanism and the strength of the adhesive bond appears to increase.

We are familiar with rubber tires and rubber inner tube repair kits. These usually contain a rubber patch, an adhesive (usually some form of solvent-carried rubber) and a piece of sandpaper or a serrated tool. The tool is used to roughen the surface of the rubber to be mended, allowing the adhesive to "key" into the substrate.

Another reason surface roughness improves adhesion is purely a matter of physical area of contact. In Fig. 6.6, is a situation where the contact between the two materials is in a plane, the minimum possible contact area between two rectangular bodies. If we can imagine Fig. 6.7 in three dimensions, we see that the surface area is increased substantially. If we believe that interfacial interactions are the basis for adhesion, we know that the sum of those interactions will scale as the area of contact. If the actual area of contact is increased by a large amount, the total energy of surface interaction increases by an amount proportional to the surface area.

Perhaps the best demonstration of the effect of surface roughness on adhesion is provided by Arrowsmith [10]. He created surfaces of varying roughness by electro-forming the surface of copper of a single thickness. Figure 6.8 is a diagram of some of the shapes he placed on the surface along with adhesive bond strength data. Note that these shapes are all in the range of a micron or so in size. He applied the same epoxy adhesive to all of the surfaces and measured the peel strength of the epoxy to the copper. As shown in Fig. 6.8, the peel strength increased, even though the adhesive and the adherend were nominally the same in all cases. We must surmise that the effect of the surface roughness is to increase the plastic deformation of the adhesive in the interphase, resulting in increased peel strength.

Surface topography of copper foil		Mean peel load lb/in
Topography	Diagrammatic representation	
Flat	————	3.75
Flat + 0.3μ dendrites		3.8
Flat + 0.3μ dendrites + oxide		4.4
3μ pyramids (high angle)		5.9
2μ low angle pyramids + 0.3μ dendrites		7.3
2μ low angle pyramids + 0.2μ dendrites + oxide		8.8
3μ high angle pyramids + 0.2μ dendrites + oxide		13.5

Figure 6.8   Experimental results reported by Arrowsmith, relating the surface roughness of electro-plated copper to the level of practical adhesion when an epoxy adhesive is removed. Note that as the level of surface roughness increases and the opportunity for mechanical interlocking increases, the level of practical adhesion increases even though the adhesive is identical in all cases. (Reproduced from Reference 10 by permission of the Institute of Metal Finishing, UK)

6.5.1   Kinetics of Pore Penetration

The above discussion is predicated on the notion that the adhesive and the adherend are in intimate contact. It is not obvious that this should be the case since all real adhesives have a viscosity. In normal bonding operations, the adhesive and adherend must come into close contact quickly. We can examine the extent to which adhesives penetrate into pores on a surface by examining the equations describing the wetting of surfaces by polymers and the penetration of liquids into a pore as provided by Packham [11]. The penetration of a liquid into a pore is described by Poiseuille's Law which states

$$x\frac{dx}{dt} = \frac{r^2 P}{8\eta}$$

where x is the distance that the adhesive can penetrate into a pore; P is the capillary pressure; t is the time; and r is the radius of the pore (or capillary, for which Poiseuille's Law is actually derived). The capillary pressure is given by:

$$P = \frac{2\gamma_{LV}\cos\theta}{r}$$

where θ is the contact angle and γ_{LV} is the liquid–vapor interfacial tension of the adhesive. The description of the wetting of a surface by a polymer is taken from the work of Schonhorn, Frisch and Kwei [12] and it is described by the following equation which was derived by Newman [13]:

$$\cos\theta(t) = \cos\theta_\infty[1 - ae^{-ct}]$$

where θ_∞ is the contact angle at infinite times and $\theta(t)$ is the time dependent contact angle. Combining these equations, we find the following relationship:

$$x^2(t) = \frac{r\gamma_{LV}\cos\theta_\infty}{2\eta}\left[t - \frac{a}{c} + \frac{ae^{-ct}}{c}\right]$$

where $\cos\theta_\infty$ and $\cos\theta(t)$ are the cosine of the contact angle at infinite time and at time t, respectively, η is the viscosity of the polymer at the temperature of the adhesive bonding operation and a and c are adjustable parameters. This equation describes the distance a pore is penetrated by an adhesive, giving an idea of the parameters necessary for expulsion of air from a pore and its replacement by an adhesive.

Let us examine the above equation by introducing parameters associated with the wetting of a surface by polyethylene. Packham assumed that the interfacial tension between the polyethylene and air was $23.5\,mJ/m^2$ under the application condition which was 200°C. He allowed a time of 20 minutes for wetting to take place. Table 6.1 shows results of his calculations.

The table clearly indicates that the amount of penetration of polyethylene into a porous surface is dependent upon the radius of the pore. The depth of penetration is inversely dependent upon the radius of the pore. For a pore radius of 1000 microns, the depth of penetration is only 220 microns. If the pore were as deep as its radius, the pore would still be mostly empty. In contrast, if the pore radius were 0.1 microns, the depth of penetration could be 2.2 microns, if the pore had that depth available. The calculation clearly says that if we wish to have as complete as possible removal of air from a pore on a surface, the pore radii must be quite small. The approximate radii of the openings of pores which are deeply penetrated is about one micron or less. The ramifications of this correlation become more clear when we discuss surface preparations in a future chapter.

Table 6.1   Packham's Calculation of Distance Penetrated by Molten Polyethylene into a Microporous Surface

Pore radius (micrometers)	Distance penetrated into "x" (micrometers)
1000	220
10	22
1	7
0.1	2.2
0.01	0.7

6.6   Wettability and Adhesion

Examine Fig. 6.7 and imagine a situation where there is a real adhesive and a real adherend. The importance of wettability to adhesion is apparent. A tortuous surface like that in Fig. 6.7 is not necessarily completely clean. There likely are contaminants on the surface, forming a "weak boundary layer" (see Section 6.10). In addition, a real adhesive has a real viscosity (as discussed in the previous section). In many cases, the adhesive will need to cure and the viscosity in these materials increases rapidly as a function of time after application. We can expect that the bottom of the pores may not be filled, leaving voids. The adhesive bond may therefore have vacancies at the interface, each of which acts as a stress concentration point. To understand this problem, we look at the situation pictured in Fig. 6.9 which is the same as Fig. 1.1. We show two situations, one is a perfect monolithic material in which there are no cracks or voids and the other of the same material containing a crack.

We can imagine a load being placed on both samples. The load is shown propagating through the unflawed material as continuous lines of force. In the flawed material, the lines of force cannot be continuous because of the flaw. The lines of force, because they must be continuous, gather at the edge of the flaw and increase in intensity. The increase in intensity can be calculated in a simple way for this elliptical crack. If the dimensions of the crack are such that the long axis is 100 times longer than the short axis, the increase in stress intensity is 201. So, a force which is a Newton at the ends of the material is more like 201 Newtons at the edges of such a crack. The factor in this discussion is a crude version of the "stress intensity factor" used in fracture mechanics [14]. An adhesive bond with a flawed interface is another example of this situation. Voids or weak boundary materials increase the applied force at the periphery of the flaw. Very often, this induces propagation of the flaw. If the material does not have mechanisms of absorbing the

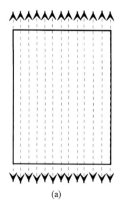

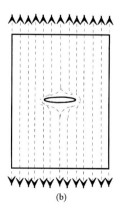

(a)   (b)

Figure 6.9   Diagram showing lines of force through a monolithic body (a) and a body containing an elliptical hole (b). The lines of force pass continuously through (a) but are unable to do so in (b). This results in a stress concentration at the edges of the elliptical hole

energy, the material fails at loads less (and sometimes even *much* less) than the theoretical strength of that material. Hence, obtaining good wetting of the surface is a matter of eliminating flaws at the interface so that the strength of the bond can be as close to theoretical as possible.

The study of adhesion cannot be separated from the study of wettability and contact angle phenomena. *For good adhesion to take place, the adhesive and the adherend must come into intimate contact.* Obtaining intimate contact of the adhesive with the surface is tantamount to saying that interfacial flaws must be minimized or eliminated. Intimate contact occurs when the adhesive spontaneously spreads over the surface to maximize interfacial contact and minimize contact with other phases. Spreading (spontaneous or not) can be determined by contact angle measurements. In this section we explore the relationship of wetting and adhesion.

A simple view of the relationship of wetting and adhesion is provided in Fig. 6.10, where the contact angle of a drop of an epoxy adhesive on a variety of surfaces is shown. The surface energy of a typical epoxy resin is about $42 \, mJ/m^2$. Thus, the drop has a low profile on materials such as cured epoxy composite or polyvinyl chloride (PVC), although wetting would not be spontaneous on PVC. On polyethylene, which has a critical wetting tension of about 31 dynes/cm, the drop has an even higher profile. In our laboratories, we have used sheet polyethylene to line our table tops because epoxies do not adhere. The adhesive has a very high contact angle on polytetrafluoroethylene (PTFE) with a critical wetting tension of 18 dynes/cm. Therefore, we could predict that an epoxy adhesive would have poor adhesion to PTFE. Low surface energy materials such as PTFE have poor adherability and are considered *abhesive* or *release* surfaces. PTFE-like materials form the basis for

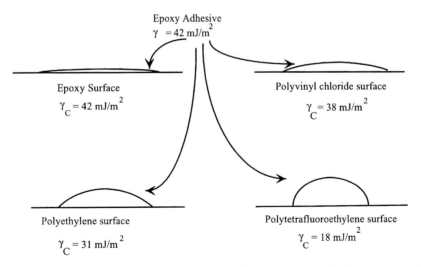

Epoxy Adhesive
$\gamma = 42 \, mJ/m^2$

Epoxy Surface
$\gamma_C = 42 \, mJ/m^2$

Polyvinyl chloride surface
$\gamma_C = 38 \, mJ/m^2$

Polyethylene surface
$\gamma_C = 31 \, mJ/m^2$

Polytetrafluoroethylene surface
$\gamma_C = 18 \, mJ/m^2$

Figure 6.10 Schematic diagram of the observation of the contact angle of an epoxy adhesive (uncured) on four surfaces of varying critical wetting tensions. Note that as the critical wetting tension of the surface decreases, the contact angle of the liquid epoxy on that surface increases

non-stick cookware. When it is demonstrated that eggs do not stick, we have a clear demonstration of the relationship between wettability, the Zisman critical wetting tension, and adhesion. Egg whites are, for the most part, proteinaceous materials. However, the proteins are in aqueous solution and the egg would be expected to have a surface tension close to 70 dynes/cm. The contact angle between the egg and PTFE is high. Wetting is poor and non-spontaneous and the egg does not adhere.

The ability of an adhesive to spontaneously wet a surface can be codified by means of the Zisman relationship described in Chapter 4. That is, an adhesive spontaneously wets a surface when its surface energy is less than that of the adherend to which it is applied. Thus a corollary to the criterion for good adhesion and wettability is *for spontaneous wetting and good adhesion, choose an adhesive with surface energy less than the critical wetting tension of the surface to which it is applied.* The background for this corollary was described in Fig. 6.10.

One of the clearest experiments relating wettability and adhesion was carried out Levine, Illka and Weiss [15]. In this work, the experimenters measured contact angles of various liquids on solid polymers. They then measured the butt tensile strength of adhesive bonds made with those plastics and a *single* adhesive. A schematic representation of their results is shown in Fig. 6.11. There is a direct relationship between the butt tensile strength and $1 + \cos\theta$, as would be predicted if there were a relationship between the thermodynamic work of adhesion and the practical work of adhesion. The Dupre Equation predicts that for a single combination of materials, the thermodynamic work of adhesion decreases as the interfacial energy increases. Figure 6.11 also shows data for the practical work of adhesion as a function of the interfacial tension. The practical work of adhesion does decrease as predicted by the Dupre Equation. Similarly, as the critical wetting tension of the solid surface goes below the surface energy of the adhesive, there is a decrease in butt tensile strength.

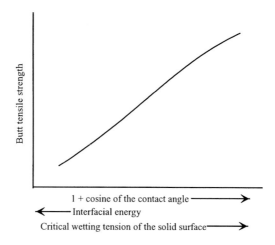

Figure 6.11   Schematic of the data presented by Levine, Illka and Weiss. Butt tensile strength of a range of plastics bonded with a single adhesive is plotted versus several wetting parameters determined from contact angle measurements

Another example of the relationship between the Young–Dupre Equation and adhesion is shown in the work of Barbarisi [16] who carried out a *surface preparation* of polyethylene. Surface preparation is an important technology in adhesion science because it has been found that many surfaces are not amenable to adhesive bonding for a number of reasons, not the least of which is low surface energy. The subject of surface preparation of various adherends is discussed in Chapter 7. The surface preparation used by Barbarisi was chromic acid oxidation. As a function of treatment time, it was found that the contact angle of water with the treated polyethylene surface went down. Therefore, $1 + \cos\theta$ increased as did the practical adhesive bond strength with the treated polyethylene as adherends. The same epoxy adhesive was used in all of these experiments. A useful reference describing the relationship between wettability and adhesion appears in the book *Adhesion Science and Technology* in the chapter by Mittal [17].

6.7   Acid–Base Interactions at Interfaces

In Chapter 4, we described various intermolecular interactions which could take place at an interface. In Section 4.2.3, we described generic acid–base interactions including the Bronsted–Lowrey acids and Lewis acids. Acid–base interactions can take place at interfaces as they do in bulk solutions. Work on this subject was done by Bolger and Michaels [18]. They used standard chemical data of acid–base equilibria to examine various interfacial phenomena. Fowkes [19] also used acid–base interactions to describe adhesion phenomena. Fowkes derived the equation which divides the surface energy of a material into its component parts and was known for his belief that polar forces played no role in interfacial phenomena. In his view, the primary interactions taking place at interfaces were due to dispersion forces. He later ascribed the remaining interactions to acid–base interactions. Thus, using the Owens–Wendt equation, in Fowkes view:

$$W_A = 2\sqrt{\gamma_1^d \gamma_2^d} + W_A^{AB}$$

where W^{AB} is the component of the work of adhesion due to acid–base interactions. From a critical point of view, it seems that this analysis just removed a term having to do with polar forces and replaced it with a term having a different designation. Fowkes borrowed from the work of Drago [20] to provide an expression for W_A^{AB}. He wrote the following expression:

$$W_A^{AB} = kN^{AB}(E_A E_B + C_A C_B)$$

where k is a proportionality constant that corrects for units and N^{AB} is the number of acid–base pairs which interact in the interphase or at the interface. The E_i and C_i are experimentally determined constants obtained from a series of detailed calorimetric experiments in which Drago and his group measured the heat of reaction of a myriad of different acid–base pairs. The purpose of the Drago experiments was to determine the electrostatic (E) and covalent (C) contribution to the enthalpy of interaction of a large series of acid–base pairs. It was a disappointment to Drago that these experiments did not provide the correlation he wanted but rather yielded a large catalog of data from which enthalpies of reaction could be calculated. Therefore, the Fowkes expression for acid–base interactions is not one that comes from first principles of intermolecular forces, but is obtained from experimentally derived constants. This is not to say that the expression is conceptually incorrect, but it unfortunately gives the impression that acid–base reactions are a fundamental force (like dispersion forces), rather than a combination of electrostatic and covalent interactions, as believed by Drago.

The effect of acid–base interactions at interfaces was examined by Fowkes and Mostafa [21] in a now classic series of experiments and more recently by Whitesides and coworkers (as described in Chapter 4). Contact angle measurements have formed the basis for a substantial amount of information on adhesion phenomena. Fowkes and Mostafa used contact angle measurements to determine the extent of acid–base interactions by creating acidic surfaces by copolymerizing varying amounts of acrylic acid with ethylene. They then used basic liquids such as dimethyl-sulfoxide and dimethylformamide (basic in the Lewis sense) and sodium hydroxide dissolved in water (basic in the Bronsted–Lowrey sense) as contact angle probe liquids. In addition, they probed the dispersion force contribution to the work of adhesion by using dispersion force-only liquids. Conversely, they generated basic surfaces by using copolymers of vinyl acetate with ethylene and used acidic liquids as probes (vinyl acetate is considered a Lewis base). The acidic liquids were composed of varying amounts of phenol in tricresylphosphate. A schematic representation of their experimental results is shown in Fig. 6.12.

There are a significant number of other studies in the literature examining the acid–base properties of interfaces including an important set which used inverse phase gas chromatography. This type of chromatography determines interfacial interactions because the retention time on the column is directly related to the enthalpy of interaction between the mobile phase and the stationary phase surface.

In addition to the Drago experimentation on acid–base pairs, there have also been a number of other methods proposed to characterize the acid or basic character of a material. Two of the important classifications are the Gutman donor–acceptor numbers [22] and the hard–soft acid–base principle. The Gutman numbers have been studied by Schreiber and co-workers [23], who have attempted to relate the chemistry of the surfaces to those numbers and then to relate those numbers to adhesion phenomena.

Despite all of the interest shown in acid–base interactions at interfaces, there are relatively few detailed studies connecting the acid–base character of interfaces with the actual forces of adhesion between those surfaces. There are experimental results implying the presence or predominance of the acid–base interaction in adhesion. It is known, for example, that silica is acidic and most glasses are basic (due to additives to the glass, such as borate). Materials thought to adhere well to silica are basic and those thought to adhere well to normal glass are acidic. In fact, many

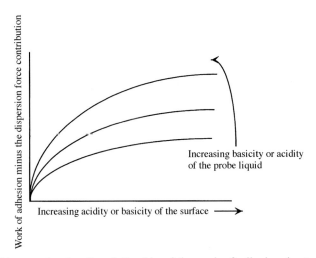

Figure 6.12   Diagram showing the relationship of the work of adhesion due to acid–base interactions versus the increasing acidity or basicity of the substrate and probe liquid. When the substrate is an acid, a basic probe liquid provides results similar to those shown. When the substrate is a base, an acidic liquid provides results similar to those shown. When an acid substrate and an acid probe liquid are used, no effect is seen. The dispersion force contribution is determined by using liquids with only dispersion force character

industrially useful inorganic surfaces are basic in character because the oxides of most metals (with the exception of tungsten) are either amphoteric or basic in character. Many adhesives are formulated to be acidic in character so that they adhere to a multitude of basic surfaces. From this discussion, we can provide another criterion for good adhesion: *determine the acid or basic character of your substrate and choose an adhesive having the opposite character.*

6.8   Covalent Bonding at Interfaces

In Chapter 4, we discussed the energetics of various intermolecular interactions. In that discussion, we made note of the fact that the deepest potential energy well that is available for the interaction between two atoms or molecules is that formed when they share a pair of electrons. That is, the deepest potential energy well is obtained when a covalent bond is formed. The generation of covalent bonds at interfaces, especially between organics and inorganics, has become an industry of its own.

Assume that we have an area of contact between two dissimilar materials that is one square meter. Let us also assume that the cross sectional area occupied by each member of a large number of carbon–carbon covalent bonds is five square Angstrom units. The number of chemical bonds is then 2×10^{19} bonds/m^2. If we assume that the energy to break a mole of these bonds is 120 kcal (which is about the amount of energy necessary to break one mole of carbon–carbon covalent bonds), then we can calculate that the total energy at this interface is on the order of 40 Joules/m^2. This is a very large number when compared to the values of surface and interfacial energy discussed in Chapter 4. This large number provides background for the reason so much research has been devoted to the generation of interfacial chemical bonds. Indeed, the bond energies described in the work of Brown [8] only approach this level. However, although it would seem necessary to have covalent bonds at interfaces to have strong adhesive bonds, often strong adhesive bonds exist in the absence of any overtly induced interfacial chemical bonds. Indeed, Fowkes [24] has calculated that the strength of a polyethylene/steel butt tensile joint is in excess of 157 000 psi when one assumes the presence of dispersion forces, exclusively, at the interface. This value is orders of magnitude higher than any experimentally observed adhesive bond strength. This comparison indicates that even though covalent bonds may be useful to have at interfaces, they are not necessary for the generation of strong adhesive bonds.

Why then, is there a desire to generate chemical bonds at interfaces? The primary reason for the need for such chemical bonds can be found in the calculation described by Kinloch [25]. We write the expression for the surface energy of any material as the sum of the polar force and dispersion force contributions, as was proposed by Fowkes [19]. In deference to the work of some adhesion science researchers, we could write the expression substituting acid–base interactions for polar interactions, as:

$$\gamma = \gamma^d + \gamma^p$$

where γ is the surface energy of a material; γ^d is the dispersion force component of that surface energy; and γ^p is the polar (or acid–base) contribution to the surface energy. Using the hypothesis of Owens and Wendt, we have:

$$W_A = 2\sqrt{\gamma_1^d \gamma_2^d} + 2\sqrt{\gamma_1^p \gamma_2^p}$$

This expression deals only with a situation where the two materials are in contact with one another and no other material is present. We could have a situation where a third material is present, with its own polar and dispersive character. In that situation, we find that the expression is a bit more complicated but derivable directly from the above relationships:

$$W_A = 2[\gamma_L - \sqrt{\gamma_1^d \gamma_l^d} - \sqrt{\gamma_1^p \gamma_l^p} - \sqrt{\gamma_2^d \gamma_l^d} - \sqrt{\gamma_2^p \gamma_l^p} + \sqrt{\gamma_1^d \gamma_2^d} + \sqrt{\gamma_1^p \gamma_2^p}]$$

where the γ_i^j are the components of the liquid surface energy of the intervening liquid. If the values of the γ_i^j are known, then the predicted thermodynamic work of adhesion at an interface in the presence of a third material such as the liquid, l, can be calculated.

Such a calculation was done by Kinloch [25]. Table 6.2 gives values of the polar and dispersive components of the surface energy for a number of familiar materials and shows a listing of the work of adhesion in the presence and absence of a third material, water.

The results in Table 6.2 provide insight as to the need for interfacial covalent or chemical bonds. In the absence of water, the work of adhesion for epoxy with silica

Table 6.2   Calculation of Work of Adhesion Based upon Polar and Dispersive Components of the Surface Energy

Surface or interface	γ^d (mJ/m^2)	γ^p (mJ/m^2)	γ (mJ/m^2)	W_A (mJ/m^2)	W_A^l (mJ/m^2)
Epoxy	41.2	5	46.2		
Silica	78	209	287		
Aluminum oxide	100	538	638		
Water	22	50.2	72.2		
Epoxy/silica				178	
Epoxy/aluminum oxide				232	
Epoxy/water/silica					−56.2
Epoxy/water/aluminum oxide					−137

or for epoxy with aluminum oxide are positive. This indicates the stability of this interface in the absence of water. With water present, the calculated values for the work of adhesion are not only decreased, they are negative. Negative values of the work of adhesion indicate that this system is unstable in the presence of water. That is, the inorganic surface would rather have water present than the epoxy resin.

An indication of thermodynamic instability should be a matter of concern here because it is hard to think of many applications where adhesive bonds made with epoxy and these substrates would not, at some time, come into the presence of water. However, an analogy can be drawn with the use of aluminum in various industrial applications. Aluminum is a highly reactive metal which is thermodynamically unstable in ambient atmosphere. If elemental aluminum is exposed to the atmosphere, it explodes. Despite this seemingly dire situation, we use aluminum for frying pans and we fly in airplanes made from aluminum. The reason we can use aluminum for these purposes is that it is insulated from the atmosphere by a thin layer of very stable aluminum oxide. The reaction of aluminum with the atmosphere is kinetically controlled by the formation of an oxide which slows down the degradation of the metal. In a similar sense, if we could place covalent bonds at the interface between organic and inorganic materials, water would first have to hydrolyze those covalent bonds before it could act on the interface. Covalent bonding at interfaces could thus be the kinetic limiter for the action of water. From this discussion comes another guideline for good adhesion: *if one expects to have an adhesive bond in adverse environmental conditions, provide for interfacial covalent bonding.*

6.8.1   Coupling Agents

An industry has been built developing agents which "couple" an organic and an inorganic phase. *Coupling agents* are materials with two chemical functions, one of

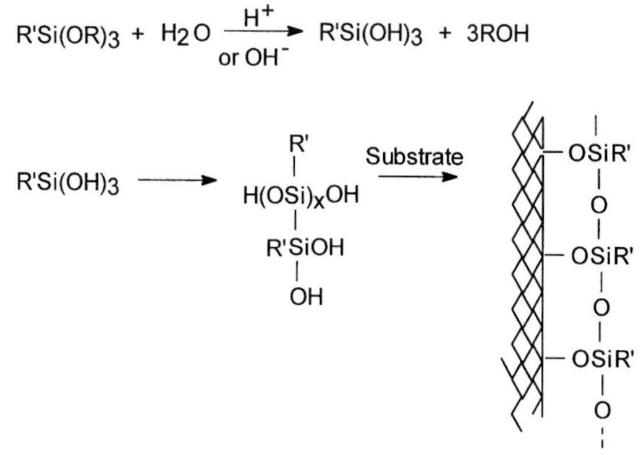

$$R'Si(OR)_3 + H_2O \xrightarrow[\text{or } OH^-]{H^+} R'Si(OH)_3 + 3ROH$$

Figure 6.13

which is reactive with the inorganic phase and the other of which is reactive with the organic phase. One class of coupling agents, based upon silanes, has found the most utility [26]. The reaction scheme thought to occur when these materials are used is shown in Fig. 6.13.

Silanes, in the presence of water, hydrolyze to silanols which spontaneously condense to yield silanol oligomers. At low molecular weights, the oligomers are usually soluble in water. If a surface containing a hydroxyl group is nearby, the silanols also condense with the surface, creating the situation shown at the end of Fig. 6.13. There is also an R' group on each silane which is retained throughout the oligomerization and condensation with the substrate. The R' group is chosen to be reactive with the matrix material. For example, if the matrix is an epoxy, a propyl amino group could be chosen as R' or if the matrix is an acrylic, then a propyl acryloyl group could be R'.

Silanes as a monolayer of oligomer on a substrate is the image early workers in this area thought to be true of these materials. However, Koenig and Ishida [27] were able to show that to be effective the amount of silane deposited on a surface needed to be substantially in excess of that shown in Fig. 6.13. In fact, they showed that an effective amount was more than hundreds of Angstrom units thick. This data has led to the hypothesis that silane coupling agents form a layer into which the matrix can diffuse and react, creating a diffuse interphasal layer between the inorganic and the organic phases. This physical action occurs in addition to chemical reaction between the matrix and the R' groups.

The first application of silanes in industry was in fiberglass. Fiberglass is a material in which a matrix resin, e.g., a styrenated polyester, is filled with glass fiber as a reinforcement. When such materials were originally fabricated, fiberglass had an increased stiffness over that of the matrix resin. However, with exposure to moisture, the stiffness decreased measurably. The hypothesis was that moisture invaded the composite material and disbonded the matrix resin from the fibers, as was predicted from the equations and analysis described above. If a silane coupling agent was

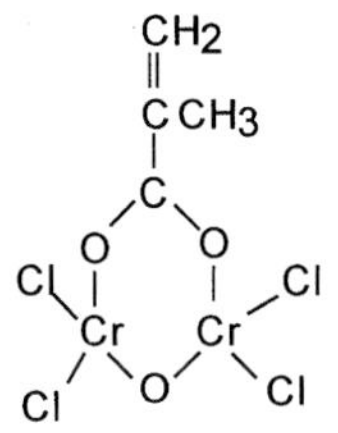

Chrome complex

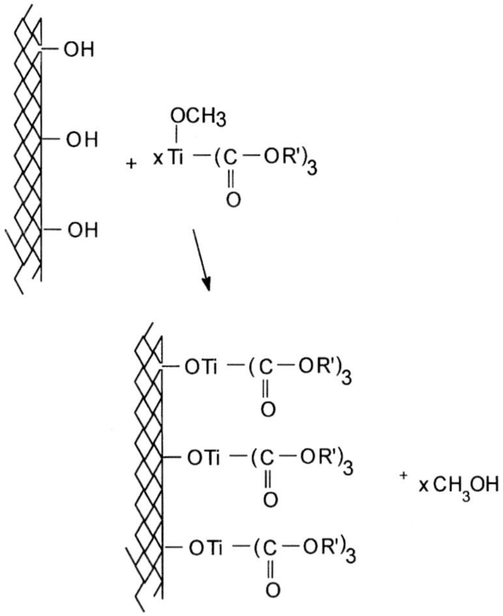

Titanate condensation on a hydroxyl
containing surface

Figure 6.14

applied to the fibers before they were added to the matrix resin, the fiberglass
retained its original modulus longer when the material was exposed to moisture. The
presence of covalent bonds in an interphase kinetically inhibited the effect of water
on an material whose performance depended on good adhesion between an organic
and an inorganic phase.

Although silane coupling agents form the largest and most successful group of
such materials, there are other combinations, as well. Chrome complexes, with
structures shown in Fig. 6.14, are formed by the reaction of chromium chloride
with methacrylic acid. The chromium oxide portion of the coupling agent reacts
with a substrate while the methacrylic portion reacts with a free-radically-curing
overlayer.

Another major class of coupling agent is the titanates [28]. Once again, this
material is a combination of an organic and an inorganic material. An example of a
titanate ester is also shown in Fig. 6.14. As in the case of the silanes, the material is
thought to react with hydroxyls on the surface of inorganics to liberate alcohols.
Titanates have been used a great deal in the modification of the viscosity of slurries
of organics in inorganics by "compatibilizing" the two materials. The R' groups
shown in Fig. 6.14 can be any one of a number of chemical functions reactive with a
number of different matrices.

6.9   The Relationship of Fundamental Forces of Adhesion and Practical Adhesion

Statements have been made as to the lack of a direct relationship between the forces of adhesion and the practical strength of an adhesive bond. In this section, we describe several experiments which have laid the basis for a way to connect interfacial characteristics and the mechanical strength of an adhesive bond.

In the description of silane coupling agents, the effectiveness of the chemistry was described as an increase in the durability of the composite. The modulus of the composite was essentially the same with or without the presence of the silane, but the retention of modulus was improved when a silane was used in the interphase.

There are also descriptions of an increase in the dry bond strength as the result of the presence of a coupling agent. Such an experiment was described by Ahagon and Gent [29]. A glass slide was coated with mixtures of vinyl and ethyl silane, at essentially monolayer coverage. The vinyl silane was available for reaction with a free-radically-curing overlayer, but the ethyl was not. We expect that increasing the percentage of vinyl silane in comparison to ethyl silane provides an improvement in adhesion. An overlayer of polybutadiene was applied to the coated slide and free radically crosslinked. The strength of the adhesive bond was measured by a 180° peel test, in which the polybutadiene was peeled from the slide at various temperatures and peel rates. The data were superimposed by means of shift factors to create a master curve for the peel tests on each treated surface. Recall the discussion in the previous chapter on master curves and the time–temperature superposition principle for polymers.

A schematic representation of Ahagon and Gent's results is presented in Fig. 6.15. The curve labeled W_1 is for a sample covered entirely with ethyl silane while W_4 is the curve for a surface covered entirely with vinyl silane. W_2 and W_3 are intermediate combinations of vinyl silane in ethyl silane. The symbol W has been chosen not only for the curves, but also for the asymptotic value of the work to break the adhesive bond. Note that $W_4 > W_3 > W_2 > W_1$. The results track well with the amount of vinyl silane in the coating.

Several things can be learned from this plot. First, a plot of peel strength (work to break) as a function of peel rate can approach an asymptotic value, which is tempting to ascribe to the intrinsic work of adhesion. Second, the plots of work to break versus reduced peel rate seem to have nominally the same shape, but are shifted in the vertical direction with respect to one another. Note that the plot is log-log. For this situation, we write:

$$\log W_B = \log W_i + \log \zeta$$

or, taking the antilog:

$$W_B = W_i \zeta$$

This equation represents an important relationship between the strength of an adhesive bond and the *multiplication* of some factor describing the intrinsic adhesion

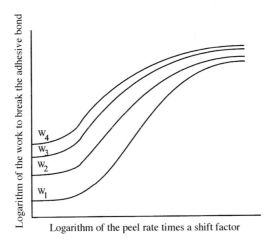

Figure 6.15   Schematic of the data of Ahagon and Gent. The log of the work to break an adhesive bond is plotted versus the reduced rate of peel. The various curves result from a variation in the surface coverage by vinyl silane

by another factor, ζ. In Fig. 6.15, the abscissa was described as a shift factor times a rate of peel. This bears a resemblance to the discussion in Chapter 5 and in particular Fig. 5.11, where the log of modulus was plotted versus the frequency times a shift factor. It is reasonable to define ζ as a function describing the viscoelastic properties of the materials involved in the adhesive bond. The final feature to note here is the value of the work to break the adhesive bond. The intrinsic levels of adhesion were found to be on the order of $200\,mJ/m^2$ to about $2\,J/m^2$, which is within an order of magnitude of the intrinsic levels of adhesion that are predicted from the Young–Dupre equation.

The above experimental results show a possible relationship between interfacial bonding, the viscoelastic properties of an adhesive, and the mechanical strength of an adhesive bond. The adhesive can be thought of as a mass of spaghetti noodles placed between two adherends. The noodles are partially cooked so that they stick somewhat to one another and they are intertwined. First, suppose that the noodles are not attached to the adherend. Pulling on the bond removes the mass of the noodles from the adherend. Therefore, if $W_A = 0$, $W_B = 0$.

Now suppose that the noodles are attached to the two adherends, but the attachment can be much smaller or equal to the attachment of the noodles to one another. If we pull on the adherends, the noodles do not detach from the adherend. Rather, the mechanical energy is placed into stretching the noodles. If the noodles are sufficiently intertwined, the mechanical energy continues to go into stretching and unraveling the noodles. The adhesion of the noodles to the adherend is not tested until at least some of the noodles are fully taut. At that point, however, much mechanical energy has already been absorbed by the adhesive. Thus, the adhesion that the noodles display to the adherend *activates* the ability of the adhesive to absorb the mechanical energy. The amount of mechanical energy which can be stored is then dependent upon the critical strain energy release rate of the materials in question. Since the adhesion displayed by the adhesive can be considered to be the conduit which activates energy absorption by the adhesive, it is not difficult to believe that the effect of increasing adhesion should be multiplicative of the energy able to be absorbed by the adhesive.

Let us formulate a more general equation describing the linkage between the practical work of adhesion and fundamental adhesion. From the discussion of the Griffith criterion for fracture, we know that for a completely brittle material, the energy necessary to break an adhesive bond is $W_B = W_A$ which is 2γ or $\gamma_1 + \gamma_2 - \gamma_{12}$, depending upon whether the failure is in cohesion in the adhesive or the failure is in adhesion. This energy can be considered to be the minimum amount of practical adhesion that one can obtain from an adhesive bond. If other modes of dissipating energy are available, then this minimum value increases. The work of Ahagon and Gent implies that the amount of increase is proportional to $W_A\zeta$, in this way:

$$W_B = W_A + f(W_A)\zeta \qquad (6.2)$$

where $f(W_A)$ says that an unknown function of the work of adhesion multiplies the function ζ which describes how mechanical energy is dissipated in the adhesive and the adherend. This expression fits our reasoning as to the relationship between fundamental adhesion and practical adhesion.

An important question to ask here is if there are any other experimental results lending credence to this equation. In one set of experiments carried out by Gent and Schultz [30], the peel strength of an adhesive/adherend combination was measured under various liquids. Instead of creating surfaces with a single interfacial energy with air, the interfacial energy in this experiment was dependent upon the liquid in which the peeling experiment was done. The work to break was measured as a function of the rate of peel and the rates were shifted in much the same way as described by Ahagon and Gent. A family of curves was obtained which were approximately the same shape, but were shifted with respect to one another. The shift was dependent upon the interfacial tension between the surfaces and the liquid used for the experiment.

In other work, Andrews and Kinloch [31] made simple fracture specimens in which an adhesive bond was simulated. They measured the crack propagation rate of the flaw as a function of the work of adhesion between the substrate and the adhesive. The crack propagation rate was reduced by a shift factor and the logarithm of the force to propagate the crack was plotted versus the log of the reduced crack propagation rate. A roughly parallel family of curves was obtained. The curves were shifted from one another by a factor approximately related to the work of adhesion. The work of Gent and Schultz and that of Andrews and Kinloch both lend credence to Eq. (6.2).

Equation (6.2) would also say that if log W_B were measured at slower and slower reduced rates (that is at very low rates or high temperatures or both) one eventually comes to the point where W_A was measured. At very low reduced rates, ζ is small. Measurements in the literature indicate that the extrapolated values of the log W_B to very low reduced rates do not actually attain W_A from the Dupre equation. Rather, the asymptotic value seems to approach several ranges, depending upon the types of bonds present at the interface. For example, in the work of Brown *et al.* [8] it was found that the asymptotic value for polystyrene in contact with polyisoprene is about $120 \, \text{mJ/m}^2$ but $W_A(\text{Dupre}) = 65 \, \text{mJ/m}^2$. With a block copolymer present at this interface, the asymptotic level increases to 400 mJ/m^2 depending upon both the aerial chain density as well as the length of the block copolymer segments. In other experiments reported by Gent, polybutadiene was partially vulcanized, attached to itself and vulcanization completed. These bonds were then peeled apart as a function of rate and temperature and a log peel force–log reduced rate plot was generated. Extrapolation to low reduced rates provided a value of the intrinsic adhesion energy of $1 \, \text{J/m}^2$. This value is close to the value we might have expected for a interface composed of carbon–carbon bonds as described in Section 6.8. We conclude from this discussion that the term described as W_A in Eq. (6.2) should be replaced with another term called W_0, also known as the *threshold level of adhesion* for a particular bonding situation. Thus, W_0 is about $50 \, \text{mJ/m}^2$ when the forces of adhesion are due entirely to van der Waals type of interactions and about $400 \, \text{mJ/m}^2$ when chain pull-out is a dominant way the interface is held together. However, W_0 is about $1 \, \text{J/m}^2$ or greater when two surfaces are primarily joined by covalent bonding. We write the equation which relates the fundamental forces of adhesion to practical adhesion as:

$$W_B = W_0 + f(W_0)\zeta$$

All of these parameters have been defined earlier. It is the goal of adhesion scientists to determine the functional form of $f(W_0)\zeta$ and to predict W_0 from first principles.

6.10   The Weak Boundary Layer

The final rationalization of adhesion phenomena is the weak boundary layer. This view of adhesion was initially proposed by J.J. Bikerman [32], who authored one of the first books about adhesion phenomena. Bikerman's theory, simply stated, is that if a proper adhesive bond is made, the bond fails in either the adherend or the adhesive, whichever is cohesively weaker. Bonds fail at less than their expected strength due to the presence of materials of low cohesive strength at the interface. These low cohesive strength materials form the "weak boundary layer." There is no doubt that if an adhesive bond has low cohesive strength materials at the interface, then the adhesive bond is weaker than expected. In fact, it has been the fallback position of adhesion scientists that any adhesive bonding situation which cannot be explained by other rationalizations is explained by the presence of a weak boundary layer.

However, it is not always true that in a proper adhesive bond, failure always occurs in either the adhesive or the adherend. For example, in our own work, we have coextruded polyethylene (PE) and polyethylene terephthalate (PET) to generate a multilayered structure [33]. The materials were mated in the melt and were thus in intimate contact. We have used the surface forces apparatus described in Section 4.5.2.2 and measured the interfacial energy between these two materials at $17\,mJ/m^2$. This is a high number. The Dupre equation predicts a low work of adhesion. This is observed in peel results. We examined the failure surface between the PE and the PET, using physical techniques, such as X-ray photoelectron spectroscopy (XPS) and Static Secondary Ion Mass Spectrometry (SSIMS), and we found that the failure between these materials was purely interfacial.

The above discussion notwithstanding, there are many adhesive failures due to a weak boundary layer. It is known that it is extremely difficult to bond to a metal surface from which mill oils have not been removed. It is extremely difficult to bond to a surface which is wet with water. Adhesive bonding to rusty steel is difficult because iron oxide is cohesively weak. Weak boundary layers, however, can also be used to advantage. For example, certain adhesive tape applications would not work without a "release liner," a material to which the adhesive tape lightly adheres and from which it can peel easily. These release liners are often chemically tailored weak boundary layers.

The discussion in this section leads to another criterion for good adhesive bonding: *in order to generate a proper adhesive bond, weak boundary layers need to be removed or modified so that they are cohesively strong.* Chapter 7 provides strategies for assuring this criterion is met.

6.11   Summary

In this chapter, we discussed various rationalizations used to describe adhesive bonding phenomena. The rationalizations include the electrostatic theory, the diffusion theory, the mechanical interlocking theory, the wettability theory, covalent bonding at interfaces and the weak boundary layer theory. Each of these rationalizations have been used to greater or lesser extent in describing various adhesive bonding phenomena. Of these rationalizations, the wettability/adsorption theory is the most widely used and appreciated. A combination of the salient features of these rationalizations leads to a set of criteria for obtaining a good adhesive bond. These criteria are:

- Choose an adhesive which is soluble in the adherend (diffusion theory), OR
- Choose an adhesive which spontaneously wets the surface (wettability theory).
- Make sure the surface has a microscopic morphology (mechanical interlocking).
- Eliminate all weak boundary layers (weak boundary layer theory).
- Choose an adhesive which has the right viscosity/cure relationship so that pores are completely wetted (wettability + mechanical interlocking).
- If the adhesive bond is to be exposed to adverse environments, provide for covalent bonding in the interphase.

Bibliography

Wu, S., *Polymer Interfaces and Adhesion* (1982), Marcel Dekker, New York
Patrick, R.L., (Ed.*), Treatise on Adhesion and Adhesives*, vol. 1, (1968), Marcel Dekker, New York
Kinloch, A.J., *J. Mater. Sci.* (1982), 17, p. 617
Kinloch, A.J., *J. Mater. Sci.* (1980), 15, p. 2141

References

1. (a) Derjaguin, B.V., *Research*, 8 (1955), p. 70. (b) Derjaguin, B.V., Krotova, N.A., Karassev, V.V., Kirillova, Y.M., and Aleinikova, I.N., in *Proc. 2nd. Internat'l Congress on Surface Activity – III* (1957), Butterworths, London. (c) Derjaguin, B.V., and Smilga, V.P., *Adhesion, Fundamentals and Practice* (1969), McLaren and Son, London
2. Hunstberger, J.R., in *Treatise on Adhesion and Adhesives*, vol. 1, R.L. Patrick (Ed.) (1967), Marcel Dekker, New York
3. Dickinson, J.T., Jensen, L.C., Lee, S., Scudiero, L. and Langford, S.C., *J. Adhesion Sci. Technol.*, 8 (1994), p. 1285
4. (a) Horn, R.G., and Smith, D.T., *Science*, 256 (1992), p. 362. (b) Smith, D.T., *Electrostat.*, 26 (1991), p. 291. (c) Horn, R.G., Smith, D.T., and Grabbe, A., *Nature*, 366 (1993), p. 442. (d) Smith, D.T., and Horn, R.G., in *Proc. Mater. Res. Soc., Symp.*, Vol. 170 (1989), Materials Res. Soc., Pittsburgh
5. Israelachvili, J.N., *J. Coll. Interface Sci.*, 44 (1973), p. 259
6. Hildebrand, J., and Scott, R., *The Solubility of Non-Electrolytes,* 3rd. Ed. (1950). Reinhold, New York
7. Iyengar, Y., and Erickson, D.E., *J. Appl. Polymer Sci.*, 11 (1967), p. 2311
8. (a) Brown, H.R., *Macromolecules*, 22 (1989), p. 2859. (b) Creton, C., Karmer, E.J., Hui, C.-Y., and Brown, H.R., *Macromolecules*, 25 (1992), p. 3075. (c) Brown, H.R., Char, K., Deline, V.R., and Green, P.F., *Macromolecules*, 26 (1993), p. 4155, (d) Char, K., Brown, H.R., and Deline, V.R., *Macromolecules*, 26 (1993), p. 4164. (e) Brown, H.R., *Macromolecules*, 26 (1993), p. 1666. (f) Reichert, W.F., and Brown, H.R., *Polymer*, 34 (1993), p. 2289. (g) Brown, H.R., *Science*, 236 (1994), p. 1411. (h) Creton, C., Brown, H.R., and Shull, K.R., *Macromolecules*, 27 (1994), p. 3174
9. DeGennes, P.G., *J. Chem. Phys.*, 55 (1974), p. 572
10. Arrowsmith, D.J., *Trans. Inst Met. Finish.*, 48 (1970), p. 88
11. Packham, D.E., in *Adhesion Aspects of Polymeric Coatings*, K.L. Mittal (Ed.) (1983), Plenum Press, New York
12. Schonhorn, H., Frisch, H.L., and Kwei, T.K., *J. Appl. Phys.*, 37 (1966), p. 4967
13. Newman, S., *J. Colloid. Interface Sci.*, 26 (1968), p. 209
14. Ingliss, C.E., *Proc. Inst. Nav. Archit.*, 55 (1913), p. 219
15. Levine, M., Ilkka, G., and Weiss, P., *Polymer Letters,* 2 (1964), p. 915
16. Barbarisi, M.J., *Nature*, 215 (1967), p. 383
17. Mittal, K.L., in *Adhesion Science and Technology*, L.-H. Lee (Ed.) (1975), Plenum Press, New York
18. Bolger, J.C., and Michaels, A.S., in *Interface Conversion for Polymeric Coatings,* P. Weiss and G.D. Cheever (Eds.) (1968), American Elsevier, New York
19. Fowkes, F.M., *Organic Coatings and Plastics Chemistry*, vol. 40 (1979), American Chemical Society, Washington, DC, pp. 13–18
20. Drago, R.S., Vogel, G.C., and Needham, T.E., *J. Am. Chem. Soc.*, 93 (1971), p. 6014
21. Fowkes, F.M., in *Microscopic Aspects of Adhesion and Lubrication*, J.M. Georges (Ed.) (1982), Elsevier, Amsterdam, p. 119

22. Gutmann, V., *The Donor–Acceptor Approach to Molecular Interactions* (1978), Plenum Press, New York
23. (a) Schreiber, H.P., and Li, Y., in *Molecular Characterization of Composite Interfaces* (1985), Plenum Press, New York. (b) Fafard, M., El-Kindi, M., Schreiber, H.P., Dipaola-Baranyi, G., and Hor, A.M., *J. Adhesion Sci. and Tech.*, 8 (1994), p. 1383
24. Fowkes, F.M., *Ind. Eng. Chem.*, 56 (1964), p. 40
25. Kinloch, A.J., Dukes, W.A., and Gledhill, R.A., in *Adhesion Science and Technology,* L.-H. Lee (Ed.) (1975), Plenum Press, New York
26. Plueddemann, E.P., *Silane Coupling Agents* (1982), Plenum Press, New York
27. Ishida, H., and Koenig, J.L., *Polym. Eng. Sci.*, 18 (1978), p. 128
28. Technical Literature of Kenrich Petrochemical Company, Bayonne, NJ,
29. Ahagon, A., and Gent, A.N., *J. Polym. Sci., Polym. Phys. Ed.*, 13 (1975), p. 1285
30. Gent, A.N., and Schultz, J., *J. Adhesion*, 3 (1972), p. 281
31. (a) Andrews, E.H., and Kinloch, A. J., *Proc. Roy. Soc Lond. A.*, 332 (1973), p. 385. (b) Andrews, E.H., and Kinloch, A.J., *Proc. Roy. Soc. Lond. A.*, 332 (1973), p. 401. (c) Gent, A.N., and Kinloch, A.J., *J. Polym. Sci.*, Pt. A-2, 9 (1971), p. 659
32. Bikerman, J.J., *The Science of Adhesive Joints* (1961), Academic Press, New York
33. Mangipudi, V.S., Pocius, A.V., and Tirrell, M., *J. Adhes. Sci. Tech.*, 8 (1994), p. 1231

7   The Surface Preparation of Adherends for Adhesive Bonding

7.1   Introduction

In the previous chapter, the criteria for good adhesive bonding were discussed. Those criteria were based on the theories or rationalizations of adhesion phenomena as well as empirical data. When adhesive bonding is used in industry, however, it is quickly found that surfaces do not necessarily have the attributes described in the previous chapter. Figure 7.1 provides a depiction of an unprepared metal surface.

An unprepared metal surface, as it comes from the mill, has surface features resulting from the rolling or forging operations and may not have the size scale necessary for good adhesive bonding. The metal surface undoubtedly is covered by an oxide or scale, but that oxide may not have the chemical characteristics for a good adhesive bond. For example, certain alloys of aluminum contain magnesium. Magnesium has high mobility in the melt and, in fact, a magnesium–aluminum alloy has a surface nominally of magnesium oxide. On top of the metal oxide is usually a layer of adsorbed organic molecules. These organic molecules could be disadvantageously adsorbed from the atmosphere or they may have been added by the mill in order to lubricate the surface for rolling. The polar organics on the surface may or may not be disadvantageously adsorbed. Water is ubiquitous and is found as an adsorbed layer on top of the organic layer and possibly as a layer of chemisorbed and physisorbed water at the metal oxide surface. In addition, water could be found as a liquid on the surface, depending upon the relative humidity of the ambient atmosphere. Depending upon the metal and its processing conditions, the layer of contaminants on a metal surface could be as thick as $0.001''$ (0.00254 cm) or more. Thus, when an adhesive is brought in contact with what is considered a "high energy surface," it is actually close to a low energy surface because of the contaminants.

A similar situation can observed in the case of polymeric materials. Most industrially useful polymeric materials (plastics) are not found in the pure chemical state but a compounded state. Compounding ingredients normally used are plasticizers, antioxidants, slip agents, etc. In addition, most plastics are not of a single molecular weight. In particular, free radically polymerized materials can have a rather broad molecular weight distribution. The low molecular weight materials (they are often called "tails") often "bloom" or rise to the surface, especially in semicrystalline plastics. The surface of an industrial semicrystalline plastic may be similar to the one shown in Fig. 7.2.

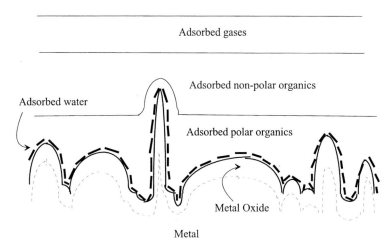

Figure 7.1   Diagram showing the layered, rough structure which could be expected on the surface of unprepared metal. Scale of surface roughness could be on the order of microns

The squiggly lines in the figure interior to the polymer signify the amorphous regions of the polymer, while the zig-zag lines represent the crystalline regions of a polymer surface. The two regions are distinct for reasons which become evident later in this chapter. On the surface of the plastic are shown some shorter, curved lines representing the low molecular weight exudate. Using adhesives with plastics has more problems than those caused by the low molecular weight exudates. Plastics are

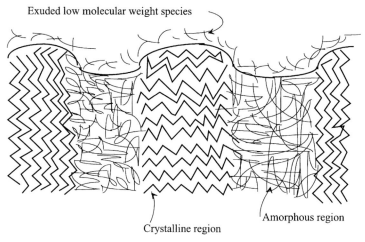

Figure 7.2   A simple representation of a semicrystalline polymer surface. The outer surface is relatively smooth but could be covered by low molecular weight exudate. The material immediately under the surface is composed of both crystalline and amorphous regions

low surface energy materials and most high strength adhesives do not spontaneously wet these surfaces. As shown in the previous chapter, a high strength (and therefore high surface energy) adhesive being used on a low energy surface should immediately be considered as problematic.

There are two other reasons for surface preparations prior to adhesive bonding which may be immediately obvious. Each of the surfaces depicted in Figs. 7.1 and 7.2 look like they have some structure. In reality, the surfaces of industrial metals and plastics do not have a specific structure or chemistry. Industrial metals are coated by various lubricants, the one used on any given day is determined primarily by cost. Industrial plastics could contain a mold release, again, usually chosen on the basis of cost. So, the first reason for surface preparation is to provide a *reproducible* surface so that the bonding operation is consistent. The second reason to use a surface preparation is durability. According to J. Corey MacMillan of Boeing Corp., "Surface Preparation – [is] The Key to Bondment Durability" [1].

In this chapter the problems associated with bonding industrial surfaces are discussed along with methods used to prepare industrial surfaces for adhesive bonding. In the discussion of these methods, surface analytical and mechanistic studies are presented to connect the concepts described in Chapters 4 and 6.

7.2   Plastic Surface Preparation

Examination of Fig. 7.2 indicates what needs to be done to generate a better surface for adhesive bonding. First, the weak boundary layer of low molecular weight exudate needs to be removed. Alternatively, it must be chemically modified to provide a cohesively strong layer well bonded to the polymer surface. Second, the surface energy of the weak boundary layer needs to be increased so that it is higher than the surface tension of the adhesive to be used. If, however, the weak boundary layer has been removed by the surface preparation, the remaining polymer surface energy must be increased. Third, the polymer surface topography should be improved to enable capillary action by the adhesive. The surface preparation methods described in the next few sections address two of these three points. The most successful surface preparations provide all three surface conditions.

There are two distinct types of surface preparation for plastics: physical and chemical methods. This classification is somewhat improper since the "physical methods" usually change the surface chemistry in addition to providing physical changes. The differentiation comes from the fact that the physical methods usually use some form of high energy radiation to change the surface. The "chemical methods" usually involve immersion of the plastic in a bath or wiping the surface with a cleaner or primer. With some exceptions, surface preparations provide surface chemical changes, whatever the method.

7.2.1   Corona Discharge Treatment

Corona Discharge Treatment (CDT) is one of the most popular methods of surface preparation for polymers. Virtually millions of yards of plastic film are treated by corona discharge annually. The purpose of this treatment is usually to make the plastic surface more receptive to an ink or functional coating. CDT has also been used to treat three dimensional plastic shapes although that is done less often. CDT is essentially an uncontrolled plasma operated at atmospheric pressure. A schematic of a corona discharge treatment station used for plastic film treatment is shown in Fig. 7.3.

The central circle in Fig. 7.3 indicates a metal roller held at ground. Above the metal roller is another bar or roller powered by a high frequency, high voltage power supply. The dark line depicts the plastic film as it travels through the apparatus. The two smaller circles are known as idler rollers or guidance rollers which hold the film in place as it travels through the apparatus. In corona discharge treatment, either the powered electrode or the grounded electrode must be covered by a dielectric material. The power supply is operated at such a voltage and frequency that the gas in the apparatus is ionized. If the gas is air, a blue glow, the "corona", occurs around the powered electrode. Because the electrical discharge causes ionization of the gas molecules in the gap between the powered and grounded electrodes, "streamers" occur in the gap. The streamers have the appearance of lightning strikes and could potentially cause physical changes as well as localized chemical changes to the plastic surface.

There are several important factors affecting the treatment of plastic films with CDT. First, the atmosphere in which the treatment is done is usually air. Treatment in air usually leads to the oxidation of the surface. If the treatment is done in air, no special precautions need to be taken although ozone should be removed from the treatment area. Other atmospheres have been described in the literature and some of

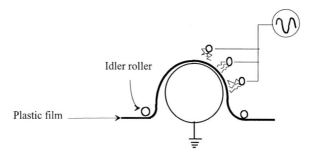

Figure 7.3   Schematic of a corona discharge treater used to increase the surface energy of plastic film. The plastic film is brought to a drum which is usually coated with a dielectric material. The drum is at ground potential. A bank of electrodes is placed near to the film's surface and an alternating current potential is applied between the electrodes and the grounded metal roller. The potential is high enough such that a "corona" forms around the powered electrodes and electrical discharges (streamers) can also be observed

these are discussed later. Second is the consumption of power. In older corona treaters, the voltage was controlled to provide a certain level of treatment. This type of control can lead to excessive power consumption, since the circuit may not be tuned to match the complex impedance of the treater with the power supply. It is important to not only control the voltage, but also the frequency of the treater's output to match impedance. Third, the speed at which the film passes under the powered electrodes is also important for control of the CDT effect.

CDT for three-dimensional plastic objects has also been developed. The electrode design of these treaters is particularly important because the proximity of the electrodes to the surface is critical for uniform corona treatment. An example of a simple corona treater is a Tesla coil, which has been used for years to detect leaks in glass vacuum systems and can also oxidize plastics' surfaces under ambient atmospheric conditions. The next few sections provide short discussions of research done to understand or optimize CDT effects on certain plastics.

7.2.1.1 Corona Discharge Treatment of Polyethylene

CDT of polyethylene is probably the most widely practiced form of surface preparation for adhesion improvement. It probably goes unnoticed since the treatment is done mostly for the adhesion of inks and coatings. As a result, there have been many studies of the surface chemistry of polyethylene as a function of surface treatment parameters. A review of these studies was written by Brewis and Briggs [2].

Cooper and Prober [3] examined the action of an oxygen corona on polyethylene and by weight loss and other experiments, they found that the gaseous product was CO_2 and water. Using infrared measurements, they also showed that a primary oxidation product on the surface of the polyethylene was carbonyl.

The effect of CDT on polyethylene was later examined by studying *autohesion*, the adhesion of a material to itself. Kim et al. [4] studied the effect of oxygen, hydrogen, nitrogen, and CO_2 based CDTs on the autohesion of polyethylene. A hydrogen corona had no effect but the remaining gases provided a measurable increase in adhesion. In the data of Kim et al., there is a loose correlation between an increase in $\cos\theta$ (θ being the contact angle) and the bond strength exhibited by polyethylene–polyethylene bonds as a function of level of surface treatment. Interestingly, a nitrogen corona also increased bond strength. Despite these data, Kim et al. chose to ignore the correlations which they presented and proposed a mechanism of adhesion based upon electret formation. They invoked the electrostatic theory of adhesion described in Section 6.3.1. There is no doubt that electrets are injected into PE with corona treatment because a nuisance static charge is often found in the process. However, is that the primary mechanism of adhesion resulting from CDT of PE?

The critical work on autohesion mechanisms on PE was done by Owens [5]. He was able to show that autohesion was strongly dependent upon the formation of certain surface chemical functions which are used to form the adhesive bond. A primary finding was that the autoadhesion bonds were very sensitive to the intrusion of any hydrogen bonding liquid, such as water. He utilized *surface chemical functionalization* which is the use of a specific organic chemical reaction chosen because it is sensitive for only one surface chemical species. It is also chosen so that the reaction does not involve anything in the bulk of the polymer.

Owens post-treated the CD-treated PE surfaces with chemicals such as acetyl chloride, nitrous acid, or bromine water. All of these reagents would react with enolic hydroxyls. When such a reaction occurred autohesion dropped significantly. If the surface was treated with phenyl hydrazine, which would react with a ketone, autohesion also dropped. This led Owens to propose the mechanism of autohesion for CD-treated polyethylene shown in Fig. 7.4. In this figure R, R' and R" stand for the remaining portions of the PE polymer. Owens proposed that oxygen, under the action of ultraviolet light present in the corona, inserts itself into the backbone of the polyethylene.

After the formation of the hydroperoxide, the treated polymer chain breaks down to yield an alkoxide and hydroxide radical. The key step in this mechanism is the breakdown of the radical into an alkyl radical and a keto-enol tautomer, as

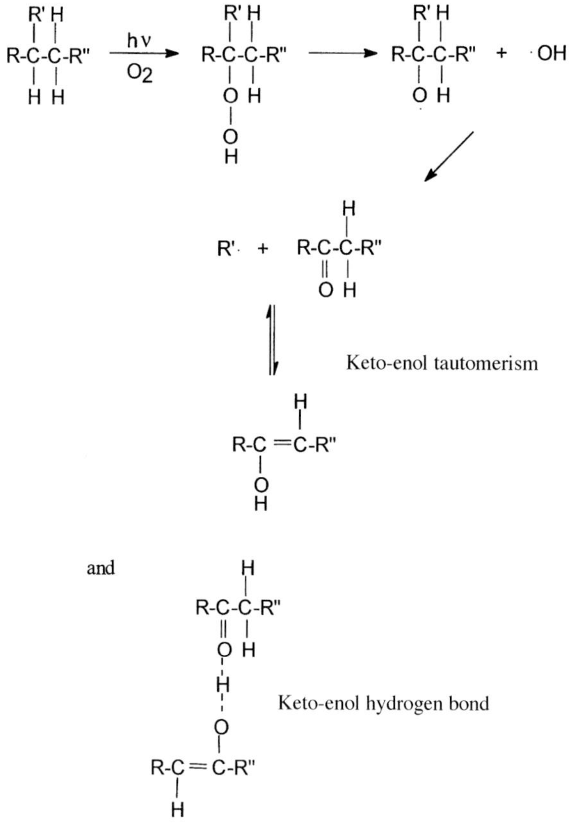

Figure 7.4   The mechanism of corona treatment induced autoadhesion of polyethylene as proposed by Owens

shown in Fig. 7.4. Owens proposed that the adhesion-inducing mechanism was the hydrogen bond formed between the keto and enol groups on either side of the autohesive bond. This mechanism is well supported by the data presented earlier. Reactants for enol reduce autohesion; reactants for ketone reduce autohesion; and water, which should disrupt such hydrogen bonds, also disrupts autohesion.

The mechanism proposed by Owens and described in Fig. 7.4 was further substantiated by Briggs and co-workers [6] who used modern methods of surface analysis such as those described in Chapter 4 in conjunction with surface chemical functionalization to prove the mechanism. A more detailed description can be found in the book by Briggs and Seah [7]. The combination of surface chemical functionalization and XPS is one of the most powerful methods of surface analysis we have today. Briggs et al. [6] used reagents similar to those used by Owens, except that Briggs' reagents also had some form a chemical "tag" attached which was easily detectable by XPS. In addition, Briggs et al. found a reagent which was selective for enol groups, chloroacetyl chloride. They used perfluorophenyl hydrazine as a tagged reagent for ketone, chloroacetyl chloride as a tagged reagent for enol and diisopropoxytitanium bisacetylacetonate (DPTAA) as a tagged reagent for normal hydroxyl. Some of the results of this work are shown in Table 7.1.

We note that CDT of the PE surface in air introduces oxygen (which supports earlier infrared work) and high values of adhesion. Detailed examination of the XPS spectrum for the carbon 1s region, shows the presence of carbonyl, aldehyde and carboxylic acid. XPS spectra can be taken at high enough resolution that the individual emission peaks for each element on a surface are examined. The regions are associated with the core level from which the electron was emitted. The primary core level peak for carbon and oxygen is the 1s peak (or "region"). The Table also shows that reaction with perfluorophenyl hydrazine results in fluorine on the surface and a complete negation of adhesion. Similar results are obtained with chloroacetyl

Table 7.1 Tabulated Results of the Surface Chemical Derivatization, XPS and Autohesion Experiments of Brigg, et al.

Treatment/ derivatization reaction	Carbon on surface?	Oxygen on surface?	Fluorine on surface?	Chlorine on surface?	Titanium on surface?	Advancing water contact angle	Autohesive peel strength (g/25 mm)
None	Yes	No	No	No	No	104	0
CDT in air	Yes	Yes	No	No	No	68	220
CDT + perfluorophenyl hydrazine	Yes	Yes	Yes	No	No		0
CDT + chloroacetyl chloride	Yes	Yes	No	Yes	No	90	12
CDT + DPTAA	Yes	Yes	No	No	Yes	86	393

chloride in that the surface now shows the presence of chlorine and a substantial, if not complete, reduction in peel strength. We note a discrepancy, however, in the results using DPTAA. Even though reaction was complete with the hydroxyls on the surface, the adhesion did not decrease or stay the same, but increased. Briggs and his coworkers attribute this result to the introduction of another adhesion mechanism: surface–surface covalent bonding due to the titanium complex which could potentially react with two hydroxyls, one on either surface. This increase in adhesion supports the discussion in Section 6.5, on the effect of covalent bonding at the interface.

7.2.1.2   Corona Discharge Treatment of Polypropylene

The chemical effects of the CDT on polypropylene (PP) are very similar to those on polyethylene. CDT in air leads to extensive oxidation of the surface as detected by the appearance of strong carbonyl bands in the infrared [8]. CDT of polypropylene in nitrogen seems to lead to unsaturation of the surface followed by oxidation [9]. The oxygen that appears on these surfaces could be due to post-oxidation when the polymer leaves the corona discharge treatment apparatus. It could also be due to low level oxygen impurities in the nitrogen gas used in the atmosphere of the corona or oxygen dissolved in the polymer which migrates to the surface during the treatment. With increasing treatment level, the wettability of the surface increases as determined by contact angle methods [10]. The primary component in the surface energy of the PP that changes is the polar component. This situation would be expected, since the number of polar groups on the surface of PP increases with increasing CDT.

There is one substantial difference in the behavior of polypropylene compared to polyethylene as a result of air CDT. In PP an oily surface layer appears at certain levels of treatment. This oily layer can be removed with water or polar solvents, leaving an oxidized surface. This oily layer has been termed "LMWOM," i.e., "low molecular weight organic material" [11]. LMWOM can either be beneficial or deleterious to the adhesion of coatings on treated polypropylene, depending upon the characteristics of the coating.

7.2.1.3   Corona Discharge Treatment of Poly(ethylene terephthalate)

Polyethylene terephthalate (PET) has a critical wetting tension of about 43 dynes/cm which is relatively high among polymeric materials. Despite the fact that many organic liquids wet PET, CDT of PET is necessary when aqueous solutions are used and it is sometimes necessary to improve the adhesion of other coatings. Owens [12] examined the autohesion of PET as a function of CDT treatment levels and found that increasing CDT led to a decrease in the temperature at which PET would autoadhere. Also, Owens found that hydrogen bonding liquids would totally disrupt this autohesive bond, as described earlier for PE. Another interesting finding reported by Owens was that heat treating PET film after CDT, but before bonding, resulted in a loss of ability to autoadhere. The loss was accompanied by a decrease in the polar component of the critical wetting tension. Owens concluded that the polar groups induced in the surface of PET by CDT are mobile and can retract into the bulk of the PET upon warming. There is a general consensus among practitioners of CDT that treated PET loses the effect of treatment over time, even at room temperature. This finding also provides an important insight: despite the fact that polymer surfaces seem stable and somewhat inert, the molecules are in motion. That motion can be induced by a means as innocuous as the application of polar liquids.

Owens completed a set of experiments which illustrate the difficulty in isolating products induced by surface treatments. He scraped and extracted the surface of several thousand feet of CD-treated PET to get enough material for analysis. Using thin layer chromatography, he found that the surface extract contained the expected PET components of terephthalic acid and its esters with ethylene glycol. The extract also contained a number of phenolic modifications of the terephthalic acid molecule, in particular, meta- and para-hydroxybenzoic acid. Owens also performed chemical derivatization experiments similar to those for PE described earlier, and found the chemical moieties responsible for the autohesive effect. The mechanism for autohesion in PET proposed by Owens is shown in Fig. 7.5; in which it is seen that the hydrogen bond is formed between a phenolic group on one surface and the carbonyl of the carboxylic acid ester on the other surface. Owens noted that phenols are actually enolic in character.

Briggs and coworkers [13] examined the work of Owens using XPS and were able to show that the surface chemistry of CD-treated PET was in accordance with Owens' proposal in that features in the carbon 1s region and the oxygen 1s region increased with CDT. Those features could be explained by the introduction of

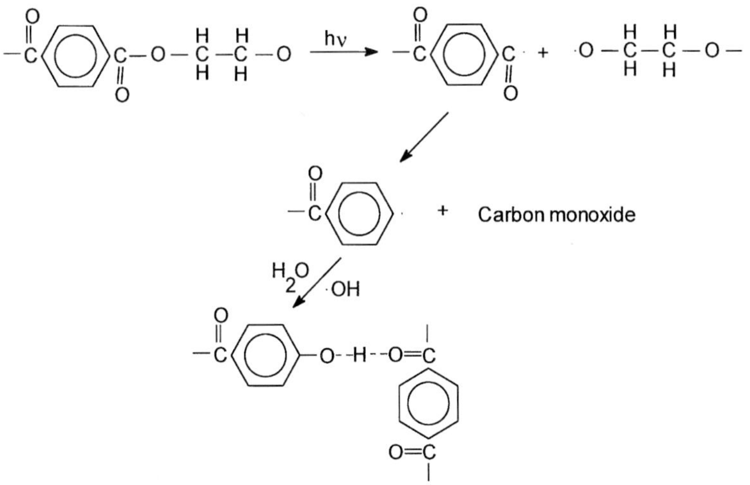

Figure 7.5   Autoadhesion mechanism proposed by Owens, involving the formation of a hydrogen bond between a phenolic group and a carbonyl group

phenolic groups to the surface. Briggs *et al.* also examined the variation of components of the PET's surface energy by contact angle measurements and found a substantial increase in the polar component after CDT. This polar component, however, decreased if the CD-treated PET was washed with water or stored and examined later. This finding is evidence that the treated PET surface is mobile and that species on the surface are of lower molecular weight than the bulk, since they can easily be removed by polar liquids. It seems that LMWOM is also created on the surface of PET by CDT.

7.2.1.4   Corona Discharge Treatment of other Materials

Cataloging the many polymers subjected to CDT is not attempted here. However, the CDT of polytetrafluorethylene and CDT of structural adherends is reviewed in the next paragraphs. Beevers [14] has shown that CDT can be used to treat a number of materials for structural adhesive bonding (structural adhesives are discussed in the next chapter). Table 7.2 shows some of his results.

"*Water Break*" *testing* is a quick contact angle test often used in industry to gauge how well a surface has been cleaned. In this test, water is sprayed on a surface. If the water sheets out onto the surface, forming a continuous film, this is considered a "good water break" behavior. If the water beads up (breaks up) on the surface, the surface is said to exhibit "poor water break" behavior. In the case of the metals used by Beevers *et al.*, the corona treated metals exhibited an improved "water break" upon corona treatment. This is an important observation because solvent cleaned metals usually exhibit poor water break properties. CDT, therefore, either oxidizes the materials left by solvent cleaning or removes them and exposes the high energy surface underneath. The results on the metals were comparable in strength to the metal surface prepared by abrasion. Beevers *et al.* also report that even though the initial bond strength was improved, the CD-treated metal adhesive bonds formed were not resistant to moisture and would not provide the durable structure usually desired with structural adhesives.

The final subject in this section is the CD-treatment of fluorocarbons. The properties which make these materials of industrial interest (chemical inertness, low surface energy, insolubility) make them equally difficult to adhesively bond. In

Table 7.2   Structural Adhesive Bonding of Corona Treated Materials [14]

Substrate	Adhesive	Lap shear strength (MPa)
Alkaline cleaned aluminum	Epoxy	16.8
Glass cloth reinforced polyethersulfone	Epoxy	13.5
Polypropylene	Epoxy	2.5
Mild steel	Epoxy	37.0
Stainless steel	Acrylic	23.0

Chapter 4, the critical wetting tension of polytetrafluoroethylene was given as 18 dynes/cm. It is hard to find liquids which can wet a surface with such a low critical wetting tension. To make materials such as polytetrafluoroethylene even more useful, surface preparations had to be developed which are discussed in future sections.

In this section, the focus is on CDT of fluorinated ethylene–propylene copolymer (FEP). In a series of patents, workers at E.I. DuPont de Nemours and Co., Inc. (DuPont) showed that mixtures of organic vapors and nitrogen in a corona chamber could be used to prepare the surface of FEP. Wolinski [15] showed that mixtures of nitrogen with monomers, such as glycidyl methacrylate or 2,4-tolylene diisocyanate, could change the adherability of FEP to Mylar from 500 to 4900 grams/inch. Similarly, McBride [16] used amines or mixtures of amines with monomers or other vapors to prepare the surface of FEP for bonding. Interestingly, unlike the air corona treatments of PE for autoadhesion, these FEP/adhesive/film laminates were not subject to degradation by water and survived boiling water tests. This last paragraph points out two new facts. First, even though perfluorinated polymers appear to be chemically inert, their surfaces can be prepared for adhesive bonding. Second, CDT can work in more than one way to prepare a surface. In most of the examples cited above, the CDT was used to oxidize the surface. In these examples, new functionality and perhaps even surface polymerization was induced by CDT.

7.2.2   Flame Treatment

Flame treatment is second to CDT in the number of square feet of polyolefins treated per year. Flame treatment of polyolefins was described by Kritchever [17]. The concept and the apparatus for this surface treatment are remarkably simple. A schematic of a flame treatment apparatus is shown in Fig. 7.6.

This equipment resembles the corona treatment apparatus in that the central drum is used as the base for the plastic sheeting. The plastic goes over the drum and under a series of burners similar to those found in a gas furnace. Of importance in the operation of a flame treater is the gas/air mix ratio. Depending upon the level of gas in the mix, the flame can have substantially different characteristics. In general, the central drum is cooled. Also of importance is the distance of the burners from

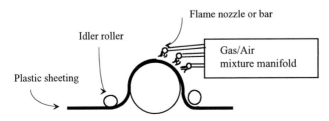

Figure 7.6   Diagram of a flame treater for polymer films

the film. If the burners are too close the film might char. If the burners are too far away, the film is improperly treated. Film speed under the burner is also of importance. Flame treatment can also be done by hand-held equipment such as a torch although uniform treatment is more difficult.

Flame treatment, CDT and plasma treatment which is discussed later in this chapter are all similar in that the treatment media is a nonequilibrium, excited gas phase. Since the operational part of a flame is a plasma under atmospheric conditions, it is expected that the primary effect of flame treatment is the oxidation of the film's surface. Briggs et al. illustrated this fact by using XPS to examine the surface of flame-treated PE as a function of natural gas/air flow rate in the burners [18]. The carbon 1s region of the XPS spectrum of the untreated polyethylene showed very little oxidized carbonaceous species. With short treatment times, the oxygen concentration went up rapidly and the carbon 1s region showed the presence of hydroxyl, ether, and ester groups on the surface. Interestingly, nitrogen was also found fixed on the surface. In general, only high energy levels of air CDT fix nitrogen on the surface. Angular resolved XPS indicated that the depth of treatment on this surface was about 40–50 Angstrom units. Unfortunately, the range of treatment levels used by these workers did not provide a substantial change in the adhesion levels. Therefore, no correlation of treatment level and bond strength was obtained.

Papirer et al. [19] highlighted the differences in the effects of flame treatment on PE and PP related to their ability to bond to styrene-butadiene rubber. They found that the wettability of both polymers increased dramatically with the level of flame treatment, with the polar component of the surface energy increasing more rapidly than the dispersive component. Interestingly, the effect of flame treatment on PE was found to be much more dramatic than on PP. XPS analysis of the flame treated surfaces showed that, as a function of the level of treatment, the oxygen concentration on PE increased much more rapidly than on the PP surface. As was found in the work of Briggs et al. [18] nitrogen is included in the flame treated PE surface but not on the PP surface. Detailed analysis of the carbon 1s region of the XPS spectrum also showed that the PE surface had a much higher percentage of carboxyl groups than the PP treated to an equivalent level. SSIMS analysis also indicated that the treated PE surfaces had a significant amount of unsaturation. Papirer et al. [19], following the work of Strobel et al. [11], found that the surface of flame treated PP contained LMWOM that was easily removable with ethanol washes. Peel tests of flame treated PE and PP from styrene–butadiene rubber vulcanized by the addition of peroxide showed that PE has a significantly higher bond strength than PP. These authors related their results to their proposed mechanism for modification of these surfaces by flame. For both olefins, according to Strobel, the flame causes oxidative scission of the backbone. For PP, the oxidative scission produces rapid attack at the tertiary carbon atom, which in turn leads to extensive low molecular weight and perhaps even volatile combustion products. These phenomena lead to rapid equilibration of the PP in the flame at low amounts of oxidation at the surface. For PE, the attack is slower and more randomly distributed along the backbone, causing extensive intrusion of oxidized functionality, but not much LMWOM. Increased unsaturation at the surface also improves the chances for covalent bonding with the peroxide-cured SBR overlayer. Obviously, these two very similar polymers respond very differently to the same surface treatment.

7.2.3   Plasma Treatment

A plasma is an ionized gas with essentially an equal density of negative and positive charges. The reactions occurring in a plasma are primarily free radical in nature and result from the interaction of materials in the plasma or the interaction of the ions and electrons in the plasma with a surface. Absorption of ultraviolet light in the plasma by the surface could also lead to surface reactions. The energy of the species in the plasma is on the order of tens of electron volts, which is enough to cause carbon–carbon bonds to break.

There is an interesting dichotomy between the level of usage of the various surface treatments described in this section of this book and the amount of academic literature that has been generated. Plasma treatment is very seldom used in industry but the academic literature is replete with examples of the effect of plasmas. CDT and flame treatment are widely used in industry, but there are relatively few articles in the open literature describing their efficacies and effects. In this book, some of the background work on plasma treatment and the adhesion of polymers, such as that reported by Schonhorn [20] is discussed. It is well beyond the scope of this book to attempt to completely review articles on plasma and polymer surfaces.

Operationally, a plasma differs from corona and flame treatment in that plasma treaters are operated at less than atmospheric pressure. This difference is also the primary reason plasma is seldom used in industry for adhesion promotion. The expense of operating a process at less than atmospheric pressure is very high. In addition, operation of a system under a partial vacuum inherently requires a batch process which also lowers cost effectiveness. A simplistic diagram of a plasma treater is shown in Fig. 7.7. The material to be treated is placed in a vessel which is evacuated. The pressure in the vessel is increased by the addition of a gas in which the plasma is to be struck. The types of gases used vary greatly. The earliest work in

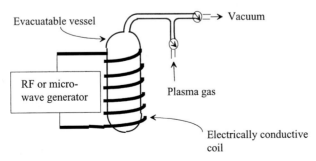

Figure 7.7   Diagram of a simple plasma treater

plasma treatment for adhesion promotion was done using noble gases such as argon and xenon [20]. Alternately, nitrogen can be used. Some workers have used oxygen as an ablative gas, while others have used fluorinated gases to perfluorinate surfaces of plastics [21]. After the active gas has been added, a radio or microwave frequency signal is placed on the coil surrounding the vessel. The coil induces a plasma inside the vessel.

7.2.3.1   Plasma Treatment of PE

The earliest work on the effect of plasma treatment on the adherability of plastics was reported by Schonhorn and coworkers who used noble or inert gases to treat the surface. These researchers coined the term CASING which stands for Cross-linking by Activated Species of INert Gases. Schonhorn and Hansen [20a] used an apparatus similar to that shown in Fig. 7.7 to treat the surface of PE. Schonhorn believed that the weak boundary layer theory of adhesion was operational under most circumstances. It was his objective to crosslink the surface of PE, increase the cohesive strength of the surface layer, and improve adhesive bond strength. They treated PE samples in an inert gas plasma. The supposition was that if the gas used in the vessel was not oxidizing, then the only reaction which could take place was the crosslinking of the surface. To determine that the surface was crosslinked, they treated a slab sample of PE and then raised it and an untreated sample to a temperature above the melt point of PE. They observed that the untreated sample melted into a puddle, while the treated sample retained its shape. This indicates that the treated sample had a crosslinked surface. Table 7.3 shows the results of adhesive bond tests using a special lap shear specimen in which a layered structure of aluminum–epoxy–PE–epoxy–aluminum was used.

The data in Table 7.3 show that the bond strength of the untreated PE to an epoxy is quite low when the bonding is done at room temperature. One has to go substantially above the melting point of the PE to produce a bond. If CASING is used, a strong bond can be effected even at room temperature. A bond produced at

Table 7.3 Lap Shear Performance of Adhesive Bonds Made With CASING Treated and Untreated PE

Treatment	Temperature of bond formation (°C)	Lap shear strength, MPA (psi)
None	25	1.4 (200)
	120	4.14 (600)
	150	15.2 (2200)
10 sec CASING	25	11.7 (1700)
	70	15.2 (2200)
	120	18.6 (2700)

70°C with treated PE yields the same strength as a bond made with untreated PE above its melting temperature.

Modern surface analytical methods confirmed the studies of Owens regarding the mechanism of autohesion. In the case of CASING of PE, Briggs and co-workers [22] disputed the "weak boundary layer strengthening" mechanism proposed by Schonhorn. They were able to show that the surface of PE, when exposed to CASING conditions, did not just crosslink. The surface of the PE was found to have a measurable concentration of oxygen, which undoubtedly contributed to the adhesion of an epoxy. The source of the oxygen was unknown since Schonhorn *et al.* took great care to eliminate that element in their apparatus. It is possible that the molecular oxygen dissolved in the slab of polymer came to the surface under the partial vacuum conditions. However, crosslinking must have happened in the CASING experiments in light of the melting experiment.

7.2.3.2 Plasma Treatment of Other Substrates

The literature on plasma treatment to improve adhesion shows that seemingly all combinations of gases and treatments have been evaluated for all the common polymers. Table 7.4 presents a very short listing of adhesive bond strengths obtained with plasma treatment on polymers by a variety of methods. In Table 7.4, we show the effect of an oxygen plasma on PE as well as for PP. In addition, the effect of more exotic plasma treatments, such as with plasmas containing acetylene and tetramethyltin, are shown. In these cases, the plasma deposits a layer of plasma-polymerized material on the surface, resulting in a surface preparation. The table also includes the effect of CASING on a number of polymers.

7.2.4 Other Physical Treatment Methods of Polymer Surfaces

7.2.4.1 Treatments Using Ultraviolet Radiation

Ultraviolet (UV) radiation is involved in the surface preparation treatments described in the previous section but there are several treatment methods which rely solely or mostly upon the effect of UV on polymers. For example, extensive irradiation of PET induces many of the same changes that CDT induces on PET [27].

One very interesting treatment method uses high energy UV irradiation available from excimer lasers. These lasers employ materials such as krypton fluoride as the active medium and generate pulses of radiation with extremely high energy. When such a laser pulse impinges on a surface, the energy can be high enough to break covalent bonds and cause ablation of the substrate. If ablation is carried out in air, the likely result is not only material removal but also oxidation of the remaining material surface. The ablation could also be carried out in a patternwise fashion, thus providing a microscopic morphology for aiding in bonding [28].

Table 7.4   Examples of the Effect of Plasma Treatment on Adhesion of Polymers Using an Epoxy Adhesive

Plastic	Type of plasma	Plasma gas	Type of adhesive bond	Bond strength, MPa (psi)	Reference
PE	none	none	Lap shear	0.16 (23)	Hall *et al.* [23]
PE	rf, capacitatively coupled	Oxygen	Lap shear	1.6 (233)	Hall *et al.* [23]
PP	none	none	Lap shear	2.6 (370)	Hall *et al.* [23]
PP	rf, capacitatively coupled	Oxygen, 30 min.	Lap shear	21.2 (3080)	Hall *et al.* [23]
Polycarbonate	none	none	Lap shear	2.8 (410)	Hall *et al.* [23]
Polycarbonate	rf, capacitatively coupled	Oxygen, 30 min.	Lap shear	6.4 (928)	Hall *et al.* [23]
Polystyrene	none	none	Lap shear	3.9 (566)	Hall *et al.* [23]
Polystyrene	rf, capacitatively coupled	Helium, 30 min.	Lap shear	27.7 (4015)	Hall *et al.* [23]
PET	none	none	Lap shear	4.3 (618)	Hall *et al.* [23]
PET	rf, capacitatively coupled	Helium, 30 min.	Lap shear	8.4 (1216)	Hall *et al.* [23]
Nylon 6	none	none	Lap shear	5.8 (846)	Hall *et al.* [23]
Nylon 6	rf, capacitatively coupled	Helium, 30 min.	Lap shear	27.3 (3956)	Hall *et al.* [23]
RTV silicone	none	none	Butt tensile	0.07 (10)	Sowell *et al.* [24]
RTV silicone	rf	Argon, 10 min.	Butt tensile	2.4 (341)	Sowell *et al.* [24]
ABS	rf	Argon, 10 min.	Unsymmetric lap shear	5.4 (783)	Ingaki *et al.* [25]
PE	rf	Argon, 10 min.	Unsymmetric lap shear	0.64 (95)	Ingaki *et al.* [25]
PE	rf	Tetramethyl tin	Unsymmetric lap shear	2.44 (354)	Ingaki *et al.* [25]
PE	AC (50 Hz), glow discharge, 750 V	Acetylene, 2 min., low flow rate	Lap shear	8.3 (1200)	Moshonov and Avny [26]
PTFE	AC (50 Hz), glow discharge, 750 V	Acetylene, 2 min., low flow rate	Lap shear	1.7 (250)	Moshonov and Avny [26]
PVC	AC (50 Hz), glow discharge, 750 V	Acetylene, 10 min., low flow rate	Lap shear	9.7 (1400)	Moshonov and Avny [26]

rf = radio-frequency

7.2.4.2   Other Vacuum Methods of Surface Preparation

In addition to the plasma methods described above, more aggressive ablative treatments of polymers have been described. Two of these methods are ion beam etching and radio-frequency sputter etching. In ion beam etching, a gas (often a noble gas) is ionized and then directed toward a target by a series of electrical lenses. The ions are accelerated to a high velocity (energy) so that when they impinge upon the surface, material is ablated. This technique is related to secondary ion mass spectrometry in that the ion source in both cases is much the same. The difference is that the ion fluxes are orders of magnitude greater in ion beam treatment than in secondary ion mass spectrometry. The usual effect of ion bombardment on semicrystalline polymers is to ablate the amorphous regions in preference to the crystalline regions. Therefore, in addition to any surface crosslinking which may take place due to the ion beam, a surface texture may also form. A similar effect can be obtained on amorphous polymers if a microscopic mask is applied to the surface. Islands of chromium (or other inorganic material) can be applied to a surface by evaporation or sputtering methods which do not ablate as fast as the polymer. Ion etching of the surface ensues in the unmasked areas, providing a microscopically rough surface which, in general, improves adhesive bond strength.

Sputter etching is a technique similar to plasma treatment. In this case, the polymer to be treated is attached to an electrode connected to a radio frequency source. Another electrode, an anode, is also within the evacuated chamber. When a gas is admitted into the chamber, a capacitatively coupled radio frequency (rf) plasma is initiated. Ions in the plasma are accelerated from the anode to the cathode, at which point the polymer surrounding the cathode is ablated by action of the ions. An effect similar to that of ion etching is obtained and similar methods as those described in the previous paragraph can be used to selectively etch amorphous polymers. The primary problem with ion etching and rf sputtering as surface preparation methods is that both are carried out in vacuum. This makes the process expensive. Ion etching is even more expensive because of the long processing times.

7.2.5   Wet Chemical Methods of Treatment of Polymer Surfaces

The archetypal means of treating polymer surfaces are wet chemical methods. The term "wet chemical" means that a solution is applied to the polymer's surface which results in either a cleaning of the surface or an actual surface preparation. The simplest wet chemical method is solvent wiping although this method is usually ineffective because the weak boundary layers often quickly reform after the treatment. Solvent wiping does not increase surface energy nor modify surface morphology. Priming is a method of surface preparation often used to increase the surface energy of polymers. In priming, a coating is applied, usually one with a higher surface energy and compatible with the polymer. Chemical and morphological modification of polymer surfaces can also be obtained by aggressive chemical treatments, several of which are described below.

7.2.5.1 Single Surface Chemical Functionalization and Chromic Acid Treatment of PE

A very important contribution to the study of chemical effects on the adhesion behavior of polymer surfaces was made by Briggs *et al.* [29]. Briggs' work has been mentioned earlier in this chapter. In this case, his work revolves around the generation of polymer surfaces containing a single distinct functionality and the effect of that functionality on adhesion. The work of Briggs *et al.* has progressed farther and several research groups have continued to explore the effect of single surface chemical functionalization on a number of properties of polymer surfaces, primarily their effect on wettability. Table 7.5 recounts the work done by Briggs *et al.* Table 7.5 shows that an epoxy resin adhesive has very little adhesion to an unmodified PE surface. If bromination under the influence of UV light is done, the adhesion increases dramatically.

Dehydrohalogenation of the brominated surface yields PE with segments of unsaturation. The adhesion drops measurably from that obtained with bromination, but is still higher than that obtained with unmodified PE. Oxidation of the unsaturated surface to give alcohol groups increases adhesion, but not markedly so. This is perhaps not unexpected since the epoxy used cured at room temperature. Epoxy-alcohol reactions usually need high temperatures. The reaction of the epoxy with surface carboxyl groups at room temperature is expected and a substantial increase in adhesion is noted. Partial reduction to ketone increases adhesion even more. This last result is very unexpected, although the amines in the adhesive could condense with the carbonyls to yield a Schiff's base. It should be noted that these increases in strength came only from the chemical functionalization, since the bulk of the polymer was unaffected. The above discussion should demonstrate the power of surface chemical functionalization and provides a prelude to the remainder of this section.

Table 7.5 Effect of Single Surface Chemical Functionalization on the Adhesion of an Epoxy to Modified PE Surfaces in a Butt Tensile Test [29]

Surface chemical functionality	Butt tensile strength, MPa (psi)
$-CH_2-$	1.4 (203)
$-CH_xCBr_y-$	6.7 (972)
$-CH=CH-$	3.7 (537)

$-CH_2-CH$
         |
        OH
	4.6 (667)

$-CH-C=O$
      |
     OH
	11.3 (1640)

$-CH_2-C-CH_2$
        ||
       O
	15.7 (2277)

One of the oldest methods of wet chemical surface preparation of PE and other polymers and metals is exposure to oxidizing acids. Chemists of earlier eras will remember the use of a commercially available cleaning agent used to clean burettes in analytical chemistry labs. This material was a combination of chromic acid and sulfuric acid which rapidly oxidized any organic contaminants on the surface of the glass burette, making it more wettable and menisci easier to observe. A similar oxidative effect can be observed when PE is exposed to aqueous chromic acid solutions. Briggs and coworkers [30] have examined the effect of chromic acid on the surface of PE using XPS. They found a good correlation between the amount of oxidized carbon on the PE's surface and the bond strength, but a poorer correlation with wettability as measured by contact angle methods. The surface contained not only oxidized carbon, but also sulphonates and chromium complexes. Adhesion to an epoxy adhesive could not be correlated with the chromium or sulfur levels as it was with the level of oxidized carbon. Interestingly, examination of the failure surface of the bonds did not show transfer of PE to the epoxy surface, indicating the absence of a weak boundary layer after treatment.

7.2.5.2   Wet Chemical Surface Treatment of Poly(tetrafluoroethylene)

Perfluorinated materials have interesting properties, all of which make adhesion difficult. Substantial effort has been made in industry to develop bondable poly-tetrafluoroethylene (PTFE). One of the first commercially successful treatments of PTFE was developed by Purvis and Beck [31] who treated this polymer with a solution of sodium in ammonia. A solution of sodium naphthalenide in tetrahydro-furan as described by Benderly [32] can also be used to treat PTFE. This last treatment is commercially available and sold under the tradename "Tetra-Etch"[1]. The surface analysis of PTFE as a function of surface treatment has become popular with researchers using XPS. Chemical groups such as -CHF- and CF_2 are easily observable because of the chemical shift effect in the carbon 1s spectrum. Dwight and Riggs [33] found that the primary effect of FEP surface treatment is defluorination and subsequent oxidation of the surface. Kaelble [34] showed that the wettability of PTFE increased substantially with sodium–ammonia treatment. This is likely a direct result of the oxidation of the surface. The surface can also contain some unsaturation normally observed as a browning or darkening. The darkening can be removed with a solution of sodium hypochlorite. Electron micro-graphs of treated surfaces show that not only has a chemical change taken place but also a morphological change in that the surface has become measurably more rough. It is likely that the roughening is due to the action of the etchants on the amorphous rather than the crystalline portions of the polymer surface. The bond strength of Tetra-Etch treated PTFE can be as much as seven times greater than untreated PTFE. The treatment of PTFE and PTFE-like materials is an example of what was necessary to obtain good adhesion as described in the previous chapter.

---

[1] "Tetra-Etch" is a registered trademark of W.L. Gore Co.

The surface must be wettable, microscopically rough, and provide possibilities for chemical bonding.

7.2.6   Priming of Polymer Surfaces

The difference between *priming* and *surface preparation* is sometimes difficult to understand. Many people in industry use the words interchangeably. In this book, the word *priming* indicates the application of a chemical or coating on a surface which does not itself modify the chemistry or morphology of the substrate surface but affects the adherability of the substrate. The primer layer itself can have a surface morphology, however. In *surface preparation*, there is a change in the chemistry of the substrate's surface and often a change in its surface morphology, as well. Many attempts have been made to prime polymer surfaces for the adhesion of another polymer. Often, primers need to have a surface preparation for them to adhere to the substrate There are a few primers, however, which function specifically as adhesion promoters, without the need for another surface preparation. We discuss two cases of this sort in the next paragraphs.

7.2.6.1   Priming of Polyolefins for Cyanoacrylates

Cyanoacrylate adhesives, discussed in Chapter 8, are the well known "Super-Glues." These adhesives have relatively high surface energy and thus, do not wet or adhere to polyolefins. Research has been conducted showing that polyolefins can be primed for adhesion to cyanoacrylates by certain chemical compounds normally considered activators for cyanoacrylate polymerization. Materials such as long chain amines, quaternary ammonium salts, and phosphines can be applied in pure form or in solution to the surface of a polyolefin. After drying, cyanoacrylates adhere well to the polyolefin. Okamoto and Klemarczyk [35] have described the efficacy of amine compounds as primers for cyanoacrylates. Garton and co-workers [36] have shown that the mechanism of action of these priming materials is not just activation of the surface, but that they diffuse into the surface of the polyolefin and initiate polymerization of the cyanoacrylate. An example of the tenets of the application of surface science to adhesion science is illustrated by this example: diffusion of adhesive materials into surfaces can substantially improve adhesion.

7.2.6.2   Chlorinated Polyolefins

Chlorinated polyolefins have recently been marketed for priming low energy surfaces. These materials are based upon either PE or PP and are usually used as solvent-based solutions. Chlorinated polyolefins can be used either as a paint additive or as a primer. Work by Waddington and Briggs [37] using XPS and SSIMS has shown that the application of chlorinated PP as a primer between PP and polyester-isocyanate paint provided cohesive failure in a layer which appeared to be a solution of the chlorinated polyolefin and the PP.

7.3   Metal Surface Preparation

In Section 7.1, the state of most metal surfaces when they are received by a manufacturing or assembly plant was described. For metal to be reliably adhesively bonded, the surface has to be changed from the one depicted in Fig. 7.1 into one clean and of predictable chemistry and morphology. The surface preparation of some metals has become a science. In this section, we outline surface preparation methods which could be used for other, less well-studied metals. For the most part, the methods which we discuss fall into two categories, electrochemical and abrasive.

There are several overall characteristics of surface preparations for metals that can be described in this introductory section. First, almost all electrochemical surface preparation processes for metals follow a flow chart similar to the one shown in Fig. 7.8.

For anyone who has prepared the surfaces of metals for adhesion, this flow chart may seem to be simplistic. However, each step is worthy of comment. Most metal, when received by the adhesive bonder, is coated with a thin layer of mill oil. If this oil is not removed by a degreasing operation, it is carried into the surface treatment bath. Eventually, the oil forms a slick on the surface of the treatment bath. When the cleaned part is withdrawn from the bath, the slick coats the metal and the surface preparation is fouled. Therefore, degreasing is essential. The rinsing steps are important to minimize the transfer of surface treatment materials from one bath to another. The rinse bath immediately after the surface treatment bath is also very important. The surface treatment ingredients continue to act if left on the surface, spoiling the surface preparation. Finally, the drying step is very important. For certain metals, water left on the surface causes flash rusting. If the corrosion products are weakly adhered or cohesively weak, the surface preparation is spoiled.

Similar problems occur in using abrasive surface preparation methods for metals. If the metal is very oily, the abrasive can just drive the oil deeper into surface

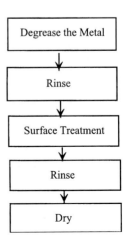

Figure 7.8   Flow chart for the surface preparation of metals by electro-chemical means

crevices. Thus degreasing is necessary before an abrasive surface treatment, just as it is before an electrochemical surface treatment. Rinse steps are also important, as debris left on a surface can act as a weak boundary layer or particulates can act as stress concentration points, weakening the overall structure. Once rinsing is used, drying becomes important for the reasons expressed earlier.

7.3.1 Surface Preparation of Aluminum for Adhesive Bonding

We begin with the discussion of surface preparation of aluminum because there is more literature available on this metal than for any other metal. In addition, the surface preparation of aluminum is more critical than that for other metals in that this metal is used for many aerospace applications which are adhesively bonded (see Chapter 1). We have already used aluminum as an example of a material that is thermodynamically unstable under normal atmospheric conditions, but that becomes useful because of a kinetic barrier to its instability, aluminum oxide. The basis for the surface preparation of aluminum is the creation of on oxide not only amenable to adhesive bonding, but also stable under the conditions to which the adhesive bond is exposed.

7.3.2.1 The Forest Products Laboratory (FPL) Etch

The FPL treatment for aluminum was first described by Eickner [38] who worked at the Forest Products Laboratory in the early 1950s. This treatment consisted of immersing aluminum in a solution similar to the chromic/sulphuric acid solution discussed in the section on wet chemical treatment of polymers. Possibly unknown to the developers of this surface treatment method, the action of chromic acid and sulfuric acid on aluminum was more than just the oxidation of organic contaminants on the surface. The treatment was electrochemically active with aluminum. A standard surface preparation method incorporating the FPL procedure is shown in Fig. 7.9

There are many variations of the FPL etch. In Europe, this treatment is known as chromic acid "pickling." In the pickling treatment, chromic acid is used instead of sodium dichromate and often deionized water is used instead of tap water. The FPL etch was used in the aerospace industry with great success after the end of World War II, when phenolic-based primers and structural adhesives were the norm.

As was mentioned in Chapter 1, structural adhesives are used extensively in the generation of honeycomb structures. Phenolic structural adhesives can not be used in this application because the high pressure requirements for their proper cure crush the honeycomb core (see Chapter 8). Luckily, at about the time this application arose, epoxy-based structural adhesives were developed. Epoxy-based structural adhesives did not require high pressures for curing. Epoxy structural adhesives became widely used in honeycomb structure as well as for metal-to-metal bonding

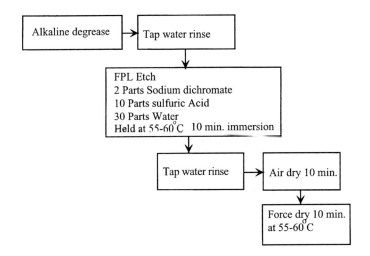

Figure 7.9   Flow chart for the FPL process for the surface preparation of aluminum

with the FPL etch as the primary surface preparation. The timeframe was the 1960s and many aircraft were deployed in Viet Nam. Under the conditions of high temperature and high humidity encountered by aircraft in that conflict, adhesive bonds failed. In addition, the Boeing Corporation found adhesive disbondments and corrosion in several of their aircraft. The aircraft industry started a significant amount of research and development work at this time to determine the cause of the failures.

A significant advance was made when Boeing engineers heeded the words of their shop workers who said that "new" FPL etch baths did not give satisfactory performance. However, if the bath was allowed to age, performance increased substantially. After considerable effort, it was found that the addition of 2024-T3 aluminum alloy to the FPL etch substantially improved the performance of adhesive bonds that were surface prepared with this etch and bonded with an epoxy. It was later shown that the action of the added 2024-T3 provided copper (copper is an ingredient of 2024-T3 alloy) [39]. The addition of copper modifies the electrochemistry of the FPL etch, making the metal surface more noble and, in fact, inducing an oscillating electrochemical reaction in which the copper participated [40]. The action of the bath was to induce a structure in the oxide on the surface of the alloy. An electron micrograph of an FPL oxide structure is shown in Fig. 7.10 and a drawing of the structure is shown in Fig. 7.11. Note that the oxide structure seems designed for adhesive bonding. The pores on the surface are small (to help with capillary forces which could displace air). The surface is clean. If the bath is properly maintained, the surface is reproducible. Examination of the chemistry of this oxide by various analytical tools showed that the oxide was essentially pure Al_2O_3. Under the oxide, however, some amount of copper could be found.

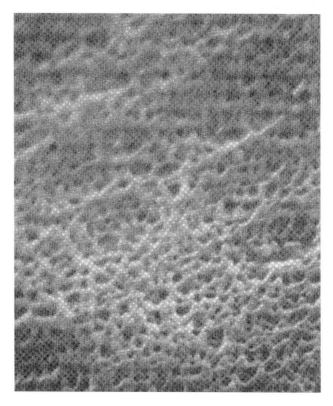

Figure 7.10   Electron micrograph of an aluminum surface generated by treating the aluminum with an FPL etch process. The magnification is 80 000×. Note the porosity of the surface. Compare this micrograph with the schematic drawings in the next figure

This demonstrates copper's participation in the electrochemistry of formation of the oxide [42].

Workers at Boeing investigated the FPL etch surface preparation in detail. They made use of fracture mechanics concepts and designed an adhesive bond test specimen now described in ASTM D3762, the wedge test (described in Chapter 3). The metal is prepared according to the procedure indicated for the surface preparation to be evaluated. The metal is then primed and bonded. A wedge is driven into the end of the specimen and the specimen is placed in an adverse environment of high humidity and high temperature. Typical results are shown in Fig. 7.12.

Here it is seen that certain bonds can lead to significant crack propagation in the interphase between the metal and the adhesive. Other bonds crack only a small amount essentially entirely in the adhesive. To investigate this effect, Boeing engineers made 1250 bonds with the FPL procedure, the variables being the time, date, and life of the etch bath. A portion of the bond was made into a wedge test, while the other parts were tested in actual aircraft. The result of the study is shown in Fig. 7.13 [1]. Most of the bonds showed no significant disbonds during their lives on

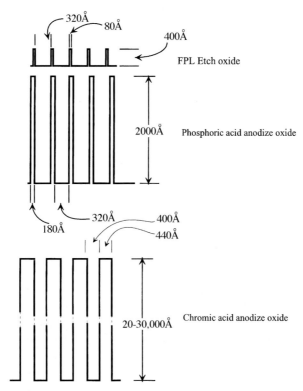

Figure 7.11   Schematic diagrams of several oxides generated on aluminum by electrochemical surface treatments. Even though the oxides are shown in two dimensions, they are three dimensional, as shown in the micrographs in Figs. 7.10 and 7.16. The oxide columns shown above repeat in an approximately hexagonal pattern over the surface of the aluminum (data from [41])

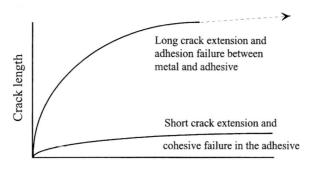

Figure 7.12   Diagram showing the type of data and the durability predictions obtainable from a wedge test specimen

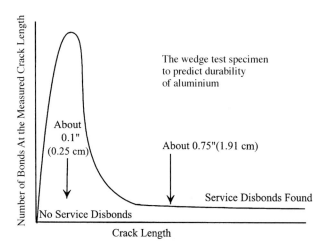

Figure 7.13   Schematic representation of data taken by the Boeing Company on wedge test specimens and in-use specimens. This type of diagram provides evidence for the ability of aluminum structural adhesive bonds (redrawn from [1])

aircraft. The largest number of bonds had wedge test crack extensions of little more than 0.1 in. However, there were crack extensions that were significantly larger than 0.1 in. Some of these did show service disbonds. These results show that a correlation can be made between a simple laboratory test like the wedge test and actual environmental exposure.

These results also indicated that the FPL etch could not consistently provide adhesive bonds with extended service life under hot and humid conditions. This led the workers at Boeing to search for an improved surface preparation which is discussed at length in the next section.

7.4   Anodization Treatments for Adhesive Bonding of Aluminum

Anodization is an electrochemical process in which the aluminum to be treated is the anode in an electrochemical cell. A schematic of an anodization cell is shown in Fig. 7.14. The cathode in this cell can be added or it can be the container itself. Materials such as stainless steel are often used as the container cathode. Alternatively, any material stable in the electrochemical solution, such as graphite, is useful as a cathode. A standard process for the anodization of aluminum for adhesive bonding is shown in Fig. 7.15.

The flow diagram in Fig. 7.15 is essentially the same as Fig. 7.9, except that the anodization step and another rinse step have been added. In this flow diagram, the degreasing step is necessary for the same reasons discussed earlier. Although

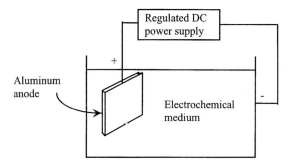

Figure 7.14   Diagram of a simple anodization apparatus. The aluminum is the anode (+) by means of a regulated DC power supply. The tank is usually made the cathode (−), although a nonreactive metal could be used as the cathode instead of the tank

anodization is the primary surface preparation step, deoxidation is necessary to remove any mill oxides of indeterminate composition before the metal piece enters the anodization bath. As a result, the electrochemistry inside the bath is reproducible.

7.4.1   Mechanism of Anodization

It is not essential to understand the mechanism of anodization to use the procedure to prepare aluminum surfaces. However, understanding the mechanism helps when problems occur during this procedure in an industrial setting. In general, anodization is done in a medium in which the oxide of aluminum is metastable. Thus,

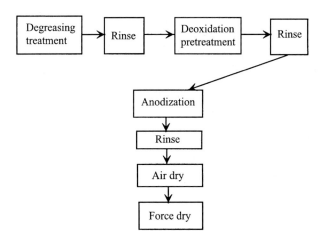

Figure 7.15   Flow diagram for the anodization process of aluminum parts

anodization can be carried out in acidic or basic media in which the oxide is soluble under normal conditions but is insoluble under the applied electrochemical potential. Usually, acidic media are used in anodizations. In anodization, a barrier layer is formed at the metal surface. At this point, anodizations, such as those used in the capacitor industry, stop. In adhesive bonding anodization, the oxide is partially soluble in the medium so the barrier layer is attacked by the medium at weak points. When a weak point is breached, the electrochemistry changes and metal dissolves but then is redeposited as oxide adjacent to the breach. Eventually, much of the surface is breached and a stochastic coalescence of these breached points fills the two dimensional surfaces. These breached points and the depositing oxide from the electrochemistry form the basis for the growth of a porous oxide which is the surface preparation.

7.4.2   Anodization Media

As indicated above, acidic or basic substances can be used as anodization media. The primary materials used in industry are sulfuric acid, chromic acid, and phosphoric acid. Of these, sulfuric acid anodization is used for architectural aluminum, while chromic and phosphoric acid treatments are used in the aerospace industry. The oxide structures from these surface preparation methods were shown in Fig. 7.11 and electron micrographs of those surfaces are shown in Fig. 7.16. Venables has discussed the formation of these oxides and their role in durability of adhesive bonds [43]. The primary difference among the oxide structures which form are the depth of the oxide, the pore size, and its chemical composition. Sulfuric acid anodization (not shown) yields an oxide that is thick and only marginally porous and containing a substantial amount of sulfate [44]. Chromic acid anodized oxide is somewhat thinner than sulfuric acid anodized oxide and its porosity is greater. By carefully controlling the anodization procedure and the use of a stepped voltage schedule, a very porous oxide can be generated [45]. The chromic acid anodized oxide is essentially pure Al_2O_3, much like the FPL etch oxide [44]. Phosphoric acid anodization yields to an oxide thinner than the other two and with a very porous, open structure. The phosphoric acid anodized oxide contains a substantial amount of phosphate ion.

7.4.3   Phosphoric Acid Anodization in the Aerospace Industry

In the previous section on the FPL etch, epoxy structural adhesive-based bonds were described as unstable under conditions of high temperature and humidity. The supposition was made that the FPL etch oxide itself in some way changed under these conditions. Since the problem seemed to be oxide instability in the presence of moisture, an oxide more resistant to moisture was sought. Marceau [46] at Boeing

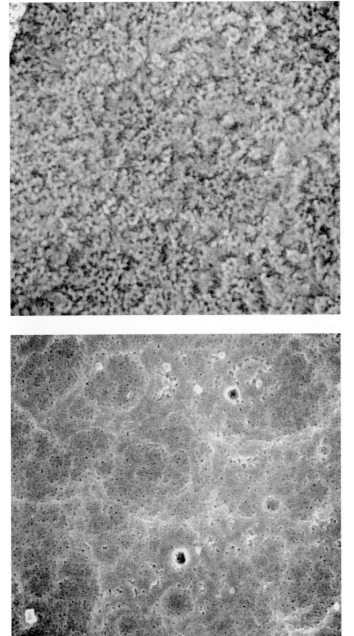

Figure 7.16 Electron micrographs of chromic (left) and phosphoric acid (right) anodized aluminum surfaces. Magnification is 30 000×. Note the greater pore size of the oxide generated by phosphoric acid anodization

proposed that an oxide resistant to "sealing" might prove resistant to environmental moisture. Sealing is a process used to improve the corrosion resistance of architectural aluminum. It is typically accomplished by soaking the anodized metal in a bath containing sodium dichromate at an elevated temperature. The pores in the oxides close as a result of this treatment providing a thick and relatively impermeable oxide layer which protects the metal from corrosion. Phosphoric acid anodize had been investigated for aluminum treatment in the 1920s. It was abandoned in favor of chromic acid anodize because phosphoric acid anodize could not be "sealed" to improve corrosion protection. Marceau correctly assumed that such an oxide would also be resistant to moisture under an adhesive.

Engineers at Boeing examined the effectiveness of the phosphoric acid anodization procedure by repeating the experiment carried out for the optimized FPL etch. They made 1,250 wedge test specimens and corresponding environmental exposure test samples using phosphoric acid anodization. The results of the wedge tests are shown in Fig. 7.17 which is a modified version of Fig. 7.13. The dashed lines in Fig. 7.17 show the results of wedge tests for the phosphoric acid anodization. The wedge test crack extensions are all less than 0.2 in. Based on the optimized FPL etch wedge test results, it was predicted that all of these specimens would be resistant to environmentally induced disbondment. None of the environmental exposure specimens showed disbondment while some of the FPL etched specimens showed disbondment over the same amount of time. Furthermore, portions of Boeing aircraft fuselages which were being rebuilt were destructively tested after they had seen significant flight time. The bonds which had been made using

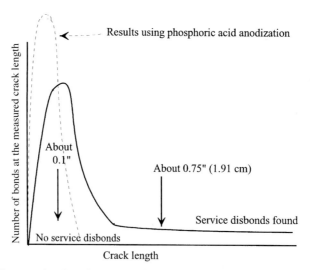

Figure 7.17   Diagram showing the relationship between wedge test data for the FPL etch and phosphoric acid anodization on aluminum. The prediction from these data was that phosphoric acid anodized metal is more durable than metal treated with the FPL etch. This was borne out by inspection of aircraft after use (redrawn from [1])

phosphoric acid anodized aluminum showed no disbondment [1]. This case study shows that the application of fundamentals in electrochemistry, surface science, mechanics, and adhesion science could be combined to solve an important industrial problem.

7.5   General Techniques for the Surface Preparation of Metals

The surface preparations for critical applications such as aircraft construction are probably the most demanding industrial uses. Simpler methods of treatment are used in industries with less stringent requirements. For aluminum, none of the methods described below provides the environmental resistance of a properly prepared phosphoric acid anodized metal surface, but can be used in a variety of applications less critical than those found in the aircraft industry and with metals other than aluminum

7.5.1   Conversion Coatings

Conversion coatings are materials and processes applied to metals to impart corrosion resistance and increase adhesion of organic coatings. Conversion coatings for aluminum are typically acidic materials applied by dipping, spraying, or brushing a solution onto an aluminum surface. The solution reacts with the aluminum surface, creating a layer with a gelatinous oxide structure comprised of both the aluminum and the ingredients in the conversion coating. The chemical composition of most conversion coatings is usually proprietary, but it is known that many of them contain chromic acid, phosphoric acid and other agents such as ferricyanide.

After drying, the gelatinous oxide collapses to form the conversion coating. In general, these coatings are smooth, uniform and organic coatings adhere well to them. In fact, conversion coatings provide the base for many architectural coatings, such as those found on aluminum siding and gutters. However, these conversion coatings do not usually provide a good base for a structural adhesive, primarily because the smooth surface that results does not provide sites for mechanical interlocking.

A well known conversion coating for steel also can provide a surface for adhesive bonding, if it is properly done. *Parkerizing* or *bonderizing* is a treatment for mild steel in which the metal, after degreasing, is dipped in a bath of phosphoric acid or a solution of zinc phosphate in phosphoric acid. This bath sets up a controlled electrochemical reaction in which the surface catalyzes the precipitation of crystals of hopeite (zinc phosphate) on the surface. This technique has long been used to adhere coatings to steel. This conversion coating also corrosion inhibits if the hopeite crystal-containing surface is dipped in chromic acid as a last surface preparation step. The size of the hopeite crystals depends upon the grain structure of the surface and also the amount of carbide there. The grains can be very large or very small and the usefulness of the surface for adhesive bonding depends upon the grain size. Large grains act as a brittle underlayer (the hopeite is crystalline) where fractures can propagate. However, if the grain size is small, the interphase acts more like a composite structure and is resistant to crack propagation [47]. An abrasive technique for refining a surface to generate smaller crystals of hopeite is discussed below. Chemical techniques can also be used to increase the number of nucleating sites on the metal surface, resulting in smaller crystals.

7.5.2   Abrasion

Abrasion treatments can involve any one of a number of media. Sandpaper can be used to prepare aluminum as well as other metal surfaces, although this method may not completely remove oily layers and may, in fact, drive the oil into crevices. Sanding also does not always provide the proper microstructure for adhesive bonding. As discussed in a previous chapter, surface roughness enhances adhesion only if the structures produced are small enough to enable capillary action and draw the adhesive into the microstructure. Many typical sandpaper grits used for substantial metal removal leave rather sizable tracks and grooves in a surface which act as flaws rather than as a surface preparation.

Grit blasting and vapor honing are two metal surface preparations used extensively for a number of metals. Using high pressure air, grit is blasted at a surface resulting in removal of material as well as a surface texture. Vapor honing involves the use of a solvent medium in addition to the grit. Depending on the size of the grit, a surface texture usable in adhesive bonding may result. These techniques may not be useful for materials such as stainless steel which work-harden under abrasive treatments, but works well for metals such as cold rolled or mild steel, nickel and in non-critical applications, titanium. Grit blasting has been used in the treatment of steel for ship construction and vapor honing has been used to treat nickel for adhesive bonding. The water break test (see Section 7.2.1.4) has been used to evaluate the cleanliness of metals prepared by these methods.

Three-dimensional abrasive surface conditioning has also been used for metal surface preparation [48]. A three dimensional abrasive is a composite material in the form of a non-woven mat that is impregnated with a resin and abrasive grit. These materials conform to the shape of a surface and provide a controlled cut of the abrasive without substantial amounts of material removal. Three dimensional abrasives, such as "Scotch-Brite"[1], have long been used to remove burrs in stamping operations. Three-dimensional abrasives with water flushing can provide clean and almost oxide-free surfaces. If the appropriate grit is selected a surface with

---

[1] "Scotch-Brite" is a registered trademark of the 3M Company

very close to the proper microstructure for adhesive bonding can result. In general, however, surfaces prepared exclusively by three-dimensional abrasive surface conditioning do not yield durable structural adhesive bonds. The oxides and microstructure are not necessarily resistant enough to moisture. Three-dimensional abrasive surface conditioning can be used as a pretreatment before other processes that prepare a reproducible surface and is a viable replacement for the deoxidation step in the phosphoric acid anodization process [48]. It has also been shown to help refine the grains in Parkerizing steel, thus making the surfaces more easily paintable [49]. An interesting combination of process and chemistry is found in using silane coupling agents with three-dimensional abrasive surface conditioning. If chosen and applied appropriately, silanes react rapidly with the new oxide surface that generated by the abrasive and could provide a durable structural adhesive bond.

7.5.3   Electrochemical Methods for Treating Metals other than Aluminum

A substantial number of etch treatments are available for treating metals, which usually provide a controlled dissolution of the metal oxide and then the metal. For example, sulfuric acid pickling is a surface preparation method for steel and stainless steel. Iron oxide and iron are soluble in the sulfuric acid, and a surface structure develops because most metals are polycrystalline and have surfaces with both anodic and cathodic sites. The anodic sites are the loci of metal dissolution and usually are the center of the grains or crystallites in a metal surface. The cathodic sites are the loci of gas evolution and are found usually at the grain boundaries. Care must be taken to avoid some pitfalls in acid etching ferrous metals. First, surfaces must be degreased before etching, as discussed earlier. Second, the time in the etch bath must be kept to an absolute minimum. Extending etching not only removes too much metal and therefore change the dimensions of the piece but can also lead to hydrogen embrittlement of the metal. Hydrogen embrittlement is the dissolution of gaseous hydrogen (often evolved in such processes) into the metal itself. Third, parts must be quickly rinsed and dried after the etching procedure, as the metal could easily flash rust after its surface has been activated by the treatment.

Titanium is an expensive but very useful metal, due to its excellent strength, low density, and corrosion resistance. However, the corrosion resistance makes the preparation of its surface difficult. There are two primary methods for the preparation of titanium for adhesive bonding, PASA jell and chromic acid anodization. PASA jel is a commercially available product that etches a titanium surface and works in the field as well as in manufacturing environments. Chromic acid anodization of titanium can be done in much the same manner as aluminum anodization except that hydrofluoric acid must be added to the bath to initiate the primary dissolution of the metal. Chromic acid anodization provides a microstructured surface of titanium dioxide and an exceedingly bondable surface.

7.6   Summary

In this chapter, the surface preparation of plastics and metals for bonding was discussed. For metals, the discussion centered around structural adhesive bonding. The methods described can used for the preparation of metals for any adhesive or coating. The primary points in this chapter are as follows:

1. The guidelines for good adhesion discussed earlier are the reasons why most surface preparations are needed:
   A. To remove weak boundary layers (grease or oils on metals, low molecular weight materials on plastics)
   B. To provide a surface which is spontaneously wettable by the adhesive (increase the surface energy of plastics, remove contaminants from metal surfaces)
   C. To provide a surface that is microscopically rough (for plastics this involves preferential removal of amorphous areas; for metals this involves etching away of crystallites or the deposition of a porous oxide)
2. Plastic surface preparations usually involve the oxidation of the surface to increase its surface energy.
3. Metals surface preparations are usually electrochemical in nature and therefore depend upon the fundamental electrochemistry of the metal.
4. Surface preparation is the key to bond durability.

Bibliography

Treatise on Adhesion and Adhesives, vol. 7, J. Dean Minford (Ed.) (1991), Marcel Dekker, New York

Minford, J.D., *Handbook of Aluminum Bonding Technology and Data* (1993), Marcel Dekker, New York

Kozma, L., and Olejford, I., *Materials Science and Technology*, 3 (1987), p. 860

Clark, D.T., Dilks, A., and. Shuttleworth, D., in *Polymer Surfaces*, Clark, D.T. and Feast, W.J. (Eds.) (1978), Wiley-Interscience, Chichester, UK, pp. 185–211

Siperko, L.M., and Thomas, R.R., *J. Adhesion Sci. Technol.*, 3 (1989), p. 157

Liston, E.M., *J. Adhesion*, 30 (1989), p. 199

References

1. McMillan, J.C., in *Bonded Joints and Preparation for Bonding*, AGARD Lecture Series No. 102 (1979), AGARD, Harford House, London, Ch. 7
2. Brewis, D.M., and Briggs, D., *Polymer*, 22 (1981), p. 7
3. Cooper, G.D., and Prober, M., *J. Polym. Sci.*, 44 (1960), p. 397
4. Kim, C.Y., Evans, J., and Goring, D.A.I., *J. Appl. Polymer Sci.*, C 15 (1971), p. 1357
5. Owens, D.K., *J. Appl. Polym. Sci.*, 19 (1975), p. 265

6. (a) Blythe, A.R., Briggs, D., Kendall, C.R., Rance, D.G., and Zichy, V.G., *Polymer*, 19 (1978), p. 1273. (b) Briggs, D., and Kendall, C.R., *Polymer*, 20 (1979), p. 1053. (c) Briggs, D., in *Adhesion 6*, Allen, K.W. (Ed.) (1982), Applied Science Publishers, London, pp. 111–121. (d) Chew, A., Brewis, D.M., Briggs, D., and Dahm, R.H., in *Adhesion 8*, Allen, K.W. (Ed.) (1982), Applied Science Publishers, London, pp. 97–114

7. *Practical Surface Analysis*, Briggs, D., and Seah, M.P. (Eds.) (1990), Wiley, New York

8. Carlsson, D.J., and Wiles, D.M., *Canadian J. Chemistry*, 48 (1970), p. 2397

9. Evans, J.M. , *J. Adhesion*, 5 (1973), p. 9

10. Kruger, R., and Potente, H., *J. Adhesion*, 11 (1980), p. 113

11. Strobel, M., Dunatov, C.A., Strobel, J.M., Lyons, C.S., Perron, S.J., and Morgen, M C., *J. Adhes. Sci. Tech.*, 3 (1989), p. 329

12. Owens, D.K., *J. Appl. Polym. Sci.*, 19 (1975), p. 3315

13. Briggs, D., Rance, D.G., Kendall, C.R., and Blythe, A.R., *Polymer*, 21 (1980), p. 895

14. (a) Njegic, A., and Beevers, A., in *Proc. Adhesives, Sealants and Encapsulants, 1985 Conf.* (1985), Network Events Ltd., Buckingham, UK, pp. 349–354. (b) Beevers, A., Thernoe, J., and Njegic, A., in *International Conf. on Structural Adhesives in Engineering, 1986* (1986), Mechanical Engineering Publications, Ltd., London, Ch. C156/86

15. Wolinski, L.E., U.S. Patent 3,274,089 (1966)

16. (a) McBride, R.T., U.S. Patent 3,275,540 (1966). (b). McBride, R.T., U.S. Patent 3,291,712 (1966). (c). McBride, R.T., and Wolinski, L. ., U.S. Patent 3,296,011 (1967)

17. (a) Kritchever, M.F., U.S. Patent 2,648,097 (1953). (b) Kritchever, M.F., U.S. Patent 2,683,894 (1954). (c) Kreidl, W.H., U.S. Patent 2,704,382, (1955)

18. Briggs, D., Brewis, D.M., and Koniezko, M B., *J. Materials. Sci.*, 14 (1979), p. 1344

19. Papirer, E.D., Wu, Y., and Schultz, J., *J. Adhes. Sci. Technol.*, 7 (1993), p. 343

20. (a) Hansen, R.H., and Schonhorn, H., *Polym. Lett.*, 4 (1966), p. 303. (b) Schonhorn, H., and Hansen, R. H., *J. Appl. Polym. Sci.*, 11 (1967), p. 1461

21. Strobel, M., Thomas,P.A., and Lyons, C.S., *J. Polym. Sci., Part A. Polym. Chem.*, 25 (1987), p. 3343.

22. (a) Malpass, B.W., and Bright, K., in *Aspects of Adhesion*, D.J. Alner (Ed.) (1968), University of London Press, p. 224. (b) Sowell, R.R., Delollis, N.J., Gregory, H.J., and Montoya, O., *J. Adhesion*, 4 (1972), p. 15

23. (a) Westerdahl, C.A.L., Hall, J.R., Levi, D.W., *Polym. Prepr. Am. Chem. Soc. Div. Polym. Chem.*, 19 (1978), p. 538. (b) Hall, J.R., Westerdahl, C.A.L., Bodnar, M.J., and Levi, D.W., *J. Appl. Polym. Sci.*, 16 (1972), p. 1465. (c) Hall, J.R., Westerdahl, C.A.L., Devine, A.T., and Bodnar, M.J., *J. Appl. Polym. Sci.*, *13*, 2085 (1969)

24. Sowell, R.R., *et al.*, *op. cit.*

25. Inagaki, N., Itami, M., and Katsuura, K., *Int. J. Adhesion and Adhesives*, 2 (1982), p. 169

26. Moshonov, A., and Avny, Y., *J. Appl. Polym. Sci.*, 25 (1980), p. 771

27. (a) Osborn, K.R., *J. Polym Sci.*, 38 (1959), p. 357. (b) Marcotte, F.B., Campbell, D., Cleaveland, J.A., and Turner, D.T., *J. Polym. Sci. Pt A-1*, 5 (1967), p. 481

28. (a) Kawamura, Y., Toyoda, K., and Namba, S., *Appl. Phys. Lett.*, 40 (1982), p. 374. (b) Srinivasan, R., and Mayne-Banton, V., *Appl. Phys. Lett.*, 41 (1982), p. 576. (c) Srinivasan, R., and Leigh, W.J., *J. Am. Chem Soc.*, 104 (1982), p. 6784. (d) Lazare, S., and Srinivasan, R., *J. Phys. Chem.*, 90 (1986), p. 2124

29. (a) Chew, A., Brewis, D.M., Briggs, D., and Dahm, R.H., in *Adhesion – 8*, K.W. Allen (Ed.) (1984), Elsevier, Barking UK, pp. 97–114. (b) Che, A., Dahm, R.H., Brewis, D.M., Briggs, D., and Rance, D.G., *J. Colloid Interface Sci.*, 110 (1986), p. 88

30. (a)Briggs, D., Brewis, D.M., and Konieczko, M.B., *J. Mater. Sci.*, 11 (1976), p. 1270. (b) Briggs, D., Zichy, V.J.I., Brewis, D.M., Comyn, J., Dahm, R.H., and Konieczko, M.B., *Surface and Interface Anal.*, 2 (1980), p. 107

31. Purvis, R.J. and Beck, W.R., U.S. Patent 2,789,063 (1957)

32. Benderley, A.A., *J. Appl. Polym. Sci.*, 6 (1962), p. 221

33. Dwight, D.W., and Riggs, W M., *J. Colloid Interface Sci.*, 47 (1974), p. 650

34. Kaelble, D.H., and Cirlin, E.H., *J. Polym Sci.*, Part A-2, 9 (1971), p. 363
35. Okamoto, Y., and Klemarczyk, P.T., *J. Adhesion*, 40 (1993), p. 81
36. (a) Yang, J., and Garton, A., *American Chemical Society Polymer Preprints*, 62 (1990), p. 916, (b) Yang, J., and Garton, A., *J. Appl. Polym. Sci.*, 48 (1993), p. 359
37. Waddington, S., and Briggs, D., *Polym. Comm.*, 32 (1991), p. 506
38. (a) Forest Prod. Lab. Tech. Rep. No. 1813, Eickner, H.W. (1950). (b) Forest Prod. Lab. Tech. Rep. No. 1842, Eickner, H.W. (1954)
39. Bethune, A.W., *SAMPE J.*, August (1975), pp. 4–10
40. Pocius, A.V. , *J. Adhesion*, 39 (1992), p. 101
41. McMillan, J.C. , Quinlivan, J.T., and Davis, R.D., *SAMPE Quarterly*, April (1976), pp 13–18
42. (a) Sun, T.S., Chen, J.M., Venables, J.D., and Hopping, R.L., *Appl. Surf. Sci.*, 1 (1978), p. 202. (b) Venables, J.D., McNamara, D.K., Chen, J.M., Sun, T.S., and Hopping, R.L., *Proc. SAMPE Tech. Symp.*, 24 (1979), p. 1188
43. Venables, J.D., *J. Materials Sci.*, 19 (1984), p. 2431
44. Wood, G.C., and Thompson, G.E., in *Corrosion: Aqueous Processes and Passive Films, Vol. 23, Treatise on Materials Science and Technology*, Scully, J.C. (Ed.) (1983), Academic Press, London
45. Brockmann, W., Hennemann, O.-D., Kollek, H., and Matz, C., *Int. J. Adh. Adh.*, 6 (1986), p. 115
46. (a) Marceau, J.A., Moji, Y., and McMillan, J.C., in *Proc. 21st National SAMPE Symposium* (1976), SAMPE, Covina, CA. (b) Marceau, J.A., Firminhac, R.H., and Moji, Y., U.S. Patent 4,127,451 (1978)
47. (a) Cheever, G.D., *J. Paint. Tech.*, 39 (1967), p. 1. (b) Trawinski, D.L., McNamara, D.K., and Venables, J.D., *SAMPE Quarterly*, 15 (1984), p. 6
48. Pocius, A.V., and Claus, J.J., in *Proc. 13th National SAMPE Tech. Conf.* (1981), SAMPE, Covina, CA, pp. 629–639
49. Wenz, R.P., *Org. Coat.*, 6 (1984), p. 373

8 The Chemistry and Physical Properties of Structural Adhesives

8.1 Introduction to Chapters 8, 9, and 10

The chemistry and physical properties of adhesives in use in industry and in the home are discussed in the next chapters. It is important for anyone who develops or uses adhesives to appreciate the range of chemistry employed in the adhesives industry. Virtually every type of polymer chemistry has been evaluated as a potential adhesive. This means we could repeat much of organic and polymer chemistry here. So we do not rewrite textbooks here, only that chemistry exploited in a major way for adhesive development or that has led to adhesives with very special properties is discussed. In the next few chapters, polymer chemistry is related to the physical properties of adhesive bonds made with major types of adhesives. This connection is particularly important for the engineer designing adhesive bonds, since relationships are drawn between strength and chemistry. This is also important to sales engineers as it helps provide guidance to customers as to the choice of adhesive. It certainly is important to chemists since the information presented here may form the basis for next generation adhesive products.

8.2 Introduction to Structural Adhesives

The first major type of adhesive discussed here is the *structural adhesive*. This group encompasses those materials with high cohesive strength used to bond adherends also with significant cohesive strength. A reasonable definition of a structural adhesive is a material used to bond other high strength materials, such as wood, composites, or metal, so that the practical adhesive bond strength is in excess of 6.9 MPa (1000 psi) at room temperature. The significance of this number becomes apparent as strengths of bonds attainable with other adhesives are described in Chapters 9, 10, and 11. Because of the demands on performance, structural adhesives are usually crosslinkable (thermoset) organic compounds, are usually polar, and of high surface energy. They are usually resistant to many types of environmental attack. In fact, in many applications, structural adhesives are required to survive in adverse environments for years, if not decades.

In discussing structural adhesives, it is often difficult to determine how to classify these materials because of the breadth of chemistry used in their formulation. In this chapter, the topic is approached in two ways: in the first part of the chapter, the basic chemistry of the major types of resins used as structural adhesives is discussed along with the major curing reactions; in the second part, formulations and modifications of the basic resin systems which have led to useful adhesives are described. In the second part, correlations among the chemistry, the cure conditions, and the physical properties of the adhesive are also reviewed.

The goals of this chapter are to describe the major classes of structural adhesives and their curing chemistries. The role of toughening or providing adhesives with fracture resistance is a central theme in Section 8.4, which includes information on the materials used to add fracture resistance as well as the mechanism by which toughening occurs.

8.2.1   Physical Forms of Uncured Structural Adhesives

Structural adhesives are available as both industrial as well as consumer products. Table 8.1 lists the physical forms in which structural adhesives are found in the uncured state. The highest technology, most expensive and highest performing structural adhesives are available in film form. The *film adhesive* contains all of the curatives necessary to obtain adhesive bond strength, need to be heat cured and often require specialized handling to effect a bond and cure. A film adhesive often contains a carrier or "scrim" which makes handling easier as well as provides bond-line thickness control during cure. Film adhesives normally require low temperature storage (usually dry ice temperatures) and are most extensively used in the aerospace and electronics industries.

Paste adhesives come in the form of *one-* or *two-part* materials and, as the name implies, are in the form of a paste or viscous liquid. One-part paste adhesives normally require heat or another form of energy to cure. One-part adhesives are sold formulated and contain all of the materials necessary for cure. They usually

Table 8.1   Structural Adhesive Types and their Physical Form in the Uncured State

Type	Form	Cure temperature (°C)
Phenolic	Heat curing films and pastes	171
Epoxy	Heat curing films and pastes	82, 121, 171
Epoxy	Two-part pastes	25
Acrylic	One part self curing liquids	25
Acrylic	One part light activated	25
Acrylic	Primer (curative) activated	25
Acrylic	Two-part pastes	25
Urethane	Two-part pastes	25
Polyimide	Heat curing films	220
Bis-maleimide	Heat curing films and pastes	200

require storage at low temperatures. Curable one-part paste adhesives are also not normally available to the consumer, but are widely used in industry, particularly in the general transportation industry.

Two part paste adhesives are quite familiar to the consumer. These adhesives are formulated such that the curatives are in one of the "parts" while the crosslinkable resins are in the other "part." These materials are storable at room temperature and the cure is effected when the two components are mixed. Such materials are widely used in industry and are familiar to the consumer, as well.

Curable liquid adhesives are also commonly available to the consumer. These adhesives usually are sold in small quantity convenience packaging through hardware stores, grocery stores, and other consumer outlets. These adhesives cure upon exposure to ambient moisture or by the exclusion of air. They are stable at room temperature as long as they are kept in their packages. More sophisticated versions of these structural adhesives are used in various industrial applications, particularly in the electronics industry, as primer/liquid combinations. In these circumstances, the primer contains the curative, while the liquid is the curable resin. Contact between the two effects the cure.

A particular form of structural adhesive is used to bond wood to produce plywood or other forest product-based articles. These adhesives are usually used in solution, particularly in water. The water or solvent is absorbed by the wood during the bonding operation. Natural product-based adhesives are often used in this application as are phenolic resin solutions.

It is important for the adhesive bond designer to know in what form adhesives are available as well as for the salesperson to know the breadth of his/her product line. The chemist needs to know these distinctions as it is the physical form in which the adhesive is packaged that often dictates the type of chemistry which can be employed. For example, a certain solid resin may be found to provide the best performance in a certain type of adhesive formulation. If the adhesive cannot be used as a solid but must be a paste, it does not matter that the solid resin provides the best performance. However, it may be possible for the formulator to find viscosity modifiers to transform the solid into a paste as long as the modifier does not compromise the most important properties of the finally formulated adhesive. The discussion in the following sections provides some insight into materials used to formulate adhesives. It also provides information on formulation balancing which must be done to provide useful structural adhesives.

8.3   Chemistry of Base Resins Used in Structural Adhesives

8.3.1   Phenolics

Phenolic resins are not only one of the basic resins used in the generation of structural as well as other adhesives, they were also the first commercially successful

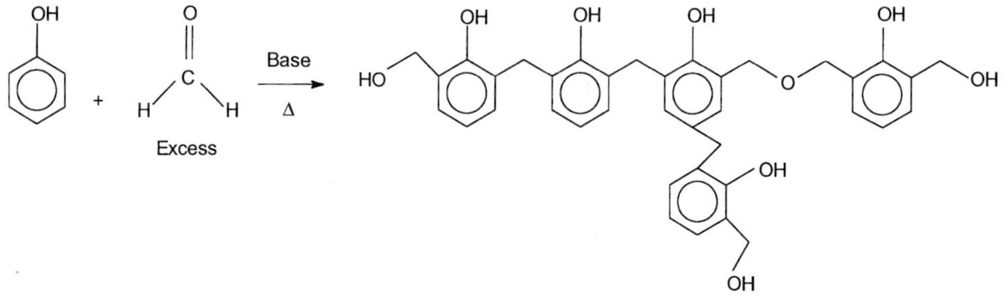

Figure 8.1   Equation for the synthesis of a resole phenolic resin

synthetic resin. Phenolic resins were first developed by Leo Baekeland [1] and were a major product of the early Union Carbide Corporation. Phenolic resins are formed by the reaction of a phenol and formaldehyde. Depending upon the ratio of reactants and the type of catalyst used, two fundamental forms of phenolic resin result. As shown in Fig. 8.1, a *resole* phenolic resin is formed by the reaction of phenol with an excess of formaldehyde in the presence of a basic catalyst, such as NaOH or KOH. The key feature of the resole phenolic resin is that it is self-curing, because of the presence of residual methylol groups which can further condense with active sites on the phenol rings to crosslink the resin and liberate water. Examine the structure as it is drawn in Fig. 8.1. Despite the fact that most phenolic resins are solids at room temperature, their molecular weight is normally quite low as shown in Fig. 8.1. It may also be concluded that with all of the possible reactive sites in a resole phenolic resin, the resultant crosslink density could be quite high. These resins also have a unique property in that they are soluble in water or in alcohol. Because of increasing concern about atmospheric pollution due to the use and venting of organic solvents, resole phenolic resins can be used in the place of others which result in significant solvent emissions. However, a limitation of resole phenolics in structural adhesives for non-porous materials such as metals is the evolution of water during cure. Cure on non-porous materials without the appropriate application of high pressure could lead to porous, spongelike adhesive layers of low strength. Another limitation of resole phenolics is that they may cure during storage which can be prevented by keeping these materials at low temperatures.

The *novolac* phenolic resin is also formed by the reaction of phenol and formaldehyde, but the phenol is kept in excess and the catalyst for the reaction is an acid. As shown in Fig. 8.2, there are no residual methylol groups in novolac phenolic resin. As a result, this material does not self cure nor is it soluble in water or alcohol. An external curative must be added to a novolac phenolic resin order to yield a crosslinked structure. The primary chemical added is hexamethylene tetraamine ("hexa") or urotropine. This chemical is a latent form of formaldehyde and is generated by the reaction of formaldehyde with ammonia. Hexa is thought to provide a crosslinked structure according to the reaction shown in Fig. 8.3. This reaction takes place at elevated temperatures, typically in excess of 150°C.

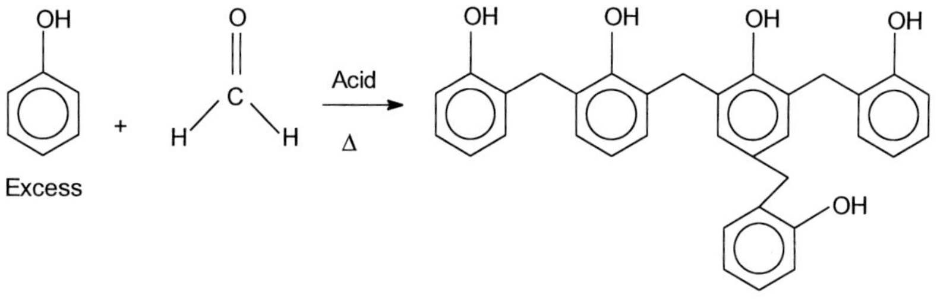

Figure 8.2   Equation for synthesis of a novolac phenolic resin

Phenol is not the only phenolic resin precursor. Other phenolic compounds, such as resorcinol, para-substituted phenol, and cresol have also been used to generate phenolic-based or modified adhesives. For example, p-*tert*-butyl phenol has been used to generate materials known as tackifying resins (discussed in more detail in Chapters 9 and 10) which are used in the modification of various types of elastomer-based adhesives. Resorcinol-based phenolic adhesives are an interesting subset of phenolic structural adhesives. The reaction of formaldehyde with resorcinol is so

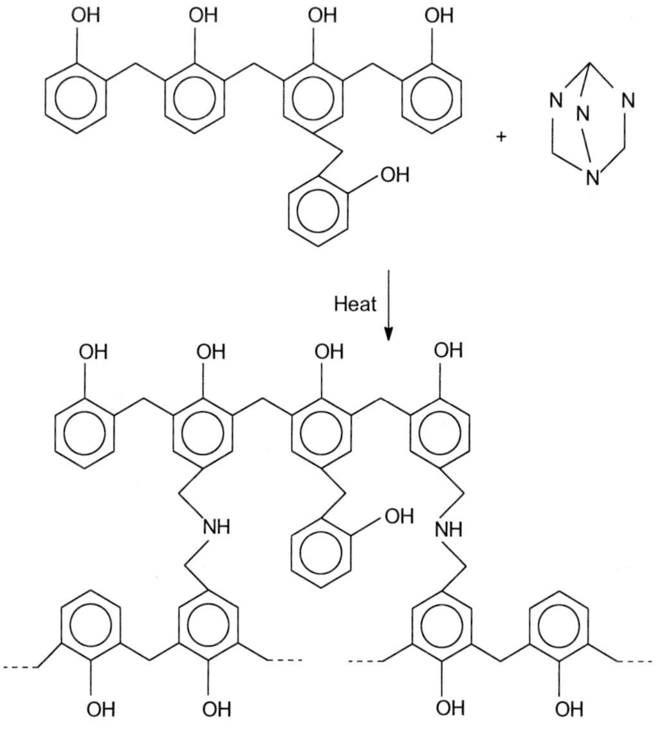

Figure 8.3   Equation describing the crosslinking of novolac phenolic resins with hexamethylene tetraamine

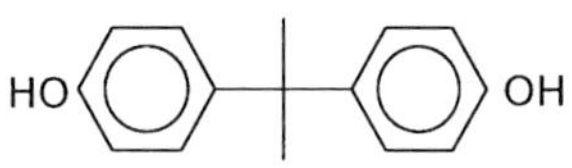

bis-phenol-A

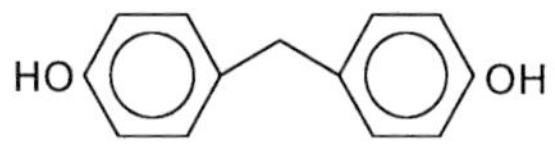

bis-phenol-F   Figure 8.4   Structures of bis-phenol-A and F

rapid and so complete, the resorcinol–formaldehyde resin must be synthesized in "novolac" form. Attempting to make a "resole" resorcinol resin typically results in an unusable gel. Resorcinol–formaldehyde resins are synthesized with a substantial deficit in the amount of formaldehyde. When mixed with the formaldehyde or formaldehyde precursors, the resin cure occurs at low temperatures. Adhesives based upon this chemistry are available as alcohol-containing solutions which can be mixed with paraformaldehyde to effect a bond to wood at room temperature.

The reaction of phenol with formaldehyde at a 2 to 1 mole ratio leads to a material known as bis-phenol-F while the reaction of phenol with acetone at the same ratio yields bis-phenol-A. The structures of these two solid materials are shown in Fig. 8.4. The commercial importance of these two basic, phenol-based chemicals is evident in a future section.

8.3.2   Proteins

Proteins used in structural adhesives come from several sources which are animal blood, fish, milk, connective tissue, and soybeans. These adhesives are ranked according to their resistance to moisture in the bond. Using this type of classification, blood is the most resistant, followed by fish, milk, connective tissue, and soybean. Connective tissue adhesives are called collagen-based adhesives while milk-based adhesives are called casein-based adhesives. Blood-based proteins actually incorporate blood albumen and are obtained by spray drying animal blood. Casein is obtained from milk by precipitation induced by acids such as lactic acid. Some of the properties of the adhesive are dependent upon the type of acid used for the precipitation. To generate protein-based adhesives, it is necessary to first ionize the protein so that it is dispersible in the application medium, usually water. Proteins, which are polyamino acids, contain ionizable groups such as carboxylic acids as well as phenol functionality. Depending upon the source of the protein, hot water, solvent leaching, or washing is necessary. Either acids or bases may be used as the ionizing medium. Once the protein has been dissolved or dispersed in water, materials such as calcium carbonate are added to form twice-valent, ionic crosslinks between two anionic groups on two protein molecules. Other means of crosslinking the protein can also be used including, sulfur based vulcanizing compounds and materials which induce oxidation, such as copper and chromium compounds. In fact, heat itself can often denature proteins in much the same manner as it affects the albumin in an egg when it is cooked.

Protein-based adhesives have been used throughout history. Their primary use in modern times is in the production of plywood. Protein-based adhesives, unfortunately, are not very resistant to adverse environments and the plywood made with this type of adhesive is limited to interior applications.

8.3.3   Epoxy Resins

Resins with an oxirane ring as their reactive moiety are known as epoxy resins. Epoxy resins form the largest variety of structural adhesives currently available. Many epoxy resins are based upon the reaction of phenols with epichlorohydrin. As shown in Fig. 8.5, reaction of 2,2′-isopropylidene diphenol, otherwise known as "bis-phenol-A" (BPA) with epichlorohydrin leads to the most common epoxy resin, the diglycidyl ether of bis-phenol-A. DGEBPA (as we call this resin) can be further reacted with bis-phenol-A to generate higher molecular weight resins which can be either epoxy or phenol terminated. High molecular weight products of DGEBPA and BPA terminated with phenol are known as "phenoxy resins". The chemistry of epoxy resin-based adhesives consists primarily of the choice of mixtures of molecular weights of epoxy resins with the correct curatives. BPF (bis-phenol-F) can also be reacted with epichlorohydrin to generate resins analogous to the DGEBPA-based resins. BPF-based resins have the important attribute of lower viscosity than the DGEBPA resins. DGEBPF resins find use as viscosity and other property modifiers of adhesives based upon DGEBPA.

Another major chemical class of epoxy resin is the epoxidized phenolic resin. Novolac phenolics of the type described in Fig. 8.2, can be reacted with epichlorohydrin in much the same way as shown in Fig. 8.5. In general, the number of epoxides per molecule is two or three. Other resins can be generated by the reaction of epichlorohydrin with aromatic amines or with aromatic amino alcohols. Thus, materials such as tetraglycidyl methylene dianiline (TGMDA) and triglycidyl p-amino phenol (TGAP) are also available as materials for the formulation of epoxy resin-based adhesives. These materials are not as widely used as those based upon

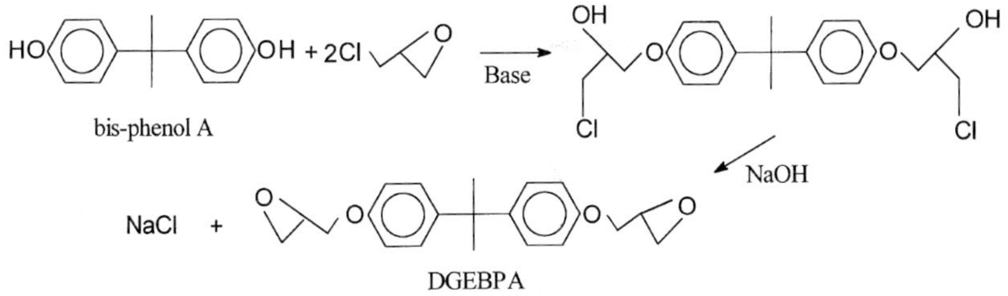

Figure 8.5   Equation describing the synthesis of the di-glycidyl ether of bis-phenol-A

DGEBPA because of problems with storage stability. Both TGMDA and TGAP contain tertiary amines and possibly residual alcohol group which can catalyze alcohol-epoxy reactions to occur slowly at room temperature. Adhesives which contain these materials usually need to be refrigerated even when used as two-parts.

Part of the reason for the wide use of epoxy resins in structural adhesives is the substantial number of crosslinking reactions to which oxirane groups are sensitive. Figure 8.6 provides a list of reactions used to cure epoxy resins. Epoxy resins can react with alcohols to generate ether alcohols. The source of the alcohol can be from phenol or from alcohols generated by the reaction of oxiranes with alcohols. This reaction does not normally take place at room temperature, but rather at temperatures higher than 120°C, in the presence of an amine catalyst. The reaction of oxiranes with phenols or alcohols is an important curing reaction and can compete with or occur simultaneously with the reaction of oxiranes with amines discussed below.

Mercaptans react with oxirane groups even at room temperature to create mercapto-ether alcohols. This reaction is accelerated in the presence of tertiary

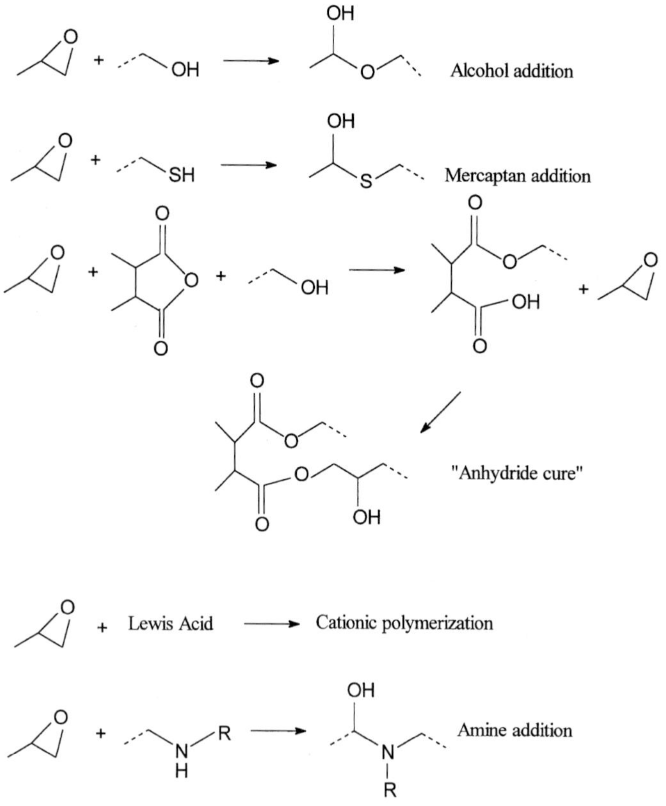

Figure 8.6   Possible curing reactions for epoxy resins

amine catalysts such as tris-dimethyl amino phenol. This reaction is the basis of "Five-minute Epoxies."

Anhydride curing of epoxy resins is infrequently used in adhesives. The reaction of anhydrides with epoxy resins leads to very hard materials and the reaction occurs at elevated temperatures. It should be noted that the reaction of an oxirane with an anhydride does not occur directly. Rather, the anhydride, in the presence of a base catalyst, reacts with alcohol to form an ester and a carboxylic acid. The carboxylic acid then reacts with another oxirane group to form the crosslink. The result is a diester.

Lewis acids can also act as curing agents for epoxy resins, although it would be more correct to say that Lewis acids act as catalysts for the cationic polymerization of oxirane-based resins. Examples of Lewis acids which can induce cationic polymerization of epoxy resins are BF_3 and $SnCl_4$. Lewis acids usually are not used in their pure state, but are complexed with an amine to render them latent or to slow down their reactivity. Latency is discussed later in this chapter.

Epoxy resins can also be polymerized anionically. One type of anionic catalyst which has become increasingly popular is based upon imidazole. Imidazole or 2-ethyl-4-methyl imidazole can be admixed with epoxy resins to generate a material with moderate stability at room temperature. The polymerization occurs rapidly at temperatures of 82°C or above. Complexes of imidazole with metal ions such as silver can be used to create a latent catalyst which causes epoxy resins to polymerize at more elevated temperatures, such as 171°C.

By far the most common curing agent used with epoxy resins is based upon amine. Primary amines react with epoxy resins at room temperature without the presence of a catalyst. Aromatic amines react with epoxy resins slowly at room temperature but rapidly at elevated temperatures. For room temperature cure of epoxy resins, the most common curing agent is based upon the primary aliphatic amine. Useful primary aliphatic amines are based upon the polymerization products of aziridine (e.g. diethylene triamine and triethylene tetramine), the reaction products of dimer acids with diamines, polyether diamines, as well as a host of other amines. One early epoxy adhesive was sold as a two-part material with one part a DGEBPA while the other part was a dimer acid-based diamine. The most common agent for high temperature cure of epoxy resins is dicyandiamide whose structure is shown in Fig. 8.7. Examination of the structure of this molecule indicates that there at least four amines available for reaction with epoxy resins. At elevated temperatures, the nitrile group can also react with alcohol to generate an amide. This reaction leads to the potential for a five-fold crosslink for this rather low molecular weight material. A substantial number of elevated temperature curing epoxy resins use dicyandiamide as the sole curative or in combination with other curatives.

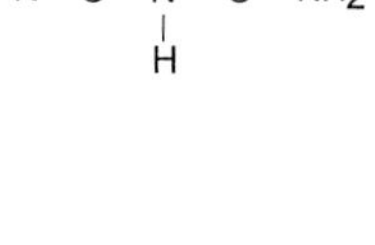

$$N \equiv C - N - C - NH_2$$

Figure 8.7   Structure of dicyandiamide

8.3.3.1   Time-Temperature-Transformation Diagrams and the Cure of Epoxy Resins

For thermosetting systems, there is a complicated and often confusing relationship among the temperature of cure, the time during which the thermoset is at temperature, and the physical state of the thermoset. An important improvement in the understanding of what happens to a thermoset during its cure was provided by Gilham and co-workers using data generated by the torsion pendulum [2] (also discussed in Chapter 5). A simplified time-temperature-transformation (T-T-T) diagram is shown in Fig. 8.8.

The diagram is read by picking a temperature and then drawing a line from the ordinate parallel to the abscissa to the time that is of interest. The state of the system is then determined by the region in which the system finds itself. The first thing to examine about the T-T-T diagram is that three T_g's are defined for the resin system, the uncured "resin T_g", the gel T_g and T_{g_∞}. The diagram also shows a gelation line which corresponds to the time at a specific temperature at which the thermoset forms a gel or crosslinked network. At temperatures below the resin T_g, the thermoset remains an uncrosslinked (non-gelled) glass for very long times. At temperatures above the resin T_g, the thermoset can gel. The time for gelation depends upon how high above the resin T_g the temperature is. Note that the higher the temperature, the closer the gelation line becomes to the ordinate. T_{g_∞} is the glass temperature for the completely crosslinked thermoset and is therefore controlled by

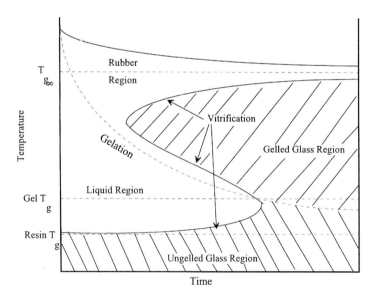

Figure 8.8   Time-Temperature-Transformation (T-T-T) diagram for a thermosetting resin system. Important regions to note are the gelled glass and the ungelled glass regions. Important demarcations to note are the gelation line and the vitrification line (redrawn from [2] by permission of Plenum Press and the author)

the chemical constitution of the thermoset. The diagram shows that at certain temperatures, the thermoset could gel before it vitrifies and at other temperatures could vitrify before it gels. The gel T_g corresponds to the temperature at which the system gels and vitrifies at the same time. *Vitrification* means the formation of a solid gel. At temperatures intermediate between the gel T_g and T_g, the thermoset could gel and then vitrify. Vitrification at this point means an incomplete chemical reaction and a resin not fully cured. The T_g of such a system is essentially that of the cure temperature. T_g could not be increased unless the temperature of the system was raised above the original cure temperature so that the system would be out of the vitrified range. However, if this "post-cure" temperature is less than $T_{g\infty}$, then the T_g of the thermoset is approximately the post-cure temperature.

The concepts described above lead to an interesting situation. If a room temperature curing thermoset (such as a two-part epoxy) is generated, can one expect the epoxy to cure fully at room temperature? Can it be expected that the glass temperature would be much in excess of room temperature? The answer to this question, according to the T-T-T diagram is no. If room temperature is not in excess of the $T_{g\infty}$, then the system either gels or vitrifies before the complete cure can be effected. It is found that in most room temperature curing epoxies the epoxy has not gone to complete reaction. It is also found that the T_g of the cured epoxy is no more than about 50–60°C. Because most measurements of T_g require that the system be exposed to elevated temperatures, the measured T_g has been effected by the application of that elevated temperature. How about measurements of lap shear strength at high temperatures of room temperature curing epoxy adhesives? If the above situation is true, we expect that at any temperature above the T_g, the lap shear strength would be low, since the modulus is lowered above T_g. However, many data sheets for room temperature curing adhesives indicate that high values of high temperature lap shear strengths can be obtained with a room temperature cure. Inherently, the data must be considered suspect since the act of increasing the temperature to measure the lap shear strength is in itself a post-cure. In most bonding situations, this scenario is not of importance since exposure of bonds to higher temperatures often occurs gradually, effecting the post-cure. However, in applications where temperature is raised rapidly and the bond is under load, failure can occur because complete cure and hence, complete strength is not attained. This situation could lead to catastrophic results if T-T-T diagrams and the data they contain are not taken into account.

8.3.4   Urethane Resins

Polyurethane resins are widely known as the basis for coatings as well as for various foam products. They are also used as a component of structural adhesives. Although they are not known for their inherent strength or modulus, these materials form tough, cured resins with the potential for substantial energy absorption. Polyurethanes can be formulated to cure at either room or elevated temperatures.

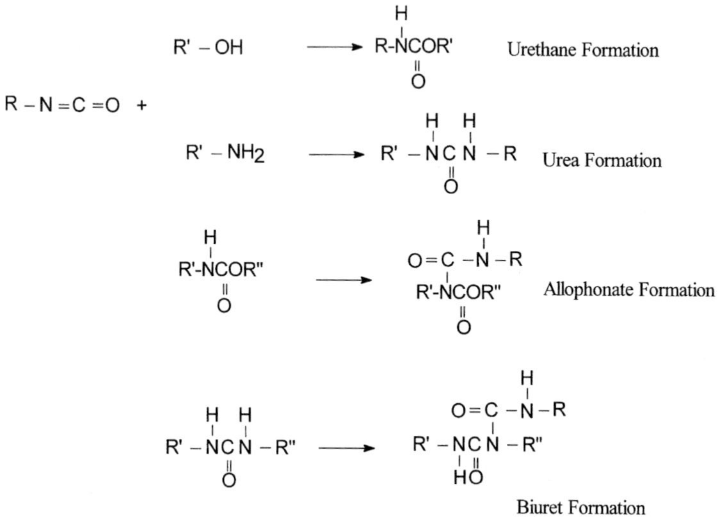

$$R-N=C=O \ + $$

$$R'-OH \longrightarrow R-\overset{\overset{H}{|}}{N}\overset{\underset{\underset{O}{\parallel}}{C}}{}OR' \quad \text{Urethane Formation}$$

$$R'-NH_2 \longrightarrow R'-\overset{\overset{H}{|}}{N}\overset{\underset{\underset{O}{\parallel}}{C}}{}\overset{\overset{H}{|}}{N}-R \quad \text{Urea Formation}$$

$$\overset{\overset{H}{|}}{R'\text{-}N}\overset{\underset{\underset{O}{\parallel}}{C}}{}OR'' \longrightarrow \overset{O=C-\overset{\overset{H}{|}}{N}-R}{\underset{R'\text{-}\overset{\underset{\underset{O}{\parallel}}{C}}{N}OR''}{|}} \quad \text{Allophonate Formation}$$

$$R'-\overset{\overset{H}{|}}{N}\overset{\underset{\underset{O}{\parallel}}{C}}{}\overset{\overset{H}{|}}{N}-R'' \longrightarrow \overset{O=C-\overset{\overset{H}{|}}{N}-R}{\underset{R'-N\overset{\underset{\underset{HO}{\parallel}}{C}}{}N-R''}{|}}$$

$$\text{Biuret Formation}$$

Figure 8.9   Reactions which can occur in the curing of an isocyanate

The general reaction for the formation of a urethane is shown in Fig. 8.9 in which an isocyanate combines with an alcohol to create a urethane or carbamate linkage. If an amine is present, a urea linkage can also form. Secondarily, cross-links form if excess isocyanate is present to create allophonate or biuret linkages. These reactions are catalyzed by various amines as well as metal catalysts, such as dibutyl tin dilaurate, triethylenediamine (DABCO Crystalline[1]), and stannous octo-ate. The cure rate of a urethane-based structural adhesive depends upon the type of polyol, the type of isocyanate, and the type and amount of catalyst used. Aromatic isocyanates usually react faster than aliphatic isocyanates; primary alco-hols react faster than secondary alcohols; urea formation reactions are the fastest in this chemical class. Urethanes are used in many types of adhesives; as structural adhesives, urethanes are found in the form of two-part, room temperature-curing adhesives.

The formulation of urethane based-adhesives depends upon the selection of the isocyanate, the polyol, and a material known as a chain extender, which can be a short chain amine or alcohol. For many years, the primary diisocyanate used to make these adhesives was toluene diisocyanate, but it was found that this material caused severe allergic reactions in a number of people, due to the chemical's volatility. To overcome this problem, oligomers with toluene diisocyanate end-caps were made available. Other diisocyanates used are based upon methylene dianiline, its dimers and trimers, and their hydrogenated counterparts. Isophorone diisocyan-ate and hexamethylene diisocyanate and its dimers are also used.

---

[1] DABCO is a registered trademark of Air Products Corporation

The most widely used polyols in polyurethane adhesives fall into three main classes, polyesters, polyethers, and polybutadiene polyols. The polyether polyols' molecular weights are generally less than 10 000 Daltons. Polyether polyols are usually based upon either the polymers of tetrahydrofuran (polytetramethylene oxide polyols) or of propylene oxide (propylene ether polyols). Polyethylene glycols are not often used because of their hygroscopicity. However, since polypropylene glycols are slow reacting, they are often capped with ethylene glycol which reacts more rapidly. Trifunctional versions are also available with base materials of glycerol or trimethylolpropane. Polyester polyols are often based upon caprolactone and also are manufactured in various molecular weights. Polyester diols can also be based upon polymers of adipic acid and various diols. Butadiene polyols are short chain butadiene polymers with hydroxyl end groups. Branched polyols are also available.

Chain extenders are part of the mechanism providing the extraordinary toughness of polyurethane-based adhesives. Materials such as ethylene glycol, 1,4-butanediol, 1,4-bis(hydroxymethyl)cyclohexane, ethylene diamine, or 3,3'-dichloro-4,4'-diamino-diphenylmethane (MOCA) can be added to the isocyanate/polyether mix. The chain extender reacts with the isocyanate which then phase-separates into domains enriched in isocyanate/chain extender blocks or "hard segments." The polyol phase separates into "soft segments." This phase-separated structure is apparently the source of the toughness displayed by polyurethane adhesives [3]. When using aluminum adherends, two-part urethanes provide about 6.9–13.8 MPa (1000–2000 psi) lap shear strength and can have quite high peel strengths in the range of 5.3–10.5 kN/m (30–60 pounds per inch width (piw)). The lap shear strength usually decreases substantially at elevated temperatures.

8.3.5   Acrylics

Acrylic structural adhesives are important because of their rapid cure and structural strength. In comparison to epoxy and urethanes adhesives, acrylics cure in less than a minute under the proper conditions. This rapid cure property is used to great advantage in the electronics industry (such as in bonding magnets into speaker assemblies) among others in maintaining high assembly line speeds.

Acrylic structural adhesives fall broadly into two classes: redox-activated and cyanoacrylate adhesives. The basic monomers used in the generation of the first type are usually combinations of methyl methacrylate, methacrylic acid, and crosslinking agents such as ethylene glycol dimethacrylate. More exotic monomers such as tetrahydrofurfuryl methacrylate and iso-bornyl methacrylate can also be used. The cyanoacrylate adhesives are based upon a particular type of acrylic monomer which we discuss later. The key difference between reduction-oxidation (redox) activated and cyanoacrylate structural adhesives is how cure is effected. In both cases, the reaction mechanism is an addition polymerization, but the redox-activated adhesives react by a free radical polymerization, while the cyanoacrylate adhesives react by an anionic addition polymerization.

Redox-activated structural adhesives rely upon some form of a redox reaction to generate the free radical initiator necessary for the inception of the polymerization reaction. The oldest structural adhesive of this type is the anaerobic adhesive. Anaerobic acrylic adhesives are based upon an initiator with a long half-life and acrylic monomers whose polymerization is inhibited by the presence of oxygen. To produce such an adhesive, materials such as diacrylates and dimethacrylates of ethylene glycol were combined with cumene hydroperoxide which generated a small concentration of free radicals. The polymerization, however, could be inhibited by a small amount of oxygen. The adhesive was stored in oxygen-permeable bottles which provided an extended shelf life. If the adhesive was brought in contact with a surface which could initiate reduction of the peroxide (such as an iron surface containing Fe^{2+} or other transition metals) and oxygen was excluded, the material polymerized. The initial use of this type of adhesive was in thread locking which involves iron bolts and the exclusion of oxygen by application of the nut. This application of anaerobic acrylic technology was responsible for the early success of the Loctite Company which is now a leading producer of these types of adhesives.

Free radical initiators could be produced in other ways besides surface-induced reduction of a peroxide. The polymerization rate of the original anaerobic acrylic adhesive depended upon the type of metal used to form the bond. For example, Fe^{2+} initiated a rapid polymerization but with Cu^{2+} it was relatively slow. Substantial advances were made in acrylic structural adhesive technology when it was found that certain organic species also acted as redox couples to cause reduction of a peroxide. One of the redox couples was N,N-dimethyl-p-toluidine and saccharin. These materials, in the presence of cumyl hydroperoxide, initiated polymerization of acrylic monomer, although the presence of either of these materials alone did not. In one type of two-part adhesive developed based upon this redox couple, either the saccharin or the N,N-dimethyl-p-toluidine is dissolved in a solvent and this solution is applied as a primer to one of the adherends to be bonded. After the solvent has evaporated, the remaining adhesive mixture (monomers and the other half of the redox couple) is applied to the other adherend. Joining the adherends initiates the polymerization in the zone where the two parts of the adhesive meet. Another type of an adhesive using this technology is a two-part mix adhesive in which half of the redox couple is mixed in each part. When the two parts are combined, initiation and polymerization ensue.

Cyanoacrylate adhesives are unique in structural adhesive technology. The structure of the basic monomer is shown in Fig. 8.10. The double bond, due to its proximity to two strong electron withdrawing groups (the nitrile and the ester group) is extremely sensitive to nucleophilic attack. In fact, this monomer, during its synthesis from alkylcyanoacetate and formaldehyde in the presence of base, polymerizes immediately upon formation. The monomer is obtained by phosphorus pentoxide/phosphine-induced depolymerization and distillation from the formed polymer. The susceptibility of the double bond to nucleophilic attack provides a monomer whose polymerization can be initiated by species as weakly nucleophilic as water. Various bases can also be used to induce polymerization of cyanoacrylates but acids inhibit the process. The extreme reactivity of the monomer results in fast

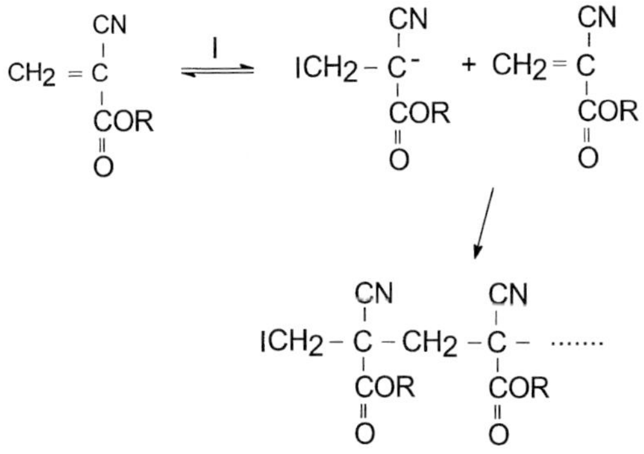

Figure 8.10   Structure and anionic polymerization of a cyanoacrylate

cure. Cyanoacrylate monomers can contain ester groups from methyl, ethyl to isobutyl and ethoxy ethyl, although the most commonly used monomers for adhesives are the first two. All of these monomers are clear, colorless, low viscosity liquids with pungent odors. Free radical stabilizers such as hydroquinone are added to improve storage stability as is sulfur dioxide which reduces the possibility of ionic polymerization. One key factor not normally recognized regarding cyanoacrylate adhesives is that these materials, unless specially formulated, are thermoplastics after cure. This makes the cured cyanoacrylate susceptible to creep as well as attack by moisture. Despite these limitations, they have become quite popular commercially and many private label packagers of adhesives have made this product available to the consumer under trade names such as "Krazy Glue" and "Super Glue."

8.3.6   High Temperature Performance Structural Adhesives

The adhesives described above are limited in their resistance to high temperatures. As already discussed, the thermoplastic nature of cyanoacrylate adhesives prevents them from resisting creep at high temperatures. The upper temperature limit for addition polymerized adhesives is normally the glass transition temperature of the cured monomer. For urethanes, at the upper temperature limit, usually between 120 and 150°C, the urethane unblocks. Epoxy structural adhesives usually exhibit a decrease in performance at about 30°C above the cure temperature. Phenolics can resist temperatures substantially higher than the cure temperature as demonstrated by the ablative material used in the Mercury and Gemini space programs. For the most part, epoxies and phenolics have an upper temperature limit for long term exposure of about 204°C. However, there are uses for materials which exhibit resistance to long term exposure to temperatures in excess of 204°C such as in internal combustion and turbine engines and adhesives for fuselage and other structure in high speed commercial airplanes. Many of the adhesives which we discuss shortly were developed to meet the needs of the SST (supersonic transport)

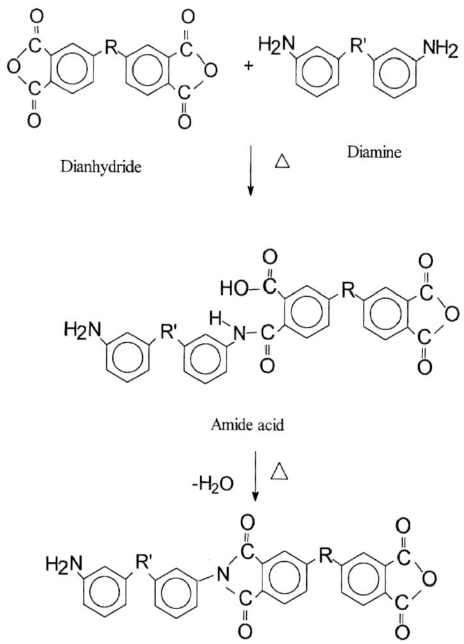

Figure 8.11   Reactions for formation of a polyimide

program of the late 1960s. One key feature which characterizes high temperature performance adhesive materials is their highly aromatic character (which provides oxidative resistance) and the plethora of bonds formed upon polymerization. To sever the polymer chain, two bonds have to be broken.

The polymer type most examined for high temperature applications is based upon polyimides. The general polyimide reaction is shown in Fig. 8.11. The diamines are aromatic and can range from methylene dianiline to diaminodiphenylether. The anhydrides can range from nadic anhydride to benzophenone tetracarboxylic acid dianhydride to 4,4'-hexafluoropropylidene-bis-(phthalic acid). Various structures of polyimide components have been studied to improve the performance of these structural adhesives. The key feature in polyimide polymerization is that each step involves the elimination of water. Both high temperature and high pressure are involved in each stage of cure to force the water out of the bond when the adherends are non-porous. Polyimide cure temperatures are usually above 220°C. Polyimides are inherently thermoplastic and creep under high loads at high temperatures.

Various schemes have been proposed for crosslinking polyimides. When nadic anhydride is used, crosslinking takes place by means of the nadic functionality. m-Amino benzoacetylene can also be used to end-cap a polyimide; at high temperatures the acetylenes condense to form an aromatic structure.

One adhesive which has a cure simpler than that of polyimides but yields a high temperature resistant material is based upon bis-maleimide. The structure of a

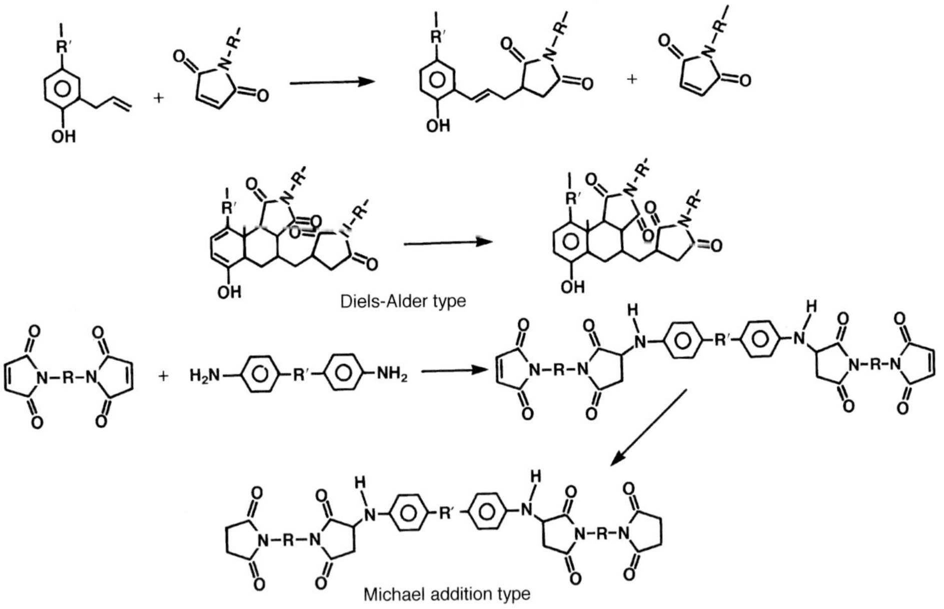

Figure 8.12   Structure and two possible curing reactions for bis-maleimides

bis-maleimide is shown in Fig. 8.12. Bis-maleimides cure by a number of mechanisms (see Fig. 8.12), including Michael addition to the maleimide double bond, and the Diels–Alder reaction with allyl phenol. In both cases, the cure temperature is more than 200°C, but since water is not eliminated during the cure, there is less need for the application of pressure to the bond than in the case of polyimides or resole phenolics.

8.4   Formulation of Structural Adhesives for Optimum Performance

All of the resins described above have a distinct disadvantage if they are used in the unformulated state or in simple formulations of structural adhesives, namely that unformulated resins are brittle and cannot sustain high loads because they cannot resist cleavage forces. Recall the energy absorption discussion of an earlier chapter. Remember that an important criterion for bond design and adhesive performance is that the adhesive be able to absorb a substantial amount of energy before it fails. In addition, recall that the weakest mode of adhesive bond strength is Mode I, or cleavage. Both of these facts lead to the conclusion that the resins used to generate structural adhesives must be formulated so they absorb energy and resist cleavage forces.

Refer to Chapter 2 and Section 5.2.2 and examine the discussion on strain energy density. A polymeric material can absorb a fair amount of energy if it is elastomeric in character. That is, high extension results in a fair amount of energy absorption before the adhesive breaks. However, elastomeric materials usually have a low modulus and cannot support a heavy load. A polymeric material can have a high modulus but be rather brittle. These polymers are stiff and can be counted upon to support a relatively high load (as one would wish for a structural adhesive, but do not absorb energy well, since their extension causes failure, i.e., the ultimate strain energy density is too low). If we have a *tough* or *leathery* material, the modulus can be relatively high and we can have a high extension to failure, indicating a high ultimate strain energy density. The goal of the formulator is to generate an adhesive with the highest possible strain energy density commensurate with the stiffness (modulus) required for the design of the adhesive joint. The next few sections describe how this has been achieved for a number of structural adhesive types.

8.4.1   Formulation of Phenolic Resins

The formulation of adhesives to resist bond cleavage forces began with phenolic resin adhesives in the 1940s. Nicholas DeBruyne described the use of polyvinyl acetal resins in the modification of phenolic adhesives [4]. The patents describe an interesting methodology in which resole phenolic was applied to metal adherends from solution by rolling or brushing. Polyvinyl butyral in powder form was then shaken onto the resin coated surface. The bond was closed and then subjected to temperatures greater than 170°C and pressures greater than 1.4 MPa (200 psi) in order to effect the bond. These were the first structural adhesives formulated for resistance to cleavage forces. The adhesive bonds, when made with aerospace aluminum, sustained loads at room temperature in excess of 20.7 MPa (3000 psi) and exhibited T-peel strengths (once again on aluminum adherends) in excess of 3.5 kN/m (20 piw). By comparison, unmodified resole phenolics exhibit lap shear strengths less than 13.8 MPa (2000 psi) and T-peel strengths of about 0.9 kN/m (5 piw). These acetal and formal modified phenolic adhesives, known as the "Redux" adhesives, were extremely successful and formed the basis for a division of the Ciba-Geigy Company. Redux adhesives were used to generate aircraft structures near the end of World War II and continue to be used today although they have lost much market share to epoxy resin-based adhesives. Bonds made with Redux adhesives were extremely stable. In one case, the author examined a fuselage which flew over the north Atlantic Ocean for over 30 years and showed little evidence of bondline corrosion or disbondment.

Despite their excellent durability, Redux adhesives did have several drawbacks including the odd application conditions and the need for high pressures to effect a bond. Currently, a Redux product is available as a structural film adhesive with the

Table 8.2 Formulation of a Nitrile-Butadiene Rubber Modified Phenolic Structural Adhesive [5]

Component	Parts per hundred	Function
Hycar 1001	46.0	Nitrile/butadiene elastomer
Carbon black	24.0	Filler/reinforcement
Stearic acid	0.5	
Zinc oxide	2.4	Vulcanizing aid
Agerite resin D	0.5	
Butyl 8	3.4	
Bakelite 18773	11.0	Phenolic resin
Durez 7031A	11.0	Phenolic resin
Captax	0.5	Vulcanizing accelerator
Sulfur	0.7	Vulcanizing agent

polyvinyl acetal dispersed in a phenolic resin. These drawbacks led to the next step in adhesive development: formulation of adhesives based upon novolac phenolic resins. Even though novolac phenolic resins modified by the addition of hexa do not liberate volatiles as do resole phenolic resins, applications are limited because of brittleness. This led formulators at 3M Company and other firms to develop novolac phenolic resin-based adhesives modified with butadiene-nitrile elastomers. The elastomers were added to novolac phenolic resins in solution and then coated out on a release liner to generate the first "structural film adhesives." A typical formulation for one of these "nitrile-phenolic film adhesives" is shown in Table 8.2.

The sulfur and Captax are added as a vulcanizing system for the nitrile-butadiene elastomer. Nitrile phenolic film adhesives have an advantage over the Redux system in that cure can be effected at relatively low pressures 0.3–0.7 MPa (50–100 psi). The cure temperatures are approximately the same as that for Redux. The bond strengths attainable using these adhesives on aerospace aluminum alloys are in the range of 27.6 MPa (4000 psi) with T-peel strengths in excess of 5.3 kN/m (30 piw), depending upon the ratio of rubber to phenolic resin. Figure 8.13 shows the relationship

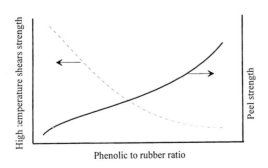

Figure 8.13   Diagram showing the effect on adhesive bond performance of a nitrile-phenolic adhesive as a function of the rubber to resin ratio

between high temperature lap shear strength, peel strength, and elastomer to phenolic ratio for a particular set of nitrile-phenolic film adhesives.

As the elastomer/phenolic ratio increases, the high temperature lap shear strength decreases and the T-peel strength increases. This phenomenon indicates a resin with the elastomer and phenolic resin in solution. The elastomer has acted as a "flexibilizer" for the brittle phenolic resin.

Nitrile-phenolic film adhesives are truly unique materials. They are used extensively in applications ranging from the adhesive bonding automotive brake linings, which takes advantage of their temperature resistance to the adhesive bonding of automotive clutch surfaces for lubricating fluid resistance to aerospace fuselage bonding for fatigue resistance and vibration damping. This wide range is surprising because of the dynamic mechanical spectra observed for cured nitrile-phenolic film adhesives. Figure 8.14 shows an example of such a curve, with $\log E'$ and $\tan \delta$ as functions of temperature. A fixed frequency of $1\,s^{-1}$ was used. The glass transition temperature for this cured adhesive falls below room temperature, indicating that cured nitrile-phenolic film adhesives are actually elastomers at essentially all temperatures of use. There are two other features to note. The first of these is the flatness of the "plateau" portion of the curve out to temperatures in excess of 200°C, indicating that the adhesive is cured and does not flow. This data indicates why these adhesives are used for brake linings and similar applications. The second feature of note is the high value of $\tan \delta$ near the glass transition temperature. This indicates that the adhesive is energy absorbing and can be used for vibration damping purposes at temperatures near the glass transition temperature.

8.4.2   Epoxy Resins

The thought behind the adhesive formulations described above is that the properties of a brittle resin can be modified with an elastomer to yield a more energy absorbing

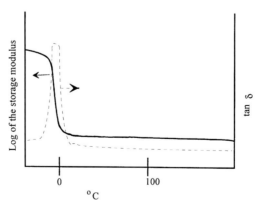

Figure 8.14   Plot of the storage modulus and loss tangent of a cured nitrile-phenolic structural film adhesive. Note the extent of the plateau region of the storage modulus

material. This thinking is best exemplified in the formulation of epoxy resin adhesives. Phenolic resin adhesives have been used with great success in the generation of durable structures. However, the cure conditions for many phenolic adhesives require temperatures too high for some substrates and pressures high enough to crush or deform other substrates. Epoxy resins do not require high pressures for cure although some may require high cure temperatures. Therefore, many of the applications which precluded the use of a phenolic structural adhesive could be handled by an epoxy structural adhesive. Formulators of epoxy-based adhesives faced the same problems encountered by formulators of phenolic adhesives: cured epoxy resins are inherently brittle, inextensible materials. Formulators of epoxy resin adhesives were able to use two mechanisms to obtain energy absorption: flexibilization and toughening by phase separation. We discuss the differences between these two methods as well as formulations of adhesives produced by them.

When an epoxy adhesive is "flexibilized," the elastomer is soluble in the resin before and after cure. Such a situation was described above for phenolic resins. The cured, formulated, flexibilized adhesive has a single glass transition temperature lower than that obtained with the unmodified epoxy resin. Elastomer modification reduces the modulus of the adhesive so that some lap shear properties, especially those measured at elevated temperatures, decrease from those for the unmodified cured epoxy resin. The resulting adhesive is also more flexible, has higher extensibility, and thus, is better able to absorb energy as the adhesive bond is loaded.

The second method of obtaining an epoxy adhesive capable of absorbing energy is toughening by phase separation. In this method, an elastomer is chosen that is soluble in the uncured epoxy resin but insoluble in the cured epoxy resin. Such an elastomer phase separates from the epoxy resin as it cures. If the elastomer is chosen properly, the elastomer phase exists as discrete balls of elastomer uniformly dispersed in the cured epoxy resin (which we now call a "matrix" resin). The epoxy resin becomes opaque as the cure progresses.

For the elastomer phase to be effective as a *toughening agent*, the particle size of the balls must be about 0.2–2 microns in diameter, thus scattering visible light. In general, flexibilized adhesives remain clear unless otherwise modified by fillers or other additives. Cured, toughened epoxy resins also exhibit two glass transition temperatures, one for the cured epoxy matrix and another for the phase separated elastomer. The glass transition temperature of the epoxy resin matrix is lowered in proportion to the amount of elastomer dissolved in the matrix. In comparison to flexibilized adhesives, toughened epoxy adhesives exhibit only a moderate increase in extensibility. Flexibilized adhesives can exhibit ultimate extensions in excess of 10% (up to 50%), toughened epoxy adhesives usually only extend up to about 10%, although this depends upon the temperature of the measurement. The approximate numbers provided here are based on room temperature measurements. Toughening results in a matrix resin which is essentially unchanged, but able now to absorb energy and to blunt cracks which may form. The mechanism of crack blunting is discussed in further detail shortly.

Flexibilized adhesives are obtained by using elastomers soluble in the matrix before and after cure. Thus, it is necessary to use elastomers with solubility

Table 8.3   Typical Formulation of a Flexibilized Epoxy Structural Adhesive [6]

Component	Approximate amount (pph)	Function
DGEBPA	47.0	Base epoxy resin
DGEBPA-based resins	19.8	Molecular weight control
Dicyandiamide	4.7	Curing agent
3-(p-chloropheny l)-1,1-dimethylurea	2.3	Curing accelerator
Hycar rubber	18.3	Butadiene-nitrile rubber flexibilizer

parameters close to those of epoxy resins. This criterion is met by acrylonitrile-butadiene random copolymers of high molecular weight and with acrylonitrile contents in excess of 25%. A typical formulation for a heat curing epoxy resin-based adhesive formulated for flexibilization is in Table 8.3. Aluminum adherends, when joined with this type of adhesive, can be expected to provide room temperature lap shear strengths in excess of 31 MPa (4500 psi) and T-peel strengths in excess of 7 kN/m (40 piw).

The above formula describes the use of a curative, 3-(p-chlorophenyl)-1,1-dimethylurea used in conjunction with dicyandiamide. Dicy, which was described earlier, is widely used as a latent catalyst for epoxy resin cures. Its latency is due to its insolubility in epoxy resins at room temperature and below. Dicy cures the epoxy resin when it dissolves at temperatures in excess of 150°C. 3-(p-chlorophenyl)-1,1-dimethylurea which is also a latent source of isocyanate, reduces the temperature at which dicy cures epoxy resins. The cure temperature can be lowered to about 121°C if the cure time is about one hour. The mechanism of action was investigated by Laliberte and Bornstein [7], and it involves the formation of an oxazolidone inter-mediate between an epoxy resin and 3-(p-chlorophenyl)-1,1-dimethylurea which liberates dimethyl amine. The dimethyl amine, at these temperatures, also acts a polymerization catalyst. However, according to these researchers, its primary pur-pose is to solubilize the dicyandiamide so that it can effect cure.

Similar formulas form the basis for toughened epoxy resin systems. The major differences from the above formulas is the use of acrylonitrile/butadiene elastomers which meet specific criteria. These criteria were originally enumerated by McGarry and co-workers [8]:

- the elastomer must contain about 18% acrylonitrile
- the elastomer must be telechelic and the end groups must be reactive with epoxy groups
- the elastomer must form a second, separate phase during the cure of the epoxy resin
- the second phase must form particles large enough to scatter light

These criteria were well met by a group of materials manufactured by B.F. Goodrich, Inc., known as RLPs (Reactive Liquid Polymers). The RLPs are random copolymers of acrylonitrile and butadiene of relatively low molecular weight, with end groups ranging from carboxyl to amine to vinyl. The carboxyl and amine terminated materials have been used to modify epoxies with the resulting adhesive exhibiting improved crack resistance while most, if not all, of the properties of the epoxy resin are retained.

RLPs have been researched extensively both industrially as well as academically. Much of the research has dealt with the mechanism of formation of the second phase, crack blunting, and how the chemistry of the elastomer particle controls that phenomenon. It is important to understand how RLPs toughen epoxies as this phenomenon is the basis for the highest performance structural adhesive technology available today.

In general, RLPs must be pre-reacted with the epoxy resin for the toughening effect to take place. For CTBN-RLPs (Carboxy-Terminated Butadiene-Nitrile Reactive Liquid Polymers), the reaction is carried out at high temperature and usually in the presence of catalyst, which can be a material such as tris-dimethylamino phenol or piperidine. In general, a chain extender such as bis-phenol-A is also added. To understand the reason for the addition of chain extenders, the stress field at a crack tip must be examined. Look at the equations for the stress at a crack tip described by Irwin [9]. The equation describing the stress state near a crack tip is known as the biharmonic equation, a fourth order differential equation. Applying the proper boundary conditions, it can be solved to yield the following relationships between the strains (in cylindrical polar coordinates) and the distance from the crack tip, r. The solutions are as follows:

$$\sigma_\theta = \frac{K_I}{\sqrt{2\pi r}} \frac{1}{2} \cos\frac{\theta}{2} (1 + \cos\theta)$$

$$\sigma_r = \frac{K_I}{\sqrt{2\pi r}} \frac{1}{2} \cos\frac{\theta}{2} (3 - \cos\theta)$$

$$\sigma_{r\theta} = \frac{K_I}{\sqrt{2\pi r}} \frac{1}{2} \cos\frac{\theta}{2} \sin\theta$$

For this discussion, it is not necessary to consider the trigonometric functions. Rather, assume that the crack is formed under either plane stress or plane strain conditions. In plane stress, we find that the following situation exists:

$$\sigma_i = \frac{K_I}{\sqrt{2\pi r}}$$

The quantity K_I is a constant resulting from the solution of the biharmonic equation, known as the *stress intensity factor*. The stress intensity factor has the same meaning as the accumulation of "force lines" that we discussed in Sections 1.1 and 6.6. That is, it is a measure of how much of the stress applied to the sample ends up accumulating at the tip of the crack. The stress intensity factor is directly related to the strain energy release rate. Under plane strain conditions, the relationship is

$$\mathcal{G}_I = \frac{K_I E}{(1 - \nu^2)}$$

We now come to a critical point in understanding this situation. If $\sigma_i > \sigma_y$ where σ_y is the yield strength of the polymer matrix, then we know that the polymer yields. From stress–strain curves, we assume that once the yield strength has been attained, the stress does not continue to increase for a substantial amount of extension. Thus, we can say that for a certain volume of material, the radius of which is r_y, near to the crack tip, has yielded. We define the radius of the volume of material around the crack tip which has yielded as being:

$$r_y = \frac{1}{2\pi}\left(\frac{K_I}{\sigma_y}\right)^2$$

This simple equation has one specific thing to say. The value of r_y is dependent upon the reciprocal of σ_y^2. That is, the radius of the yielded zone is proportional to the square of the stress intensity factor and it is inversely proportional to the square of the yield strength of the matrix. Hence, for us to have a large radius of yielded material near the crack tip, we must have a low enough σ_y. The radius in the equation above should not be associated with a two-dimensional situation. It is a radius in cylindrical coordinates and maps out a volume. The bigger the radius, the bigger the volume of yielded material. The bigger the volume of yielded material, the more crack energy which has been absorbed. Therefore, chain extension is done to lower the yield strength to such a point that energy is absorbed in the matrix by yielding. A material with a high yield point has a difficult time in providing a large r_y and in absorbing the energy in the crack.

The "plastic zone," as the region mapped out by r_y is called, is not just a mathematical construction. It can be observed as a whitening around the crack tip, as demonstrated by Hunston [10]. The ramifications of the yielded or "plastic" zone on other properties of an adhesive bond is now examined. It is well known that structural adhesive bonds have a maximum in their strength dependent upon bond line thickness. This phenomenon can be explained by an examination of the effect of the plastic zone. For any particle-resin system, the yield strength and the radius of the plastic zone is defined. What would happen if the radius of the plastic zone were confined to a smaller value due to the proximity of the adherends? Examine Fig. 8.15. In Section (a) of this figure, the plastic zone is confined too greatly between the adherends and the actual volume of the zone is decreased because of that confinement. This has the effect of lowering the fracture resistance of the joint. In Fig. 8.15(c), the plastic zone is not confined at all. The resistance to fracture is that of the bulk material. If, however, the thickness is in a range in which the constraint of the adherends extends the volume of the plastic zone beyond the crack tip, a maximization of fracture resistance results. This situation is shown in Fig. 8.15(b). This phenomenon is observed both in fracture mechanics specimens as well as in lap shear specimens. Figure 8.15 also shows a plot of the observed dependence of fracture toughness on the thickness of the adhesive. This phenomenon was first observed by Bascom and co-workers [11a,b] and was explained in this manner by Kinloch and Shaw [11c].

The main difference between an unmodified epoxy system and one with a phase separated elastomer is that in the latter, a second, weaker phase is distributed

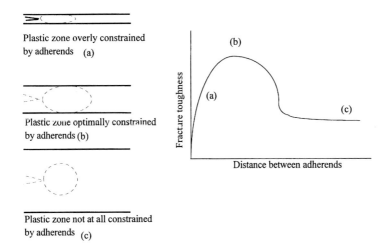

Plastic zone overly constrained
by adherends   (a)

Plastic zone optimally constrained
by adherends (b)

Plastic zone not at all constrained
by adherends   (c)

Figure 8.15   Diagram showing the relationship between fracture toughness and the extent of constraint of the plastic zone by the adherends. The designations in the figures on the left correspond to the sections of the curve on the right (redrawn from [11c])

through the cured epoxy matrix. A discontinuity in the properties of a material results in a stress concentration at the boundary of a discontinuity. The same is true of toughened epoxy matrices. Thus, when a crack is propagating through a toughened epoxy, the energy propagating the crack sets up a stress field in the region ahead of the crack. If that region contains a particle, the boundary of the particle and the matrix is a discontinuity, resulting in a stress concentration. This stress concentration yields the matrix, causing plastic deformation.

It is suspected that the viscoelastic properties of the matrix, as they are reflected by the yield stress, has an effect on the resulting resistance to fracture. This is found to be true in that the fracture properties of a modified as well as an unmodified epoxy resin can be modeled by examination of the effect of temperature and rate on the yield stress of those systems [12]. It has been found that both modified and unmodified epoxy resins have much the same features in their fracture resistance behavior as a function of temperature. The difference is that the modified epoxy has much larger resistance to fracture. It is also interesting to note that as temperature is decreased and the glass temperature of the rubber has been passed, the properties of the elastomer become similar to those of the epoxy and the fracture resistance of the modified and unmodified epoxy resins become very similar to one another. The fracture resistance of modified and unmodified epoxy resins have been modeled by a modified Dugdale fracture mechanism as well as by application of the Eyring rate equation [12b].

A typical formula for a toughened epoxy resin adhesive and a comparable, non-toughened counterpart are shown in Table 8.4. An examination of the formulae show several interesting features. First, the CTBN-RLP has been pre-reacted with the epoxy resin. If the criteria for toughening epoxy resins are examined, it is noted

Table 8.4 Comparison of Formulary of Modified and Unmodified Epoxy Adhesives and their Physical Properties [13]

Component or test results	Unmodified adhesive (parts)	Modified adhesive (parts)
DGEBPA Resin	100	100
DGEBPA/CTBN 1300X13 adduct (40% elastomer)	0	25
Alumina filler	40	40
Silica filler	5	5
Dicyandiamide	6	6
Melamine	2	2
Room temperature lap shear strength, MPa (psi)	18.5 (2680)	20.5 (2970)
Room temperature T-peel strength, kN/m (piw)	1.1 (6.3)	5.5 (31)

that McGarry indicated that the phase-separated particle should be "well-bonded" to the matrix. The presence of this pre-reacted CTBN-RLP is a manifestation of this need. Second, dicyandiamide and melamine are used in the formula. The dicyandiamide is the primary latent curing agent (as described above) while the melamine is a co-curative, probably acting to reduce the high cure temperature required by dicyandiamide. Third, the lap shear strength increases as does the peel strength. These increases can easily be misunderstood as an improvement in the shear strength of the resin. Examination of the Goland–Reissner analysis reminds us that lap shear specimens have a substantial component of normal (peel) forces. The toughened adhesive has been formulated to be resistive to peel forces, which results in a bond with a higher load to failure, even though the shear strength of the adhesive is, at best, the same as that of the unmodified material. This final point is of particular importance to the engineer designing adhesive bonds. Use of ASTM D1002 lap shear specimens can give a false reading of the actual shear performance of an adhesive, as discussed in detail in Chapter 3.

A similar situation is noted when examining the formulation of room temperature-curing, two-part epoxy adhesives. The physical properties of such adhesives are dependent upon the mix ratio (stoichiometry) used in the adhesives as well as the crosslink densities as determined by the molecular distance between amine groups in the crosslinking agent. This is important to consider for room temperature-curing epoxies, since these systems are limited in the amount of chemistry included to reduce the yield stress of the cured resin. In the earlier discussion, the dependence of the toughening effect on the yield strength of the matrix was emphasized. The dependence of the toughening effect in room temperature curing epoxies on the choice of curing agent can then be appreciated. In addition, it is doubly important that the rubber particle be firmly attached to the matrix. Work by N.C. Paul *et al.* [14] has shown that for room temperature curing epoxies, the elastomer must be pre-reacted with the epoxy resin to achieve the desired performance. In addition, a

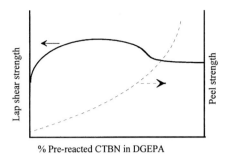

Figure 8.16   Plot of lap shear strength for epoxy adhesives formulated with varying percentages of CTBN pre-reacted with DGEBPA (redrawn from [14])

polyether diamine was chosen as the curative in these studies, to provide the appropriate crosslink density for toughening. Work in the author's laboratory examined the effect of crosslink density in a homologous series of crosslinking agents in which the only variation was the number of polyether units [15]. In this case, it was shown that the optimum distance between amine groups was two ether linkages. It is interesting to examine the dependence of shear strength on the amount of elastomer used in a room temperature curing toughened adhesive. This was done by Paul and co-workers with results shown in Fig. 8.16.

The lap shear strength of adhesive bonds made with increasing elastomer content seem to rise, and then go through a maximum. Beyond the maximum the lap shear strength is still higher than that for the unmodified adhesive. This is a further demonstration of the Goland–Reissner effect. Addition of the elastomer to the adhesive probably reduces the shear strength of the adhesive. However, the resistance to cleavage makes the lap shear strength appear to increase. These effects can be detected and accounted for by using specimens with longer laps or thicker adherends.

8.4.3   Acrylics

Various types of monomers have been used to generate both anaerobic as well as other types of acrylic structural adhesives. Although methacrylate esters are used widely in these adhesives, other monomers have also been used. A primary problem with methacrylic esters is their pungent and, for some people, objectionable, odor. Much effort has been put into the generation of monomers with less objectionable odors but with similar performance. Monomers used are the reaction products of hydroxyethylmethacrylate and anhydrides, polyurethane methacrylates (as described below), iso-bornyl methacrylate, tetrahydrofurfuryl methacrylate, as well as cyclohexyl and dicyclopentyl methacrylate. In general, methacrylate, rather than acrylate, functionality is used due to the somewhat slower speed of cure and higher stiffness.

Initiator and redox systems are the basis for this type of adhesive. Some of the initiator materials have been described earlier. Many peroxides can be used for this application, although it is important that they be room temperature stable in the absence of the redox couple. tert-Butyl peroxide and potassium persulfate could be used for this application. The saccharin/aromatic amine couple described earlier as well as others like it have been described as capable of initiating acrylic polymerization.

A key problem with acrylic structural adhesives is that the monomers normally have very low viscosity. Methyl methacrylate has a viscosity similar to that of water. An adhesive based upon this material alone would run out of the adhesive bond during its application. Various materials have been added to acrylics as flow control agents. Perhaps the simplest technique is to use higher molecular weight polymeric acrylates and methacrylates, although materials such as hydrophobic fumed silica can also play a role.

Unmodified acrylics have a high modulus and are brittle. In much the same way that the toughened epoxy adhesive evolved, acrylic adhesives were first flexibilized and then toughened. Anaerobic acrylics were first modified by urethane elastomers end capped with acrylic functionality [16]. These materials, when incorporated into the acrylic matrix, resulted in an increase in fracture resistance as well as a decrease in matrix T_g. A major improvement occurred with the development of toughened structural acrylics done by the addition of chlorosulphonated polyethylene to the acrylic mixture. Table 8.5 shows several features which characterize modern structural acrylics. The adhesive contains both methyl methacrylate monomer as well as methacrylic acid. Although not specifically proven, it is suspected that the methacrylic acid acts to enhance the adhesion and the methyl methacrylate homopolymerizes and thus, reduces the yield stress of the material. This formulation should be compared with the early anaerobic adhesives in which most of the adhesive mix was made from crosslinking monomers such as ethylene glycol dimethacrylate. Some of the components of the anaerobics still are in this formula, e.g., the cumene hydroperoxide and the aniline derivative. This adhesive performed excellently with lap shear strength on aluminum in excess of 17.2 MPa (2500 psi) and T-peel values in excess of 6.1 kN/m (35 piw).

Investigation of the properties of this adhesive by Charnock and Martin [18] demonstrated that the cured adhesive had a phase separated character. In addition,

Table 8.5   Formula for a Toughened Acrylic Structural Adhesive [17]

Component	Amount	Function
Chlorosulphonated polyethylene	100 g	Toughening agent
Methyl methacrylate	85 g	Primary monomer
Glacial methacrylic acid	15 g	Adhesion enhancer
Ethylene glycol dimethacrylate	2 g	Crosslinking agent
Cumene hydroperoxide	6.06 g	Free radical polymerization initiator
N,N-dimethylaniline	2.02 g	Reducing agent

Table 8.6   Formulation of a Cyanoacrylate Adhesive [19]

Component	Amount (pph)	Function
Ethyl cyanoacrylate	91	Resin former
Poly(methyl methacrylate)	4	Thickener, flow control
Dimethyl sebacate	5	Flexibilizer
p-methoxyphenol	0.1	Free radical inhibitor
Sulfur dioxide	0.005	Anionic polymerization inhibitor

plots of shear performance versus elastomer content were similar to those shown in Fig. 8.16 in which a maximum is observed. The explanation for the maximum is the same as that described earlier.

A typical formulation for a cyanoacrylate adhesive is shown in Table 8.6. The methyl and ethyl cyanoacrylates are probably the most widely used monomers. Thickeners are typically higher molecular weight acrylates soluble in the cyanoacrylate monomer. Hydrophobic fumed silica can also be used to generate gels. The most important stabilizer for a cyanoacrylate is sulfur dioxide which stabilizes against anionic polymerization. The primary benefit from the use of cyanoacrylates adhesives is the rapidity of cure on a number of substrates. Adhesives based on unmodified cyanoacrylates have several drawbacks, one of which is sensitivity to substrate acidity. In general, this can be solved by using primers to make the substrate basic. Cyanoacrylates also have difficulty in bonding with porous or cellulosic substrates. This problem can be ameliorated by the addition of materials such as crown ethers [20]. Another major problem is the fact that the adhesive is still a thermoplastic after cure and is therefore, subject to creep at higher temperatures. This problem has been addressed by the addition of either crosslinking agents, heat resistance modifying monomers, or both. Crosslinking monomers such as bis-cyanoacrylates or alkenyl cyanoacrylates can be used to generate some amount of crosslinking in the adhesive.

As with all of the resin systems described, the cyanoacrylates suffer from brittleness. Modification of cyanoacrylates is less straightforward than that for the epoxies and acrylics because of their extreme reactivity. Thus, many of the materials which might normally be considered as toughening agents for acrylates do not work for cyanoacrylates since they initiate polymerization. Materials used for toughening cyanoacrylates include copolymers such as ABS (acrylonitrile-butadiene-styrene) rubber [21a], ethylene-methyl acrylate copolymers[21b], SBR grafted with styrene and methyl methacrylate [21c] as well as other copolymeric and grafted species. Many of the formulations are described as "milky and white", implying that the toughening agent forms a phase separate from the cyanoacrylate. In general, the concentration of the toughening agent was 15–20%, very close to that required for other systems such as the epoxides or normal acrylates. Plasticizers have also been used to impart some level of flexibility to the matrix. Materials such as aliphatic esters, aromatic phosphates, and phthalates as well as other materials have been used to flexibilize cyanoacrylates [22]. Typical properties for an unmodified cyano-acrylate structural adhesive with aluminum adherends in an ASTM D-1002 lap shear are in the range of 17.2 MPa (2500 psi). Peel performance is essentially nil as is impact resistance. Lap shears can be improved by 10–30% by rubber modification and peel resistance and impact resistance can be much improved by the same technique.

8.4.4   High Temperature Performance Structural Adhesives

Although the chemistry of high temperature performance structural adhesives is perhaps the most researched of the systems described, the use in industry of these materials has been relatively limited. Therefore only some of the salient features of the chemistry and the resultant properties of these materials are discussed.

Adhesives based upon polyimides has occupied much of the interest or research-ers and synthetic chemists in this area. Subrahmanian [23] has described the require-ments for a high temperature performance polymer as:

1. Only the strongest chemical bonds should exist in these polymers. Aromatic units are preferred; alkyl and alkylene units are to be avoided.
2. The structure is in its minimum energy state with no pathway for thermal rearrangement.
3. Resonance stabilization (highly aromatic) structures should be maximized.
4. The structure should have chemical bonds in their most stable configuration so that if bonds are broken thermally, they can easily re-form.
5. Ladder polymers (as described earlier) with multiple bonds in the backbone should be maximized so that single bond cleavage would not result in loss of molecular weight.

To these requirements, add the following:

6. The polymer should be processable at as low a temperature as possible.
7. The polymer should have a yield stress low enough so the polymer can itself absorb fracture energy or such that the polymer can be toughened.

The last two requirements are contrary to most of the first five and the technology necessary to balance them continues to be unavailable.

In polyimide-based structural adhesives, two major development paths have been followed. The first has been to generate anhydrides or diamines which impart some level of flexibility in the backbone while still maintaining oxidative stability. This has been accomplished to some degree with the use of monomers such as bis(3,4-dicarboxyphenyl ether dianhydride) or 1,3-bis(3,4-dicarboxyphenyl)hexa-fluoropropane dianhydride as well as 4,4'-diamino diphenyl ether. Much of the work to generate these materials has taken place at NASA and at the Air Force Materials Laboratories and their literature can be consulted for structure property relationships [24].

Problems associated with the use of polyimides have been volatiles generated during cure and the necessity to crosslink the adhesive to maintain solvent and creep resistance. Workers at NASA-Langley [25] have synthesized thermoplastic, crystallizable polyimides which are melt processable with no volatiles. When they crystallize, these materials have solvent and creep resistance in much the same manner as that obtained with polyether ether ketones (PEEK).

Other temperature resistant materials have been evaluated as high temperature adhesives including polyphenylquinoxaline which is the polymerization product of 3,3'-diaminobenzidine and p,p'-oxydibenzil. This material is of particular interest in that very high lap shear performance is obtained even at temperatures as high as 232°C. On chromic acid anodized titanium, the polyphenylquinoxalines gave room temperature lap shear strengths of more than 34.5 MPa (5000 psi) and 232°C lap shear strengths of 19.3 MPa (2800 psi). The remarkable thing about these materials as well as polyimides is that they retain a substantial portion of their lap shear strength at high temperature even after the bond is exposed to temperatures as high as 232°C for thousands of hours.

As with all of the previous structural adhesives, attempts have been made to toughen the high temperature performance structural adhesives with elastomers. Attempts were made to toughen a polyimide known as LARC-13 with various elastomers, including silicones, as well as the HYCAR-RLPs [26]. Even though a phase separated structure was obtained, very little increase in toughness was observed, undoubtedly due to the lack of ductility in the polyimide matrix. An attempt has been made to toughen bis-maleimides with HYCAR-RLPs. Toughness could be obtained but only after quantities of RLP were added that were large enough to result in poor modulus retention.

8.5   Summary

In this chapter, the types of structural adhesives currently in industrial use have been reviewed. The description of these adhesives has been in terms of their chemistry, their physical form before cure and their cured physical properties. In general terms, acrylic adhesives are the easiest to use but are hampered by either their thermoplastic character or odor. Phenolic adhesives provide durable bonds, but are difficult to use. Polyimide adhesives have the highest temperature resistance but are extremely difficult to use. Epoxy adhesives have the broadest range of chemistry and utility. All of the materials used as matrix resins are brittle and must be modified to obtain optimum structural character. The modification usually takes the form of an addition of elastomeric material. The mechanism of action of these elastomers requires that the matrix have the correct ductility to allow energy absorption to take place.

Bibliography

Hartshorn, S.R. (Ed.), *Structural Adhesives, Chemistry and Technology* (1986), Plenum Press, New York

Patrick, R.L. (Ed.) *Treatise on Adhesion and Adhesives*, vol. 2 (1969), Marcel Dekker, New York

Lee, H., and Neville, K., *Handbook of Epoxy Resins* (1967), McGraw-Hill, New York

May, C.A., *Epoxy Resins: Chemistry and Technology* (1988), Marcel Dekker, New York

Riew, C.K., and Kinloch, A.J. (Eds.), *Toughened Plastics I: Science and Engineering* (1993), American Chemical Society, Washington, DC

Riew, C.K. (Ed.), *Rubber Toughened Plastics, Advances in Chemistry Series 222* (1989), American Chemical Society, Washington, DC

I. Skeist (Ed.), *Handbook of Adhesives*, 2nd Ed. (1977), Van Nostrand Reinhold, New York

References

1. (a) Baekeland, L.H., *Ind. Eng. Chem.*,1 (1909), p. 3. (b) Baekeland, L.H., U.S. Patent 939,966 (1909). (c) Baekeland, L.H., U.S. Patent 942,852 (1909)
2. Gilham, J.K., in *Proc. Joint U.S.–Italy Symposium on Composite Materials*, J.C. Seferis (Ed.) (1983), Plenum Press, New York, pp 127–141
3. Estes, G.M., Cooper, S.L., and Tobolsky, A.V., *J. Macromol. Sci. Rev. Macromol. Chem.*, C4 (1970), p. 313
4. (a) DeBruyne, N.A., British Patent 577,823 (1946). (b) DeBruyne, N.A., U.S. Patent 2,499,134 (1950)
5. Bolger, J.C., in *Treatise on Adhesion and Adhesives*, vol. 3, R.L. Patrick (Ed.) (1973), Marcel Dekker, New York, p. 41
6. Pagel, W. C., U.S. Patent 3,894,113 (1975)
7. Laliberte, B.R., and Bornstein, J., *Govt. Rept. #AMMRC-TR-81-34, NTIS#AD-A104658*
8. (a) McGarry, F.J., and Willner, A.M., *ACS Div. Org. Coat. Plast. Chem. Preprints*, 28 (1968), p. 512. (b) Sultan, J.N., and McGarry, F.J., *Polym. Eng. Sci.*, 13 (1973), p. 29
9. Irwin, G.R., *Appl. Materials Res.*, 3 (1964), p. 65
10. Hunston, D.L., Kinloch, A.J., and Wang, S.S., *J. Adhesion*, 28 (1989), p. 103
11. (a) Bascom, W.D., Cottington, R.L., Jones, R.L., and Peyser, P., *J. Appl. Polym. Sci.*, 19 (1975), p. 2545. (b) Bascom, W.D., and Cottington, R.L., *J. Adhesion*, 7 (1976), p. 333. (c) Kinloch, A.J., and Shaw, S.J., *J. Adhesion*, 12 (1981), p. 50
12. (a) Kinloch, A.J., Shaw, S.J., Tod, D.A., and Hunston, D.L., *Polymer*, 24 (1983), p. 1341. (b) Kinloch, A.J., Shaw, S.J., and Hunston, D.L., *Polymer*, 24 (1983), p. 1355
13. Stamper, D.J., in *Synthetic Adhesives and Sealants*, Wake, W.C. (Ed.) (1986), John Wiley and Sons, Chichester, UK, Ch. 3
14. Paul, N.C., Richards, D.H., and Thompson, D., *Polymer*, 18 (1977), p. 945
15. Pocius, A.V., Schultz, W.J., Thompson, W.L., and Adam, R.E., *J. Adhesion*, 41 (1993), p. 189
16. Gorman, J.W., and Toback, A.S., U.S. Patent 3,415,988 (1970)
17. Briggs, P.C., and Muschiatti, L.C., U.S. Patent 3,890,407 (1975)
18. Charnock, R.S., and Martin, F.R., in *Adhesion and Adhesives, Science and Technology* (1980), Plastics and Rubber Institute, London, Ch. 16
19. Millet, G.H., *Adhesives Age*, 24 (1981), p. 27
20. Motegi, A., Isowa, E., and Kimura, K., U.S. Patent 4,171,416 (1979)
21. (a) Gleave, E.R., U.S. Patent 4,102,945 (1978). (b) O'Connor, J.T., U.S. Patent 4,440,910 (1984). (c) Kato, K., Sasaki, T., and Narizawa, H., Japanese Patent Showa 47-51807 (1972)
22. Shantha, K.L., Thennarasu, S., and Krishnamurti, N., *J. Adhesion Sci. Technol.*, 3 (1989), p. 237
23. Subrahamanian, K.P., in *Structural Adhesives, Chemistry and Technology*, S.R. Hartshorn (Ed.) (1986), Plenum Press, New York, Ch. 7

24. (a) Hill, S.G., Peters, P.D., and Hendricks, C.L., NASA Contractor Report 165944 (July, 1982). (b) Hanky, A.O., and St. Clair, T.L., *Int. J. Adh. and Adhesives*, 3 (1983), p. 181. (c) Progar, D. J., and St. Clair, T.L., in *The Science of Adhesive Bonding*, L.H. Sharpe and S.E. Wentworth (Eds.) (1990), Gordon and Breach, UK, pp. 287–300. (d) Shaw, S.J., *Materials Sci. Technol.*, 3 (1987), p. 589. (e) Fowler, J.R., *Materials and Design*, 3 (1982), p. 602. (f) Hergenrother, P.M., *Chemtech.* (August, 1984), pp. 496–502. (g) St. Clair, A.K., and St. Clair, T.L., in *Proc. 1st Technical Conference on Polyimides*, K.L. Mittal (Ed.) (1984), Plenum Press, New York

25. St. Clair, A.K., and St. Clair, T.L., NASA Technical Memorandum 84516 (June, 1982)

26 (a) St. Clair, A.K., and St. Clair, T.L., in *Proc. National SAMPE Tech. Conf.*, 12 (1980), SAMPE, Azusa, CA, p. 729. (b) St. Clair, A.K., and St. Clair, T.L., U.S. Patent 4,497,935 (1985)

9 The Chemistry and Physical Properties of Elastomer-Based Adhesives

9.1 Introduction

Of the classes of adhesives, elastomer-based adhesives are probably the most familiar to the consumer. Many of the baby boom generation remember solvent-thinned, rubber-based paper adhesives used for elementary school projects. Many of the pieces of furniture we have in our homes and offices are laminated wood. The adhesive used for lamination is most often based on an elastomer. Probably the most widely recognized elastomer-based adhesive is coated on a backing and used as a pressure sensitive adhesive tape. In this chapter, the chemistry and physical properties of pressure-sensitive adhesives as well as other types of elastomer-based adhesives is discussed. The physical properties of pressure-sensitive adhesives is emphasized as these demonstrate many of the concepts discussed in this book. Other elastomer-based adhesives are discussed in terms of their chemistry, because fundamental information on these materials is limited.

The objectives of this chapter include the development of an understanding of the chemistry of elastomer-based adhesives. Knowledge of the parameters necessary to formulate this type of adhesive and an appreciation of the test methods evaluating pressure-sensitive adhesives should be gained. Most important is the discussion on how the dynamic mechanical properties of pressure-sensitive adhesives are related to their mechanism of action.

9.2 Pressure-Sensitive Adhesives

The Pressure-Sensitive Tape Council [1] has defined pressure-sensitive adhesives as materials with the following properties:

1. Aggressive and permanent tack
2. Adheres with no more than finger pressure
3. Requires no activation by any energy source
4. Has sufficient ability to hold onto the adherend
5. Has enough cohesive strength to be able to be removed cleanly from the adherend

The above definition of a pressure-sensitive adhesive (PSA) includes some concepts yet to be discussed but that are extremely important for this class of materials. The property we first notice about PSAs is their *tack*. We know what tack feels like but how do we describe it and, for that matter, how do we generate materials with tack? Tack is generated by adding certain low molecular weight materials to elastomers in a process called *tackification*. These *tackifiers*, because of their low molecular weight, decrease the cohesive strength of the elastomer. However, a PSA must have tack *and* sufficient cohesive strength to hold two things together. In this section, we see how a balance of properties is generated so that a PSA combines these seemingly mutually exclusive properties to yield a material with "sufficient ability to hold onto the adherend" as well as "be cleanly removed from the adherend."

For the most part, PSAs are used in coated form as the adhesives in pressure-sensitive adhesive tapes (PSATs). There is substantial technology associated with the manufacture of pressure-sensitive tapes but much of the information regarding PSATs is proprietary to those companies which manufacture them. The information about manufacturing does not yield more understanding as to how these materials perform and therefore, it is not discussed in this book.

9.2.1   Chemistry of the Base Resins Used in PSAs

A large variety of elastomers have been used as PSAs. The first material to gain widespread use was a natural rubber-based adhesive. Natural rubber is poly(*cis*-isoprene) and is obtained from the *Hevea* rubber plant as a natural latex. The structure of poly(*cis*-isoprene) is shown in Fig. 9.1. The latex is coagulated and then the rubber is usually smoked to eliminate bacteria and fungi which can degrade the rubber before it can be processed. The PSA manufacturer receives the natural rubber as a slab of smoked material which is often worked mechanically to reduce its molecular weight. The mechanically worked rubber is then dissolved in an appropriate solvent, mixed with the tackifier and coated or otherwise packaged. Natural rubber-based PSAs are still used in a number of PSAT applications including masking tape where they exhibit excellent removability after painting and baking. One of the primary attributes of natural rubber-based PSAs is their low cost, but they also are used extensively because of their high peel strength when properly formulated. The properties of natural rubber-based PSA lead to most of the discussion on PSA performance, which follows in a later section.

Natural rubber-based PSAs were the basis for all of the early PSA products. However, these adhesives had one primary flaw. Because of unsaturation in the backbone of the base polymer, the adhesive had a noticeable tendency to yellow and to crosslink, thus becoming brittle. The problem could in some ways be ameliorated by the addition of antioxidants, but, in general, natural rubber-based PSAs were unstable to long term exposure to the environment. This problem led to the introduction of a number of new base resins which did not suffer from these deficiencies.

A group of base elastomers to do this were the acrylates. The two primary acrylates used in PSAs are 2-ethylhexyl acrylate and iso-octyl acrylate. High polymers of these two monomers can be generated by standard free radical polymerization in solution. In a later section, it is shown that the molecular weight of the polymer plays a substantial role in the performance of the PSA. Polymers based on these monomers do not necessarily perform well as PSAs on their own. Early in the 1950s, researchers found that the performance of poly-2-ethylhexyl acrylate and polyiso-octyl acrylate could be substantially improved by adding certain amounts of acrylic acid [2]. A substantial patent literature has developed regarding PSA performance as a function of the type of polar monomer polymerized with the non-polar, long chain acrylate. The performance of an acrylic PSA is fine tuned by a selection of various monomers at specific ratios. Example structures of acrylic polymers used in PSAs are shown in Fig. 9.1.

Acrylic adhesives are usually not tackified to make them into PSAs. Their pressure-sensitive character results from the inherent physical properties of the polymer. The performance of acrylate PSAs can be improved by crosslinking the base polymer. Acrylic-based PSAs are used in a wide variety of applications from transparent tape to medical tapes. In comparison to natural rubber-based PSAs, acrylates are more expensive, but they have excellent weathering characteristics.

Both natural rubber and acrylate-based PSAs need to be crosslinked to obtain the cohesive strength necessary to meet all of the requirements of a PSA. Another group of base resins for PSAs, the block copolymer-based elastomers meet these requirements through phase separation. Thus, A-B-A block copolymers of isoprene with styrene or butadiene with styrene yield a phase separated structure in which the polystyrene segment phases out from the polyisoprene or polybutadiene. Examples of these polymer structures are listed in Fig. 9.1. The phase-separated styrene blocks reinforce the PSA by acting as a physical crosslink rather than a chemical one. Block copolymer-based PSAs are used in a wide variety of applications but most commonly in packaging tapes. Tackification is necessary for block copolymers to attain PSA-like character. They are less expensive than acrylates but, because of the unsaturation in the "B" blocks, these elastomers suffer from oxidative instability in much the same way as natural rubber-based adhesives. In addition, due to the styrene content, these elastomers tend to be on the high modulus side of PSA base elastomers and thus are more difficult to formulate into general purpose PSAs.

The above three types of base elastomers form the majority of PSAs. There are several other types which fill in smaller, but also important, niches in the PSAT market, such as the important silicone-based PSA. Silicones have not yet been discussed in this book. The primary base polymer of silicone PSAs is polydimethylsiloxane which can also have some content of diphenyl siloxane units, as shown in Fig. 9.1. In general, the addition of phenyl groups increases the peel performance of silicone-based PSAs. These polymers are unique materials in that they have a great degree of chemical resistance. They have a very low glass transition temperature and very flat dynamic mechanical properties over a wide range of temperatures plus high temperature performance. Silicones have an inorganic backbone, but are sheathed in organic groups. The low surface energy of silicones (about $21 \, \text{mJ/m}^2$) allows them to

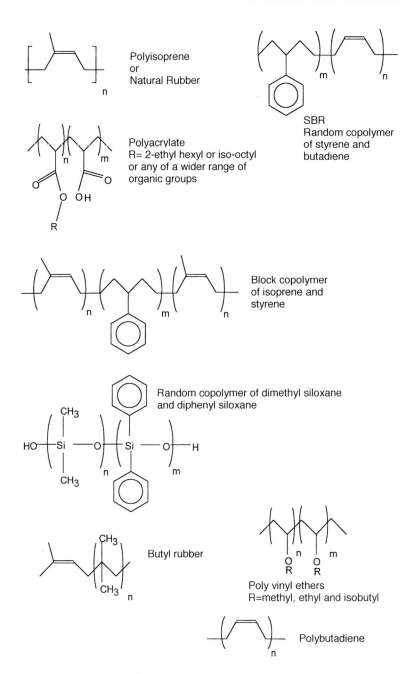

Figure 9.1   Chemistry of base resins for pressure sensitive adhesives

wet a wide range of surfaces and they can even be used as a PSA for Teflon. Silicone elastomers must be tackified as well as crosslinked to get PSA performance. Of the base elastomers used in PSAs, silicones are by far the most expensive, but the advantages in terms of high and low temperature performance as well as their hypoallergenic character can often outweigh the extra cost.

Poly iso-butylene, polyvinyl ethers and polybutadiene can also be made into PSAs. The structures of these three polymers are also shown in Fig. 9.1. In comparison to the other classes of PSA base elastomers, these three form the smaller portion of the market. Polyvinyl ethers were once thought to provide performance equivalent to that of the polyacrylates. However, the polyvinyl ethers had a feel of "dry tack" which did not provide the "thumb appeal" which the acrylates exhibited. Polyvinyl ethers are usually not modified with tackifiers, but rather are blends of high and low molecular weight polymers. Poly iso-butylenes are unique polymers in terms of their resistance to oil as well as their low moisture permeability. Because of its saturated chemical character, these polymers are weatherable. Similarly, they are difficult to crosslink and thus exhibit poor shear characteristics. Poly iso-butylenes are tackified to achieve performance. Polybutadiene can be made into a PSA and it is eminently crosslinkable. Combined with its low glass transition temperature and good electrical properties, this material has found use in electrical tapes.

9.2.2   Chemistry of Tackifiers

Tackifiers are a unique class of materials. They normally have low molecular weights and are resinous, but yet they have glass transition and softening temperatures often much above room temperature. It is this combination which makes these materials useful in the formulation of PSAs. Tackifying resins are usually based on natural products or petroleum streams. In the following discussion, these materials are classified according to the materials from which they are synthesized.

9.2.2.1   Natural Product Based Tackifiers

The class of materials based upon rosin acid derivatives are the oldest known tackifiers. The structures of abietic acid and pimaric acid, which are components of rosin, are shown in Fig. 9.2. Abietic acid itself can be used as a tackifier, but most often the material is chemically modified in some way. The unsaturation of abietic acid can be expected to lead to oxidation and discoloration. Hydrogenation of those double bonds can eliminate that problem. Rosin acid is also used in esterified form. Typically abietic acid is esterified with glycerol or pentaerythritol to generate higher softening point materials. Rosin acids are obtained as wood by-products such as gum rosin, wood rosin, and tall oil. Rosin acid and their esters are most often used in the formulation of natural rubber-based PSAs.

Another natural product based tackifier is that based on α- or β-pinene whose structures are also shown in Fig. 9.2. This class of materials is known as the

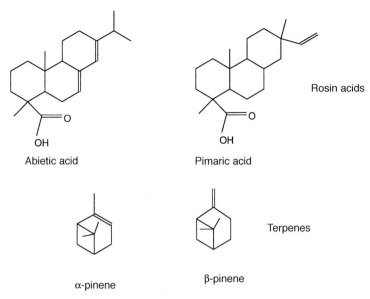

Figure 9.2   Chemistry of rosin- and terpene-based tackifiers

"terpenes." α- or β-pinene is usually used in the polymerized state. The polymerization is done cationically by aluminum chloride catalysis. The softening point of this resin strongly depends upon its molecular weight and is remarkably high for a low molecular weight material. For example, at a molecular weight of about 1200, the softening point can be about 120°C. Terpenes are obtained from citrus peels or wood by-products.

9.2.2.2   Petroleum Based Tackifiers

Since petroleum is a natural product, it is difficult to classify the next set of resins as being "synthetic." This class of tackifiers is differentiated from those described above in that they are obtained from petroleum cracking products and not directly from flora. Petroleum-based tackifiers are also not used as obtained from the petroleum stream. They are polymerized to raise their softening points to the level that they become useful in PSAs. The same process used to polymerize β-pinene resins is used for petroleum-based tackifiers. These tackifiers are broadly classed into two types, the aromatic and aliphatic resins. The aromatic resins are further classified into coumarone-indene resins, aromatic petroleum resins, and heat reactive resins. The aliphatic resins are also known as "C-5" resins since much of their chemistry revolves around polymerized pentene and cyclopentene.

The structures of the compounds used in coumarone-indene aromatic resins are shown in Fig. 9.3 as are those used in the aromatic petroleum resins and the heat reactive resins. Cationic polymerization of combinations of these compounds leads to a large class of materials. The coumarone-indene resins and the aromatic resins

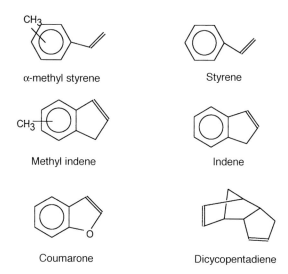

Figure 9.3   Chemistry of petroleum-based aromatic tackifiers

are often used with natural rubber-based adhesives. Care must be taken in the formulation of block copolymer-based PSAs to insure that the tackifier does not dissolve in the polystyrene phase. The cohesive properties of block copolymer-based adhesives depend upon the phase separation and glassy nature of the polystyrene phase. If the polystyrene phase is not glassy, the effect of the phase separated particle is diminished. The aromatic resins discussed here are most likely not useful in block copolymer-based adhesives, since their solubility properties are similar to the polystyrene phase and would thus plasticize that phase. The C-5 resins, which are more compatible with the polyisoprene phase are more likely be used in block copolymer-based PSAs.

The chemical structures of the monomers used in the generation of C-5 aliphatic resins are shown in Fig. 9.4. Once again, these materials are copolymerized in various ratios using aluminum chloride catalyzed cationic polymerization. The aliphatic resins have no tendency to yellow as would the aromatic materials discussed earlier. These resins are used in natural rubber-based PSAs as well as the block copolymer-based PSAs. Even though the classifications described above have been made, aliphatic-aromatic resins and C5–C9 resins can be made by taking materials from the two streams and copolymerizing them. Table 9.1 provides a listing of a number of tackifying resins, their classification, molecular weights, and softening temperatures.

9.2.2.3   Other Tackifiers

There are two more classes of tackifiers to be discussed in this section. One of these tackifiers is used specifically in silicone-based PSAs and is known as MQ resin. A proposed structure is shown in Fig. 9.5. The material is generated from a hydrolyzed

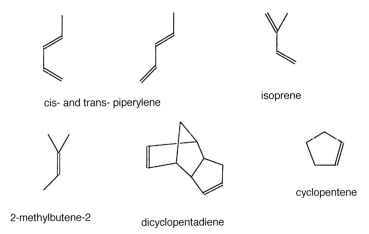

cis- and trans- piperylene

isoprene

2-methylbutene-2

dicyclopentadiene

cyclopentene

Figure 9.4   Chemistry of petroleum-based C-5 tackifiers

quadrafunctional silane matrix (the "Q") which is subsequently capped with tri-methyl silane (the "M"). The result is a material which still has functionality and is reactive with the silicone gum (the hydroxyl terminated polydimethyl siloxane-co-diphenyl siloxane) through condensation. The MQ resin is highly polar and provides an increase in cohesive strength as well as tack.

The other tackifier is tertiary butyl phenolic resin. The structure of this resin is also shown in Fig. 9.5. This tackifier is not usually used in PSAs but is used in other rubber-based adhesives which are discussed later in this chapter. This tackifier increases the heat resistance of certain rubber-based adhesives.

Table 9.1   Incomplete Listing of Commercially Available Tackifying Resins and Illustrative Properties

Commercial resin	Type	Glass Transition Temperature (°C)	Softening Temperature (°C)
Piccolyte HM-85 (Hercules)	Styrenated terpene	35	85
Nirez K-105 (Reichhold)	Polyterpene	54	105
Regalrez 1094 (Hercules)	Hydrogenated Aromatic	37	94
Piccovar AP-25 (Hercules)	Aromatic	−50	25
Wingtack 10 (Goodyear)	C-5	−28	10
Escorez 1310 (Exxon)	C-5	40	94
Foral 85 (Hercules)	Glycerine Rosin Ester	40	85
Foral 105 (Hercules)	Hydrogenated Pentaerythritol Rosin Ester	57	105
Zonarez A-100 (Arizona)	Terpene	55	106
Escorez 2101 (Exxon)	Mixed Aliphatic/Aromatic	36	92

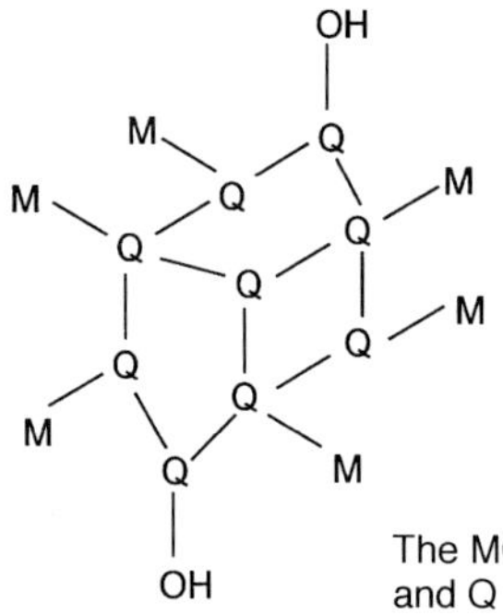

The MQ resin structure, where M is monofunctional trimethylsilane and Q is hydrolyzed quadrafunctional silane

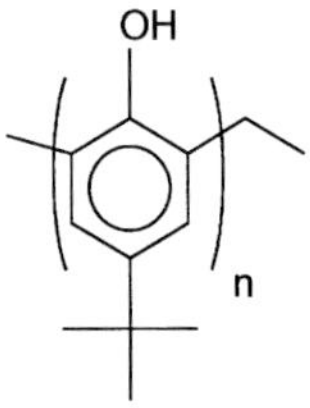

Tertiary butyl phenolic resin

Figure 9.5   Chemistry of the MQ resin and the t-butyl phenolic resin

9.2.3   Testing of Pressure-Sensitive Adhesives

It is necessary to discuss mechanical tests for PSAs before we discuss the relationship among chemistry, mechanical properties, and performance. In Section 9.2.4, use is made of the knowledge gained from previous chapters in understanding PSA performance. Many of the test methods and specifications for PSAs are provided by the ASTM, but the Pressure-sensitive Tape Council (PSTC) also publishes test methods and specifications for these products.

9.2.3.1   Measurements of Tack

One of the primary features of PSAs in contrast to other adhesives is their ability to bond with little applied pressure. Known as "tack", this capability if defined by the PSTC as "the condition of the adhesive when it feels sticky or highly adhesive. Sometimes used to express the idea of pressure sensitivity." [3] The ASTM provides another definition: "the property of an adhesive that enables it to form a bond of measurable strength immediately after the adherend and adhesive are brought into contact under low pressure." This definition includes some important features of tack, including "measurable bond strength" and "low pressure." A simple definition is that an adhesive is said to display "tack" when the application of light finger pressure enables one to deflect or lift the backing on which the adhesive is coated.

The next section shows that tack is a viscoelastic property of the adhesive. Therefore, the rate and temperature of the test must be controlled variables in tack testing. In particular, it is important that all PSA tests are done under conditions of controlled temperature and humidity and that the test samples are conditioned at the test temperature for a minimum of 24 hours prior to the test.

A number of methods can be used to measure tack. The PSTC describes two methods for tack measurement [1], "quick stick" (PSTC-5) and the rolling ball tack test (PSTC-6). The quick stick method involves the application of tape under no load conditions. The tape specimen is held taut over a pre-cleaned substrate and then allowed to drape smoothly over the substrate with no applied load. The adhered tape is then loaded into a tensile testing machine and tested using the 90° peel fixture described shortly. The tape is removed at a crosshead speed of 30.5 cm/min (12″/min) and the force to remove the tape is recorded. The recorded force is the "quick stick" value. This test, although functionally measuring the level of tack, does not provide the information necessary to understand tack, since the pressure and the rate of application of the tape are not controlled. The backing stiffness also has a marked effect, since stiffer backings do not allow easy intimate contact of the adhesive to a surface.

In the rolling ball tack test (PSTC-6) a ramp is constructed having a specified angle of 21°30′ with respect to the horizontal. The ramp is grooved so that a steel ball having a diameter of 1.11 cm (7/16″) rolls on the edges of the groove. The top of the ramp is 6.51 cm (2.562″) from the bottom. A piece of tape is placed at the bottom of the ramp and held there securely. The ball is placed on a catch mechanism which releases the ball at the desired time. The tack is recorded as the distance the ball travels down the length of tape. High tack tapes stop the ball as it comes off the ramp while low tack tapes stop the ball at longer distances of travel. This test, although functionally testing tack, also does not provide the level of control needed to understand tack, since the rate of application of force varies somewhat as the ball travels the length of the tape. This test does eliminate the backing as a variable, however. ASTM D3121 also describes a related tack test [3].

A tack test not published by either of these standards agencies is the loop tack test. In this test, a loop of PSA tape is attached to the jaws of a tensile testing machine. The loop is brought into contact with the pre-cleaned substrate by lowering the loop at a specified rate so that it touches a certain area of the panel. The tensile testing machine is then reversed and the force to remove the tape is recorded. The virtue of this test is that the rate of contact and withdrawal are controlled. However, the backing stiffness once again has a dramatic effect on the wetting contact of the adhesive with the substrate.

The test which best controls all parameters having an effect on tack is known as the probe tack test, described in ASTM D2979. A schematic of the test apparatus is shown in Fig. 9.6. In this apparatus, the effect of the tape backing is eliminated because the tape is either rigidly affixed to a steel plate or mounted on an annular ring of known weight. The probe is usually made of stainless steel which must be cleaned before the test. Any surface roughness at the tip of the probe should be known as well as its cross sectional area. Usually, the tip is highly polished. The key features of the probe tack apparatus are the controlled rate of approach as well as

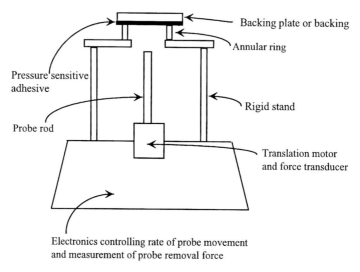

Figure 9.6   Diagram of probe pack tester. This test is described in ASTM D2979

the rate of detachment. The results of probe tack are reported as force per area of probe tip at a specific rate of attachment and detachment and at a specified temperature. Once again, since PSA performance is determined by viscoelasticity, these parameters must be scrupulously controlled to obtain meaningful data.

9.2.3.2   Measurement of Peel

Before peel tests are discussed, it is necessary to look at "roll down", a testing parameter important for PSAs when determining peel or shear. Since the performance of a PSA depends highly upon the degree of contact under the application of a light pressure, the parameters surrounding the application of the tape are exceedingly important. It is important to have a "roll down" methodology used before the testing of tape. The roll down methodology usually requires the tape to be laid down on a substrate with little or no applied pressure (such as that described above for the quick stick test). A roller of known weight and dimensions is rolled over the tape at a specified rate and number of times up and down the tape. The roll down conditions control the degree the PSA "wets out" the substrate.

Peel, in addition to tack, is one of the parameters by which PSA performance is easily recognized. We have all removed a box sealing tape from a package and either exclaimed or complained about how hard it was to remove. In general, that removal was accomplished by peeling back the tape. Peel is tested most commonly by the 180° and 90° peel tests. The first peel test is easier to describe and is shown schematically in Fig. 9.7.

The PSA tape is applied and rolled down onto the stiff, usually stainless steel or glass adherend. The tape is then folded back over itself, forming a long tab. The top of the stiff adherend is clamped into a tensile testing machine, as is the end of the

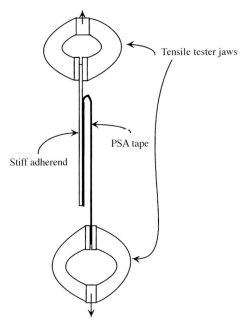

Figure 9.7   Diagram of a 180° peel test, showing the specimen configuration in the jaws of the tensile testing machine

long tab. The 180° is formed by the tape backing against tape backing. The angle of peel is not truly 180°, since the backing interferes with the actual attainment of a 180° angle. The actual angle depends upon the backing stiffness and the backing thickness. The measurement is usually conducted at a constant crosshead speed and at a few temperatures although better data is obtained if the experiment is carried out at several temperatures and as many rates of peel as possible.

The 90° peel experiment is slightly more complicated than the 180° peel measurement. The key difference between the two is how the peel angle is kept constant. Figure 9.8 provides a schematic of an apparatus for measuring 90° peel.

The adherend in the 90° peel test is cleaned and the adhesive is properly rolled down on it. The adherend is then clamped firmly into a trolley. The entire trolley mechanism is clamped into the bottom clamp of a tensile testing machine. The trolley is designed as to roll freely in the direction perpendicular to the movement of the jaws of the tensile testing machine. The trolley is connected through a pulley and rod to the upper, moving jaw of the tensile testing machine. The pulley arrangement is set so that an upward movement of the upper clamp provides a corresponding lateral movement of the trolley. In this way, the peel angle is kept at 90°.

9.2.3.3   Measurement of Shear

In Chapter 3, various measurements of the shear strength of adhesive bonds were discussed. If the shear strength of a PSA were measured using methods described in

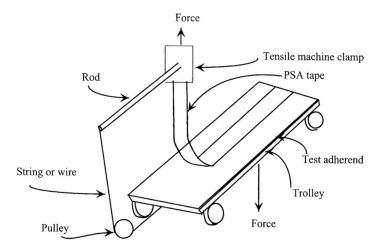

Figure 9.8   Diagram of a test fixture for 90° peel of a PSAT. Note that the test adherend is attached to a moveable trolley which traverses horizontally, while the tensile testing machine clamp moves vertically

Chapter 3, a low value, on the order of only a few psi would be obtained. In general, PSAs are not judged by their shear strength. Rather, PSAs are expected to sustain a low load for the time period of use. Thus, if masking tape is used, one would expect the tape would hold its own backing or perhaps a backing and some covering material on that substrate for the time period of the paint job. If the application were to hold a picture up on a wall, the tape would be expected to hold a few psi load for an indefinite period of time. So, the factor of interest is not shear strength, but rather the resistance of the material to a constant small shear stress for a period of time. The PSA industry has applied the term "shear holding power" to this PSAT performance parameter. This term is definitely a misnomer since there is no aspect of power (as defined in physics) in the test. Rather the test is a constant load creep test. Nonetheless, the term is pervasive in the industry and it is used interchangeably with "constant load creep test" in this book. A schematic of the shear holding power test is shown in Fig. 9.9.

The rigid adherend is appropriately prepared. The adhesive tape is applied to the edge of the specimen as shown in Fig. 9.9. The adhesive is rolled down and excess is removed to provide a known and specified area of contact. The other end of the tape is looped around a rod attached to a hook to which a weight can be added. The rigid adherend is placed in a fixture and held firmly during the measurement. It is very important that the temperature and humidity be carefully controlled. The elapsed time between the attachment of the weight and the point when it drops is recorded. The measurement can, of course, be mechanized so that a timer is switched off when the weight falls. Thus "shear holding power" is recorded as the time to failure at a specified load. Typical loads are 0.5 to 1 kg.

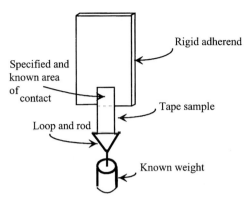

Figure 9.9   Diagram of a "shear holding power" test of a PSAT. The important test parameters are the applied weight, the contact area, and the conditions of the test (temperature and humidity)

9.2.4   Balance of Properties

The properties of a pressure-sensitive tape seem to be at odds with one another. The tapes are expected to wet quickly, have enough resistance to peel, and also have shear holding power. Attainment of this balance of performance is the main objective of the formulator. For PSA tapes, formulation tools are the rubber to resin ratio and the degree of crosslinking placed in the system. Figure 9.10 shows the usual balance of performance obtained for a single elastomer and a tackifier resin when the ratio of the rubber to the resin is varied.

As the resin to rubber ratio increases, the shear strength usually goes through a shallow maximum (this assumes that the crosslinking is constant for the formulations in this figure). The peel strength usually rises as the resin to rubber ratio increases while the tack goes through a maximum. It is the job of the PSA formulator to maximize all three of these performance parameters to meet the specifications of the customer. The following sections describe the physico-chemical phenomena controlling the performance parameters shown in Fig. 9.10.

9.2.5   PSA Performance Viewed as a Timescale in Viscoelastic Response

When a pressure-sensitive tape is applied to a substrate, the adhesive is expected to spontaneously spread on the surface with little or no applied pressure. That is, the PSA is expected to act as a liquid. However, when the adhesive is peeled or a weight is hung from it, we expect the adhesive to resist the force. That is, it should act as a solid. This contradictory behavior is available from viscoelastic materials. Consider the timescale of the two processes discussed above. A PSA tape is not applied to a substrate rapidly. In fact, the tape is often allowed to sit on the substrate for a while after application. Thus, the timescale of application is long, usually on the order of a

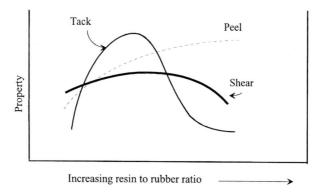

Figure 9.10   Diagram of the relationship of performance properties to the rubber-to-resin ratio in a natural rubber-based PSA. Note that the highest value of each performance property is not obtained at the same rubber-to-resin ratio. Optimum performance of a PSAT is obtained with the best balance of properties which meet the customer's expectations (redrawn from Satas)

second or more. When a PSA is removed, the timescale is much shorter. Typical peel measurements are usually done on the order of inches per minute which, when looked at from the point of view of the adhesive, is on the order of tenths of a second. Therefore, a PSA is expected to behave as a liquid for timescales of seconds or longer and to behave as a solid for timescales of tenths of seconds or less. At any particular temperature, these are properties which a viscoelastic material can achieve. The formulation of PSAs is the attainment of viscoelastic properties which allow wetting (liquid-like properties) at long timescales and peel (solid-like properties) at short timescales at the temperature of use.

9.2.6   PSA Viscoelasticity and Tack

Tack is the instantaneous wetting of a substrate under little or no applied pressure to rapidly develop a measurable strength. Since tack requires the adhesive to act as a liquid, it might be expected that if the adhesive becomes too stiff (too high a modulus), then the adhesive does not display tack. This phenomenon was studied in detail for rubber-resin adhesives. It is that work which forms the basis for this discussion.

The variation of probe tack with temperature is one key to understanding which property of materials leads to the phenomenon of tack. The discussion above indicates that the timescale of the probe tack test is important. Figure 9.11 represents the measurement of probe tack as a function of temperature when the measurement is taken at a withdrawal rate of a few centimeters per second and a contact time on the order of a second.

There are several important features in Fig. 9.11. First, probe tack goes rapidly to zero as the temperature falls even slightly below room temperature. Second, tack

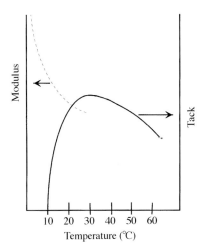

Figure 9.11 Plot of the tack and modulus measured at a rate of 1 Hz for a rubber-resin adhesive. Note that the tack reaches a maximum when the modulus drops below a certain level. The modulus value which corresponds to the onset of a high tack is known as the Dahlquist criterion

is maximized near room temperature (this is done by formulation). Third, tack falls slowly as the temperature is increased.

Examine the modulus (dashed line) of the adhesive as a function of temperature using a rate of application of stress similar to the rate of the probe tack experiment in Fig. 9.11. The modulus of this rubber resin adhesive decreases rather dramatically as a function of temperature. In fact, as the temperature nears room temperature (the point at which the probe tack increases to a maximum), the modulus decreases to less than 3×10^6 dynes/cm^2. (Figure 9.11, which is only for demonstration, does not have units other than temperature.) In fact, it is found that the room temperature modulus of any tacky adhesive is less than 3×10^6 dynes/cm^2 when measured at a frequency of about 1 Hz. This finding is a criterion for tack and has been given the name "Dahlquist criterion for tack" after the scientist who studied this phenomenon [4].

Figure 9.10 showed that the way in which tack is obtained in a PSA is through the addition of a tackifying resin to an elastomer. As the resin concentration in the elastomer is increased, various practical adhesion properties change. Figure 9.12 shows a schematic of the modulus of a natural rubber/resin PSA as a function of the frequency of measurement and of the resin content.The dotted line shows the variation in modulus with frequency. The modulus curve is flat and is also above the Dahlquist criterion. As tackifier is added, the modulus decreases and at the frequencies in the graph, the second curve goes below the Dahlquist tack criterion. If the peel resistance of this PSA were measured, it would be relatively low. If we increase to another level of tackifier, we would find that now the modulus at low frequency was much below the tack criterion and the modulus at high frequency was now increased measurably. If the peel strength of this PSA is measured, it would be

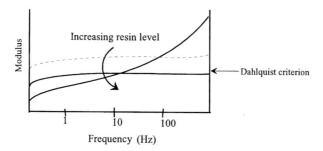

Figure 9.12   Plot of modulus of a pressure sensitive formulation as a function of frequency at three different resin levels in the adhesive

found that it had now increased to a substantial value. Understanding this phenomenon is key to understanding the tack and peel performance.

Another way of examining this phenomenon is to plot of the shear modulus of a PSA base elastomer as a function of temperature measured at about 1 Hz as well as that of the tackified base elastomer, as shown in Fig. 9.13. This type of data is similar to the dynamic mechanical data presented in Chapter 5. The base elastomer is shown as the dashed line. The glass transition temperature, when measured at 1 Hz is somewhat below room temperature. The dynamic mechanical determination of the shear storage modulus of the tackified adhesive is shown as the solid line in Fig. 9.13. The very interesting effect of having the tackifier act as an anti-plasticizer, that is, increasing the T_g of the tackified adhesive is seen. Above the T_g, however, the plateau modulus is decreased. It is indicated that the storage modulus has decreased below that required by the Dahlquist criterion.

The time–temperature superposition principle states that the effects of time and temperature on a viscoelastic material are inversely related. Therefore, when the same physical properties as shown in Fig. 9.13 are measured at a higher frequency, one might expect to obtain the plot shown in Fig. 9.14. When measured at 100 Hz, it is

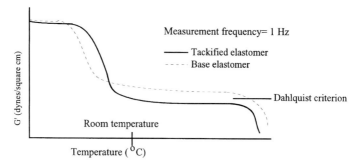

Figure 9.13   Dynamic mechanical spectrum of a PSA-based elastomer in the tackified and non-tackified state. The measurement is done at a single frequency but as a function of temperature. Note that the tackified elastomer has a plateau modulus below that of the Dahlquist criterion

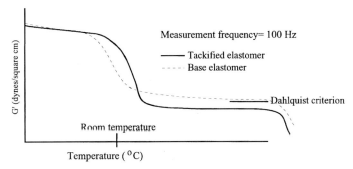

Figure 9.14 Plot of the shear modulus of a PSA elastomer with and without tackification measured as a function of temperature but at a frequency of 100 Hz. Note that the curves have shifted towards higher temperatures as the frequency was increased

seen that the entire dynamic mechanical spectrum of the shear storage modulus of the adhesive has shifted to higher temperatures. The T_g of the tackified adhesive is now above room temperature. This adhesive would be expected to exhibit greater stiffness and thus provide some physical strength when the tape is tested.

The above discussion implies that the resin must be completely miscible with the base elastomer. Indeed, if the resin were not soluble, one would not expect a change in the physical properties of the base elastomer. Instead, two glass transition temperatures, with no change in the T_g of the base elastomer, would be expected. In systems where two materials of substantially differing T_gs are mixed and these materials are soluble in one another, the overall glass transition temperature of the solid solution can often be predicted by the Fox equation [5]:

$$\frac{1}{T_g} = \sum_i \phi_i \frac{1}{T_{g,i}}$$

where the ϕ_i is the weight fraction of the ith soluble component in the mixture and $T_{g,i}$ is the glass transition temperature of the ith soluble component. The Fox equation can often be used to predict the T_g of elastomer/resin solid solutions and in fact, can show that components are not soluble in one another.

If the elastomer and the tackifier are not soluble in one another, what sort of physical situation might be expected? In the case of normal polymer solutions, several results could occur. One possibility is gross separation of the two phases, particularly when the interfacial tension between the components is large. When the incompatibility and the interfacial tension are not that large, microscopic phase separation occurs similar to that discussed in Chapter 8 on toughening epoxy resins. In this situation two T_gs are exhibited. In a particularly sinister situation, the resin could phase separate into microscopic phases, and by surface tension effects, phase separate into a solid layer at the surface of the PSA. Since the resin is glassy, it would not exhibit tack and the PSA would not perform as expected. Therefore, care must be taken to choose tackifiers that are completely soluble in the elastomer to be tackified.

Tack depends upon more than the resin to rubber ratio and the rate of the tack test, however. Tack also depends upon the probe material (or the material to which the tape is adhered). The general dependence of tack on the constitution of the substrate is almost exactly what would be expected if the guidelines for good adhesion presented in Chapter 6 were followed. That is, for any particular PSA, the tack level increases with increasing critical wetting tension of the solid surface. The tack force usually plateaus when the critical wetting tension of the substrate exceeds that of the adhesive. So, in the regime of low rates that is associated with the attachment of PSAs, the liquid-like nature of PSAs exhibit the same wetting behavior as liquids of equivalent surface energy.

9.2.7   PSA Peel and Viscoelasticity

Figure 9.10 indicates that peel performance normally improves as resin concentration increases, primarily because the increase in tackifier increases the stiffness of the PSA at higher rates. The more tackifier, the stiffer the PSA. Obviously, a point is reached when the adhesive is too stiff and PSA character disappears. PSA viscoelasticity also plays a role in PSA performance when it is tested at various rates of peel and temperature. In fact, a master curve much like the ones we described in Chapter 5 can be constructed for PSA peel on any given substrate. An example of such a master curve is shown in Fig. 9.15.

The curve in Fig. 9.15 is similar to one published by Kaelble [6] for the peel adhesion of a PSA to polystyrene. The data is presented in a manner analogous to the WLF concepts discussed in Chapter 5 and Chapter 6. The peel force, F, becomes a reduced variable when it is multiplied by the ratio of the measurement temperature, T, and a reference temperature T_0. The peel rate is reduced by a shift factor

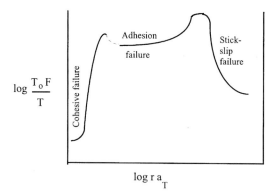

Figure 9.15   Reduced peel force as a function of reduced peel rate for a rubber-resin PSA drawn according to the data of Kaelble [6]. Note that not only is there a substantial dependence of peel force on peel rate but the mode of failure changes as a function of peel rate

that was calculated from the following relationship:

$$\log a_T = 9.8 - \frac{17.44(T - T_g)}{51.6 + T - T_g}$$

As in Chapter 5, a_T is the shift factor; T is the absolute temperature; and T_g is the glass transition temperature.

The primary interesting feature associated with the curve in Fig. 9.15 is that the peel data can be condensed into a single peel curve with multiple segments. This definitively demonstrates that the peel performance of a PSA is dependent upon its viscoelastic properties. The next interesting feature is that the peel force–peel rate curve can be divided into three segments. The first segment occurs at very low peel rates and the failure mode is cohesive within the adhesive. That is, some of the adhesive remains on the substrate. At some peel rate-temperature combination, the peel failure mode changes from cohesive failure within the adhesive to adhesion failure. This abrupt change occurs with an initial decrease in peel force, but this peel force increases with increase in rate. In both cases, increase in peel force is a consequence of the stiffening of the adhesive at either increasing rates or decreasing temperatures. The third segment of the curve, however, seems to show decreasing peel force with increasing peel rate. This region of "stick-slip" behavior is one that is marked by various degrees of oscillation in the peel force. That is, steady peel force is not achieved but rather a "shocky" peel occurs. This region of the peel force–peel rate curve is associated with a glassy response of the adhesive.

Since tack depends upon the wetting behavior of the PSA, peel force exhibited by a PSA is expected to depend upon the surface to which the PSA was adhered. Zosel [7] has investigated this behavior with results shown schematically in Fig. 9.16.

The effects of the liquid-like wetting behavior of a PSA are shown in this figure. First, the peel force after short contact time is heavily dependent upon the critical wetting tension of the substrate. If the wetting tension of the substrate is substantially lower than the surface energy of the adhesive, there is a lower peel force. The

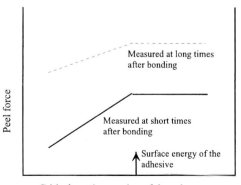

Figure 9.16   Peel force of a polyisobutylene-based PSA as a function of the critical wetting tension of the substrate to which is applied. The plot is drawn according to the data presented by Zosel [7]

bigger the mismatch, the lower the peel force because incomplete wetting means interfacial flaws which mean lower forces to failure. Once the critical wetting tension of the substrate exceeds that of the adhesive, wetting is complete and the peel force no longer increases. The dashed lines in Fig. 9.16 show what happens when the wetting of a surface by a PSA is not complete immediately after the PSA has been attached. If tack is a low rate phenomenon, then conditions in which the PSA is allowed to flow with little or no load is a very slow rate process and the adhesive behaves like a liquid. Indeed, the data in Fig. 9.16 shows that wetting does occur in this regime and the strong dependence of peel force on critical wetting tension of the substrate is somewhat decreased when the adhesive is allowed to remain in contact with the substrate for an extended time.

The dependence of peel force on substrate is also demonstrated by showing how peel force affects peel rate. However, these results are not necessarily as expected. If the peel force-peel rate curve of the same adhesive used in Fig. 9.14 is measured on a substrate which is low in critical wetting tension (such as polytetrafluoroethylene), a curve is obtained like that in Fig. 9.17. Not only is the level of the peel force decreased with respect to the higher energy surface, but also the positions of the transitions from cohesive to adhesion and adhesion to stick slip failure have changed. This indicates that the activation of the stiffening behavior of a PSA depends upon the substrate to which the adhesive is bonded. The change in the position of the first transition is not hard to explain. The transition of cohesion failure in the adhesive to adhesion failure of the adhesive to the substrate occurs at a lower reduced rate because the adhesive does not need to have as high a cohesive strength to exceed the forces of adhesion to the lower energy surface. The change in the higher peel rate transition is more difficult to explain and the appropriate criteria for explaining this change are still under study.

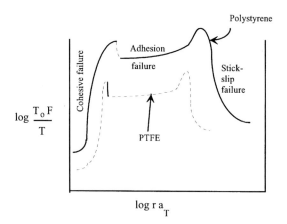

Figure 9.17   Reduced peel force versus peel rate master curves for a single PSA on two surfaces drawn according to the data of Kaelble [6]. Note that, with a change in substrate, the peel force changes and the position of the failure mode transitions changes

9.2.8   Shear and Creep Behavior of PSAs

The behavior of PSAs when exposed to a shear stress is not determined in the same manner as for structural or semi-structural adhesives. As indicated earlier in this chapter, PSAs are ranked in terms of their "shear holding power" which is the same as a "constant load creep" test. In Chapter 5, the entanglement molecular weight was discussed. In various portions of this book, dynamic analysis of viscoelasticity has been discussed. All of these subjects play a role in forming the basis for the following discussion.

When a PSA is placed under a shear load, the adhesive immediately provides an elastic response which then viscously relaxes. The rate at which the relaxation takes place gives a measure of the creep compliance. The initial application of shear stress in a creep experiment is on a short timescale, so the adhesive responds elastically. However, for the remainder of the experiment, the load application rate is extremely slow, so the viscous properties of the adhesive dominate. The quantity of interest here is the steady shear viscosity of the adhesive at the temperature of use. The steady shear viscosity of a material is directly dependent upon the molecular weight of the polymer. As discussed in Chapter 5, above the entanglement molecular weight, M_e, the viscosity varies as the 3.4 power of the molecular weight. For good creep resistance, the adhesive has a molecular weight above its M_e. In fact, the higher the molecular weight is above M_e, the better should be the shear holding power. As an illustration, examine the following equation which has been proposed to describe the time to failure under a shear load [8]:

$$t_f = \frac{L^2 W \eta}{2hMg}$$

where t_f is the time to failure; L is the lap length in centimeters; W is the lap width in centimeters; η is the viscosity in poise; h is the thickness of the adhesive layer; M is the load in grams; and g is the gravitational constant. If η depends on the 3.4 power of the molecular weight above M_e and k is a conversion constant for the dependence of the viscosity upon molecular weight, then:

$$t_f = \frac{L^2 W k (MW)^{3.4}}{2hMg}$$

It is easy to see that doubling the molecular weight above M_e provides a $2^{3.4}$ increase in the time to failure of the adhesive under shear load.

One way to determine the potential resistance of an adhesive under a steady shear load is to do an actual creep experiment such as that described in Chapter 5. For another way to determine how an adhesive might respond to shear loading, measure dynamic mechanical properties. As shown in Fig. 5.9, the extent of the plateau modulus of an polymer provides a measure of the molecular weight and hence, the resistance to a shear loading.

Higher levels of tackifier decrease the shear holding power of a PSA. As discussed earlier, a tackifier acts as an anti-plasticizer at high rates and as a plasticizer at low rates. Thus, even though we may have a PSA base polymer with a high molecular weight, the addition of a tackifier increases mobility and the PSA acts as if it is actually a lower molecular weight. The behavior is exemplified in Fig. 9.10 with the shear performance decreasing as a function of increasing resin to rubber ratio.

There are essentially two ways to increase the shear performance in a PSA. The first method is to increase molecular weight by crosslinking. As discussed in Chapter 5, crosslinking of polymer chains can lead to very high if not infinite molecular weight. Crosslinking can be achieved in a number of different ways. If the adhesive is one based upon natural rubber or any of the base polymers containing double bonds in the backbone, crosslinking can be induced by any number of free radical sources, such as UV radiation or peroxides. Acrylate adhesives, especially those containing acrylic acid, can be crosslinked by any additive bireactive with carboxylic acids. In addition, specific acrylate monomers could be added in the synthesis of the PSA base polymer, which can be crosslinked later thermally or through actinic radiation.

The other ways of improving shear creep resistance in a PSA have already been mentioned. If a PSA is made from a block copolymer in which one of the blocks phase-separates from the other and if the separated phase is glassy, then the phase-separated material acts as a crosslink. Thus, block copolymer PSAs are, in general, not crosslinked in their processing and could be potentially remelted with retention of properties.

9.2.9   Summary

In this section, a basis for the understanding of the phenomenon of PSA adhesion has been provided. In short, most of the performance of a PSA comes from the formulation and optimization of the viscoelastic properties of certain polymers. Tack is dependent upon the slow rate modulus of the material at room temperature, which must meet the Dahlquist criterion. The peel performance of a PSA depends upon the fast rate modulus of the adhesive which is in turn dependent upon the position of the glass transition temperature of the adhesive. The shear performance of a PSA is dependent upon the molecular weight and the crosslink density of the PSA base polymer and can thus be characterized by the plateau modulus in a dynamic mechanical spectrum. Optimization of this performance depends upon the proper formulation of the PSA or by proper molecular design of the base polymer.

9.3   Rubber-Based and Contact Bond Adhesives

The formulation of rubber-based and contact bond adhesives is affected by considerations similar to those for PSAs. The primary difference between PSA performance and that of other elastomer-based adhesives is that non-PSA elastomer-based adhesives must hold a load for substantially longer times than do PSAs.

In addition, the shear strength requirements are those of a semi-structural adhesive. Typical lap shear strengths attainable with rubber-based adhesives is on the order of 1–3 MPa (several hundred psi) and peel strengths of 2–8 kN/m (several tens of piw). The base polymers used in rubber-based adhesives discussed in this section differ somewhat from those used in PSAs. Instead of being called "non-PSA elastomer-based adhesives" these materials are referred to as "rubber-based adhesives" or "RBAs."

The uses of rubber-based adhesives abound in industry. Essentially all furniture made from a laminate of Formica on a less expensive wood base is fabricated with a rubber-based adhesive. RBAs are used to bond fabric to foam core in many upholstered furniture applications and are used to a large extent in the shoemaking industry. Many consumers are familiar with the construction mastics used in modern home construction and the RBAs used to apply plywood paneling. RBAs are used to apply floor and wall ceramic tile and are finding increasing use in the bonding of carpet tile to floors. Another basic use of rubber-based adhesives is in the generation of paper cements.

9.3.1 Formulation of RBAs

RBAs are based in large part on elastomeric polymers. They differ from PSAs in that the adhesive, after application, may or may not be tacky but it is expected to hold loads that are semi-structural. By our definition, "semi-structural" loads are approximately mid-way between PSAs and structural adhesives. RBAs can be broadly classified into solvent-based and latex-based systems. Although the performance of solvent-based systems is generally superior to that of latex-based systems, the present day drive to eliminate solvents from the home and workplace has caused rapid development of systems that do not employ these volatile chemicals. The formulation of both types of adhesives is discussed in this section. RBAs can be further classified into curing and non-curing types and how these are formulated is also reviewed.

9.3.2 Base Polymers

The strength of an RBA comes primarily from the elastomeric base polymer. The structures of a number of these base polymers have already been shown in Fig 9.1. Of the polymers shown in Fig. 9.1, the polymers used in RBAs are natural rubber, SBR, and butyl rubber. The base polymers useful for RBAs that are not necessarily useful for PSAs are shown in Fig. 9.18. Of these base polymers, the workhorse of the RBA industry is chloroprene (also called Neoprene[1]).

---

[1] Neoprene is a registered trademark of E.I. DuPont de Nemours and Co.

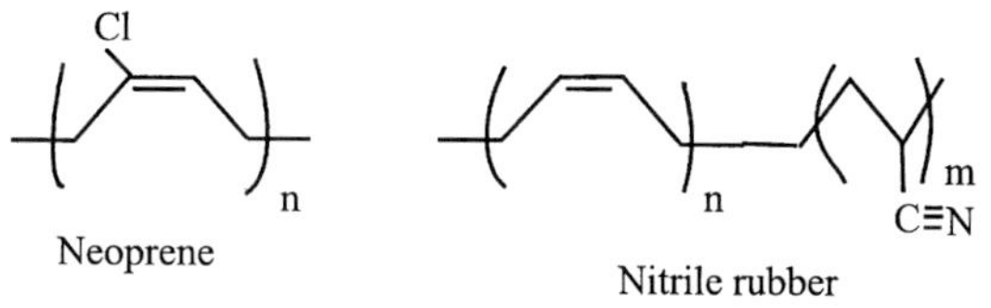

Figure 9.18   Structures of elastomers that are used in RBAs, but not necessarily in PSAs

Chloroprene is a homopolymer of 2-chloro-1,3-butadiene, usually prepared by emulsion polymerization. Depending upon the temperature of polymerization, chloroprene has a greater or lesser amount of the trans configuration; the higher the polymerization temperature, the more polymer with *cis* content. The higher trans content form of chloroprene is the more rapidly crystallizing form of the polymer. The rate and degree of polymer crystallization in the final adhesive controls the rate of strength buildup and the final cohesive strength, respectively. Like polybutadiene polymers, chloroprenes also contain a certain amount of vicinal vinyl groups as a result of 1,2 addition rather than 1,4 addition. These vinyl groups have been used for grafting from the polymer backbone to generate other forms of chloroprene. Another classification of commercially available chloroprenes is the linearity of the backbone. The chloroprene forms most often used in solvent-based adhesives are highly linear and soluble. Latex-based chloroprenes have varying degrees of gel structure and are marginally solvent-soluble, if they are soluble at all. Solvent-soluble chloroprenes are obtained from emulsion polymerization. They are then coagulated, often by the addition of salt. Lower molecular weight chloroprenes can be dissolved by simply stirring in solvent, while higher molecular weight materials often have to be broken down on a mill before easy dissolution is possible. Latex chloroprenes are often stabilized with rosin acid-based emulsifiers which are therefore anionic stabilizers. One type of chloroprene is nonionically stabilized and is also copolymerized with methacrylic acid.

Figure 9.18 also shows the structure for nitrile rubber, which has already been discussed in this book in terms of its use in the modification of phenolic and epoxy-based structural adhesives. Nitrile rubber is a copolymer of 1,3-butadiene and acrylonitrile. As in the case of chloroprenes, the nitrile rubbers are prepared by an emulsion polymerization process. The result is coagulated and then resolvated for use in these adhesives. The level of acrylonitrile varies widely in these polymers and can be as high as 50%, although the primarily used nitrile rubbers have an acrylonitrile content of about 25%. Nitrile rubbers, especially those with high acrylonitrile content, are well known for their resistance to gasoline and fuels.

Returning to Fig. 9.1, natural rubber is used as the base for a number of RBAs. The earliest RBA was simply natural rubber dissolved in naphtha. This adhesive was, at one time, extensively used in schools for paper craft work. Natural rubber latex can also be formulated into a useful water-based RBA. SBR rubber is a random copolymer of styrene and butadiene formed through emulsion polymerization. As in the previous cases, it can be coagulated and redissolved or used in the latex. As a random copolymer, this material does not crystallize and its properties are highly dependent upon the ratio between the butadiene and the styrene. As in the case of nitrile and chloroprene rubber, many of the properties can be controlled by the polymerization temperature. In addition, acid functional monomers can be incorporated into the emulsion polymerization, resulting in SBR latexes with extra performance and reactivity.

The final polymer useful for the generation of RBAs is butyl rubber. Butyl rubber is not to be confused with polyisobutylene. Butyl rubber is a copolymer of butylene with a small amount of isoprene. As a result, butyl rubber has a certain number of double bonds available for curing. Polyisobutylenes are fully saturated and do not crosslink by normal chemical means. Butyl rubbers are available in solutions, solids, and as ionically stabilized latexes. Polyisobutylenes as well as butyl rubber are known for their inertness and excellent vapor impermeability properties.

9.3.3 Tackifiers

The same tackifiers described for use in PSAs are also useful for RBAs. The rules for the choice of tackifier for an RBA are similar to those for a PSA. However, the tackifier levels can be substantially higher than those for a PSA, since the RBA does not have to be tacky without the presence of the solvent. Higher levels of tackifier provide the opportunity for increasing the T_g of the adhesive, since tackifiers act as anti-plasticizers. The Fox equation can be used to predict the T_g of the resultant adhesive as long as the tackifier and the base elastomer are completely compatible.

The choice of tackifier for the RBAs is the same as that described for natural rubber-based PSAs. One tackifier particularly useful in chloroprene-based RBAs is the t-butyl phenolic resin discussed below. Other resins used in this type of adhesive are based upon rosin esters as well as the coumarone-indene resins. Nitrile RBAs can also be tackified with coumarone-indene resins but hydrogenated rosins have also been used. In both of these cases, the base elastomer can also be modified by the addition of other polymers for particular applications. For example, chlorinated rubber has been added to both chloroprene as well as nitrile rubber RBAs to improve adhesion of the RBA to metal. SBR-based adhesives use the full range of tackifiers which we described as being useful for PSAs, including rosins, coumarone-indene and other aromatics as well as pinene-based resins. It is perhaps obvious that the formulation of latex-based RBAs requiring tackification starts with the availability of latex-based tackifiers. Since tackification depends upon the solution of the tackifier in the elastomer, materials used to formulate a latex-based RBA are required to quickly fuse and dissolve as the latex coagulates. This extra requirement is often difficult to achieve; often, the tackifier is added to the elastomer and the combination is emulsified. As indicated above, it is also possible to use rosin acids as the emulsifying agents for latex RBAs and these emulsifiers can also act as tackifiers.

9.3.4   Pigments and Fillers

Pigments and fillers are added to adhesive products for various purposes. The most common purpose is to reduce the cost of the product, since many non-surface-treated pigments are very inexpensive compared to synthetically produced resins. Clay and talc fillers are often used to reduce the manufacturing cost of an adhesive formula. Another common purpose for the use of fillers is to opacify the product. Certain applications require opacity for aesthetic reasons or as an indication of how uniformly the adhesive is applied. Titanium dioxide is often used to make the adhesive opaque.

Another primary use for pigments and fillers in RBAs is for viscosity or sag control. In many applications, an RBA is used on a vertical surface such as in a wall tile cement. Fillers for sag control to prevent the cement from running down the wall before the tile can be applied are fumed silica and treated fumed silica. For latex based RBAs, clays, which impart a yield stress to an RBA formula provide excellent sag control.

Two other pigments act as those described earlier but also modify the performance or the resistance to adverse environments, namely zinc oxide and magnesium oxide. Zinc oxide has long been part of a system for rubber vulcanization. It can be used in the same way in RBAs, especially RBAs with internal double bonds such as natural rubber. How zinc oxide helps vulcanize rubber is discussed in the next section.

Magnesium oxide plays a crucial role in the performance of chloroprene-based RBAs by aiding the stabilization of chloroprene against dehydrohalogenation. When unstabilized chloroprene is exposed to temperatures in excess of $87°C$ ($190°F$) for extended periods of time, the chloroprene evolves hydrochloric acid. Adhesive performance decreases and degradation of the adherend can occur through acid attack. The process is auto-catalytic, but can be greatly inhibited by the presence of acid acceptors, which not only neutralize the acid but also inhibit the autocatalytic effect. Zinc oxide apparently acts synergistically with magnesium oxide in this process and the two are often used as a stabilization package for chloroprene. Magnesium oxide plays another important role to be discussed in the next section.

9.3.5   Crosslinking/Vulcanization of RBAs

RBAs can and have been used without crosslinking. *Vulcanization* is the crosslinking of natural rubber with sulfur and the crosslinking of elastomers in general. The terms vulcanization and crosslinking can be used interchangeably for RBAs. Essentially all of the crosslinking agents normally used in the vulcanization of natural rubber can be used for crosslinking RBA elastomers which contain internal double bonds. A common system is to use a combination of sulfur with sulfur-curing accelerators such as zinc oxide and/or mercaptobenzothiazole. Such a crosslinking system requires heat to work. Other sulfur-based crosslinking systems work at room temperature. The accelerators for such a curing system are zinc dibutyldithiocarbamate and/or zinc mercaptobenzothiazole. If the formulation is very active, a two-part adhesive is generated. The sulfur and the accelerator are placed in a separate component which is mixed into the adhesive just before application. Natural rubber also contains a certain number of hydroxyl groups which react with added isocyanate in urethane formation. Nitrile rubber RBAs can be formulated in much the same manner as natural rubber RBAs when cure is necessary. A common system for curing nitrile rubber involves sulfur in combination with benzothiazyl disulfide and zinc oxide. Common free radical curing agents can also be used. Carboxylated SBRs can be cured through reaction with the carboxyl groups or an ionic crosslink can occur by using zinc salts. The ionic crosslink is stable in most conditions except when the "cured" RBA is exposed to very acidic conditions.

Polyisobutylene does not contain unsaturated sites and is therefore, not curable. However, butyl rubber RBAs can be crosslinked, again by sulfur. A crosslinking system useful for butyl rubber, as well as other unsaturated elastomer systems is the quinoid cure, in which p-quinone dioxime is combined with an inorganic oxidizing agent such as lead dioxide or benzothiazyl disulfide. The crosslinking apparently takes place through the nitroso groups which form when quinone dioxime oxidizes. The quinoid cure is usually formulated in a two-part system since it is active at room temperature.

Many curing systems can work with chloroprene-based RBAs, as described above, with sulfur cures particularly effective if accelerators are involved. However, chloroprene RBAs have been formulated without these crosslinking agents and still retain the heat resistance required in many applications. As described earlier, t-butyl phenolic resins have been used as tackifiers in chloroprene RBAs. In addition, the role played by magnesium oxide in this type of adhesive has been mentioned. It has been found that a synergistic effect takes place when MgO is used with the tertiary butyl phenolic resins in chloroprene-based RBAs. When solvent is removed from these systems, the phenolic groups in the resin react with MgO to crosslink. This crosslinking increases the heat resistance of the chloroprene RBA much above that of the unmodified resin or elastomer [9]. Thus, the 80°C bond strength of a chloroprene-based RBA increases threefold when the concentration of the phenolic resin is doubled. Care must be taken, however, because the *tack open time* decreases with the increase in tackifier level. *Tack open time* is the time available after the adhesive is applied during which the product remains tacky enough for the application of the adherend.

9.3.6   Solvents

In older RBAs, the solvent played a crucial role in the performance of the product. The solvent was the carrier for the system and all of the components of the adhesive (less fillers) had to soluble in the chosen solvent. A particular type of RBA, usually based on chloroprene, is called a *contact bond adhesive*. A contact bond adhesive, within a certain time after application, has enough cohesive strength and *knitting ability* that two surfaces coated with the adhesive have *green strength* immediately after they are mated. *Knitting ability* is an autohesion phenomenon in which chloroprene elastomer molecules are mobile enough to quickly form a bond (likely through interdiffusion) immediately after contact with little or no applied pressure. Few elastomers have this ability. *Green strength* indicates that the adhesive bond is strong enough to be handled a short time after the adherends are mated but much before full cure is obtained. One can imagine the utility of such an adhesive in mass production operations where it is much less expensive to store a part during cure than to slow down the production line to allow the adhesive time to set up. The choice of solvent in such an adhesive system is critical. A combination of solvents is usually chosen with a rapidly evaporating solvent as the primary carrier and a slower evaporating solvent to provide tack during bonding.

Because of increasing regulation on the use of organic solvents, the use of latex-based adhesives has increased markedly. Such systems, however, often have problems due to slow evaporation of water, less tack, and microbic buildup in the wet adhesive. For such systems to be useful in production lines, infrared heaters or ovens are often used to aid in the evaporation of the solvent. In addition, wetting plastic or other polymeric substrates is often problematic when latex-based RBAs are used. Often a small amount of solvent, called a *coalescing aide* which is soluble in both the elastomer and water, is added to latex systems to aid in wetting as well as to improve the coalescence of the latex particles. A recent improvement in the usability of latex-based RBAs has come with the development of a new application method. A salt solution is spray-applied simultaneously with the latex RBA, the latex is destabilized during the operation and it coagulates almost immediately upon application with the expulsion of water. This improves the drying production line speeds where latex based adhesives are used.

9.4   Summary

Elastomer-based adhesives come in two primary forms, the pressure-sensitive adhesive (PSA) and the rubber-based adhesive (RBA). The formulation of these two types of adhesives are quite similar in that a base elastomer provides much of the performance which is modified by the addition of tackifiers and crosslinking agents. The primary difference between the two materials is that the PSA is dry and ready to use in its commercial form while the RBA usually comes in a carrier (solvent or water) which must be removed before the bond can be effected. The ultimate holding power of the PSA is substantially less than that of an RBA, which should be considered semi-structural in character. The performance properties of a PSA were discussed in detail, especially as they related to dynamic mechanical properties. In particular, the properties of tack and peel were related to dynamic mechanical properties.

Bibliography

Handbook of Adhesives, 2nd Ed. Skeist, I. (Ed.) (1977),Van Nostrand Reinhold, New York
Handbook of Pressure Sensitive Adhesive Technology, Satas, D. (Ed.) (1989), Van Nostrand Reinhold, New York
Wragg, A.L., in *Aspects of Adhesion – 3.* Alner, D.J. (Ed.) (1966), CRC Press, Cleveland, OH
Whitehouse, R.S., in *Synthetic Adhesives and Sealants*, Wake, W.C. (Ed.) (1986), John Wiley, Chichester, UK
Wake, W.C., in *Treatise on Adhesion and Adhesives*, Patrick, R.L. (Ed.) (1969), Marcel Dekker, New York

References

1. *Test Methods for Pressure Sensitive Adhesive Tapes* (1994), Pressure Sensitive Tape Council, Chicago, IL
2. Ulrich, E.W., U.S. Patent 2,884,126 (1959)
3. *1990 Annual Book of Standards*, Vol. 15.06, Adhesives (1990), American Society for Testing and Materials, Philadelphia, PA
4. Dahlquist, C.A., in *Adhesion Fundamentals and Practice*, The Ministry of Technology (1966), McLaren and Sons, Ltd., London
5. Fox, T.G., *Bull. Am. Phys. Soc.*, 1 (1956), p. 123
6. Kaelble, D.H., *J. Adhesion*, 1 (1969), p. 102
7. Zosel, A., *Adhesives Age*, 32(11) (1989), p. 42
8. Dahlquist, C.A., in *The Handbook of Pressure Sensitive Adhesive Technology*, Satas, D. (Ed.) (1989), Van Nostrand Reinhold, New York
9. (a) Gerrard, J.A., and Mattson, R.C., U.S. Patent 2,918,442 (1959). (b) J. Kermadjian, *Adhesives Age*, 5(6) (1962), p. 34

10 Thermoplastic, Pseudothermoplastic and other Adhesives

10.1 Introduction

In this chapter, some types of adhesives not classified as either structural adhesives or as elastomer-based adhesives are discussed. These adhesives are based primarily on thermoplastics or materials which appear to be thermoplastic. The two primary types described in this chapter are hot melt adhesives and emulsion adhesives. In both cases, the main polymer utilized is polyvinyl acetate. Also some miscellaneous classes of adhesives, such as those based on natural products are discussed.

The primary objective of this chapter is to become acquainted with the chemistry and physical properties of hot melt and emulsion adhesives. The types of polymers used in hot melt adhesives as well as the materials used to modify their performance should become familiar. Many of the adjuvants described in previous chapters are used in these adhesives so the discussion mostly revolves around how these materials affect the performance of these adhesives. The chapter describes the chemistry of the primary type of emulsion adhesive and ends with a description of several types of natural product-based adhesives which have not been described earlier. These materials are either thermoplastic or pseudothermoplastic in character.

10.2 Hot Melt Adhesives

10.2.1 Introduction

A hot melt adhesive is defined as an adhesive applied from the melt, gaining strength upon solidification and crystallization. Hot melt adhesives are applied without solvents. The increase in solvent emission regulations have increased the demand for hot melt adhesives. Certain types of hot melt adhesives cure over time after application. However, with the general purpose hot melt adhesive, the material is applied as a thermoplastic melt and the resulting adhesive is also a thermoplastic. Attention has to be paid to the type of polymers forming the adhesive, since the resultant material has to be low viscosity in the melt (for easy application) but must solidify into a cohesively strong material.

Hot melt adhesives are divided into two classes; the first class depends upon formulation design. That is, the properties of the hot melt come from the combination of components which give the desired balance of properties. This situation should now be familiar, as it was encountered for elastomer-based as well as structural adhesives. In the second class of hot melt adhesives, adhesive performance is molecularly designed. That is, the hot melt performance does not come from formulation, but rather from the choice of monomers used to make the base polymer. Later in this chapter, the primary shortcomings of hot melt adhesives are discussed as well as how these shortcomings are addressed through the use of post-application crosslinking.

10.2.2   Polymer Physical Properties and Hot Melt Adhesives

The primary characteristic that distinguishes hot melt adhesives from other adhesive materials is the fact that they are applied in the melt and the adhesive's strength comes from resolidification. Melt properties, wetting while in the melt, resolidification, and the properties of the adhesive after solidification are all important. The dynamic mechanical properties of a thermoplastic polymer are dominated by two transitions, shown in Fig. 10.1. There is a substantial difference between the two dynamic mechanical spectra, as one is for a semi-crystalline polymer while the other is for an amorphous thermoplastic. For comparison, the curves for the two polymers are drawn so that they have the same glass transition temperature. Figure 10.1 shows that the plateau region in a plot of modulus versus temperature is higher and longer for a semi-crystalline polymer than for an amorphous polymer. The reason for this phenomenon is that the crystallites in the semi-crystalline polymer reinforce

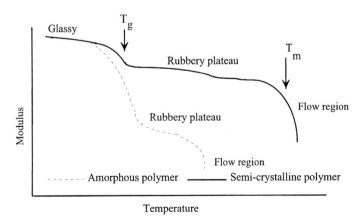

Figure 10.1   Dynamic mechanical spectrum of two polymer types: amorphous and crystalline. The plot shows that the range of temperature over which reasonable values of modulus can be obtained is, in general, larger for crystalling thermoplastics

its rubbery, amorphous regions. This gives rise to a higher plateau modulus than in the corresponding amorphous material. The plateau region of the amorphous polymer can be increased in height and length if the polymer is crosslinked or if its molecular weight is increased dramatically (i.e., the number of entanglements is increased). At the melt temperature of the semicrystalline polymer, the modulus drops drastically as the crystallites melt. For the amorphous polymer, at a certain temperature, the polymer starts to flow. The curves shown in Fig. 10.1 are very similar to the curves obtained for semi-crystalline versus atactic polypropylene. The reason for discussing these dynamic mechanical spectra is that they define the region in which polymers can be used as hot melt adhesives. In Fig. 10.1, the dynamic mechanical spectrum is divided into a glassy region, a rubbery plateau and a flow region. In the glassy region, the material behaves as a glass, and is usually brittle. It is possible to increase the strain energy density of glassy hot melts by the same means as described for structural adhesives. Polymers in the flow region have no strength. In the rubbery region, the polymer is likely to have its highest strain energy density at failure. The best performance for any load bearing adhesive occurs when the energy absorption properties of the polymer are maximized. Therefore, the operational range for a hot melt adhesive is between the melt temperature and the glass transition temperature:

$$\Delta T = T_\mathrm{m} - T_\mathrm{g}$$

It is the objective of the hot melt formulator to have ΔT as large as possible and the plateau modulus high enough to support the loads for which the adhesive is designed.

There are substantial limitations in our ability to maximize ΔT. T_m cannot be very high since worker safety and heating system capabilities become a concern with high temperatures. T_m should actually be as low as possible to pevent problems in these areas. Typically, hot melt adhesives have melt temperatures below 170°C. The performance of a hot melt adhesive is usually maximized at near room temperature. Therefore, the T_g of the hot melt should be at least 20°C below room temperature. As was the case with the elastomeric adhesives discussed in the previous chapter, there are few polymeric materials that meet these criteria.

Another important criterion for the usefulness of a hot melt adhesive is its melt viscosity. Excessively high melt viscosities result in adhesives that are exceedingly hard to apply perhaps requiring specialized equipment. The melt viscosity depends upon the molecular weight of the polymer so it should be low. As stated earlier, the only way amorphous polymers can exhibit higher and longer rubbery plateau is to increase its molecular weight to increase the number of entanglements. For a hot melt adhesive, such a high molecular weight, substantially above the entanglement molecular weight, quite likely means that the melt viscosity is too high for easy application. Hence, most of the materials discussed as hot melt adhesive base polymers are semi-crystalline in character. Amorphous materials are not often workable as hot melt adhesives.

The hot melt adhesive industry does not typically refer to the melt viscosity of a polymer as we defined it in Chapter 5. Rather, the industry uses a quantity known as the *melt flow index* (MFI) or *melt index*. The MFI is measured various ways, one of which is described in ASTM D1238. In this test method, the polymer or hot melt adhesive is raised above its melt point in an apparatus in which it is pressurized and then forced through a capillary of specified size and length. There is an obvious relationship of this test to the actual method of application of hot melt adhesives. The melt flow index is given as the weight of polymer in grams which can be forced through this apparatus under the specified conditions of pressure, temperature and time. There is a inverse relationship between the melt flow index and the melt viscosity of a polymer.

The ability of a hot melt adhesive to wet a surface depends upon not only the wetting relationships discussed in Chapter 6 but also depends upon the time the adhesive is in the melt state. Rapidly crystallizing polymers, while perhaps rapidly building strength after application, are problematic in terms of providing complete wetting before the polymer solidifies. Another problem for hot melt adhesives is wetting substrates of high heat conductivity, such as metals, because the heat present in the applied hot melt is rapidly dissipated. The adhesive sets too much before it can wet the surface. The contact interface is the first region to solidify in such a bond. Metallic adherends almost always have to be heated before application of a hot melt adhesive in order to allow the adhesive to wet the surface.

As discussed in Chapter 6, wetting is not only an interfacial phenomenon, but also depends upon the viscosity of the material. The equations described in Chapter 6 for the time dependent contact angle are not immediately useful for the hot melt situation, since they were written with the supposition that the melt viscosity was constant. If the melt viscosity is not constant, then the equation for the time dependent contact angle is:

$$\frac{d \cos \theta_t}{dt} = \frac{\gamma_{LV}}{\eta(t)L} (\cos \theta_\infty - \cos \theta_t)$$

where θ_t is the time dependent contact angle. If $\eta(t)$ is constantly increasing, then the rate of change of the contact angle as it approaches equilibrium is ever decreasing, indicating that the length of time necessary for the contact angle to come to equilibrium is constantly increasing. The formulation of a hot melt must balance the need for rapid strength buildup with the need for complete wetting.

10.2.3   Formulation of Hot Melt Adhesives

The primary polymers used to formulate hot melt adhesives are shown in Table 10.1.

Paraffin wax is the base for the oldest hot melt adhesive, sealing wax. Paraffin wax is used in low melting hot melt adhesives, yielding an the adhesive with generally poor strength. Low density polyethylene provides a higher strength hot melt adhesive with much the same structure as the paraffin wax, but with more

Table 10.1   Base Polymers Used in the Formulation of Hot Melt Adhesives

Polyvinyl acetate-co-polyethylene (EVA)
Low density polyethylene
Polyethyl acrylate-co-polyethylene
Paraffin waxes
Polypropylene
Styrene-butadiene block copolymers
Styrene-isoprene block copolymers
Phenoxy resins

branch points in the polymer. The workhorse of the industry is the poly(ethylene)-co-poly(vinyl acetate) polymer also known as ethylene-vinyl acetate polymer, or simply EVA. These materials are random copolymers of ethylene and vinyl acetate with vinyl acetate levels of about 18% to 52%. The melt index can vary from 0.6 to 500 g/10 min. This wide range of material choices provides substantial latitude for the formulator to find the best balance of properties. The base polymer, whatever its composition, is the primary strength-providing material in a hot melt adhesive formulation.

The primary other ingredients in a hot melt adhesive formulation are the tackifying agent, a flexibilizer, a wax, and an antioxidant. Tackifying agents were discussed in the previous chapter. The role of the tackifying agent in a hot melt adhesive is similar to the role it plays in a PSA. However, the tack of a hot melt adhesive is fleeting and only special formulations of hot melts are tacky after they have reached room temperature. The same criteria exist for hot melt adhesive tack as for PSAs. However, the time when the adhesive meets the Dahlquist criterion for tack is the time when the adhesive has a modulus less than 3×10^6 dynes/cm^2. Once the adhesive has solidified, the tackifier modifies the T_g of the solid adhesive. The ultimate T_g can be predicted from the Fox equation if the components are completely compatible.

The same tackifiers discussed in the previous chapter are useful for modifying hot melt adhesive performance. Some consideration has to be given to the heat stability of the tackifier in the melt. Tackifiers with unsaturation could potentially gel while the adhesive is in the melt and not be useful. In addition to those discussed in the previous chapter, chlorinated polyolefins are tackifiers for hot melts that improve their ability to wet surfaces.

Flexibilizers can be added to a hot melt adhesive to make it permanently soft or flexible. Phthalates, tricresyl phosphate and polybutenes find a role here. These materials act opposite to the tackifiers in that they decrease T_g, while tackifiers increase this quantity. The plasticizer must be completely soluble in the base resin or undesirable phase separation can take place during storage or application. Another important criterion in choosing a plasticizer is its volatility at the melt temperature. Undesirable effluent could result.

One of the most important ingredients in a hot melt formulation is the wax. Waxes decrease the viscosity of the melt and the surface tension of the liquid adhesive. As hydrocarbonaceous materials, waxes, in general, have a lower surface tension than the base polymer of the hot melt and thus, lower the surface tension of the overall adhesive. Certain waxes, known as microcrystalline waxes, not only reduce melt viscosity and melt surface tension but they also reinforce the hot melt by forming crystallites that resist deformation under load.

Fillers are also used in hot melt adhesives. Materials such as clay and talc can be used to control the melt viscosity of the hot melt and to opacify the material. Most often, they are added to reduce the manufacturing cost of the formulated adhesive. The final formulation ingredient is the antioxidant. Since these adhesives may spend long times in a hot melt applicator before use, an antioxidant is mandatory, especially for those adhesives based on ethylene. Materials such as hindered phenols are used for such purposes.

It is important to consider the structural features of a hot melt base polymer such as EVA as they affect the final properties or applications of the adhesive. From the discussions in the earlier chapters in this book, we already know that increasing vinyl acetate content in the base polymer increases the cohesive strength of the material, making it stronger under load. However, increasing vinyl acetate content also increases the surface tension of the melt, thus making it more difficult to wet lower energy substrates. Increasing the vinyl acetate content also lowers the solubility of waxes in the adhesive, making them more difficult to formulate. Melt flow index also significantly effects the strength of an adhesive bond. High melt flow index materials are lower in molecular weight and thus, have less strength than a low melt flow index material.

Formulation-based hot melt adhesive are used in an ever increasing number of applications. One of the primary uses is in paper joining. Many corrugated boxes are sealed by formulation-based hot melt adhesives as is much of the packaging material used to hold and display products. Formulation based hot melt adhesives are also extensively used in bookbinding, although early hot melts used to bind inexpensive paper-backed books were not very good for long periods of time. However, improvements in adhesive formulation over the past 20 years resulted in more permanent bindings for paperback books and even many hardcover book publishers now use hot melt adhesives as part of the binding process. Hot melt adhesives are also used in woodworking. A woodworker can join parts using a hot melt as a fixturing aid, while a standard wood adhesive is allowed to set. In general, however, hot melts are not used in furniture manufacture because of their thermoplastic character which means they are likely to creep under load. The lap shear strengths exhibited by hot melt adhesives (above their glass transition temperature) are typically 0.7–3.5 MPa (few hundred psi) and peel strengths are usually 0.9–3.5 kN/m (few tens piw). Hot melt adhesives, below their glass transition temperatures, can have properties that are almost structural in character, However, peel strengths can be low, since these materials tend to be brittle glasses because their molecular weights are low to keep their MFIs high.

10.2.4 Synthetically Designed Hot Melt Adhesives

The formulation ingredients described in the previous section can also be used with the materials described in this section. However, the materials discussed here are those based primarily in synthetic design, rather than in formulation design. That is, the base polymer forms essentially the entire adhesive and, with the exception of antioxidants, few other ingredients are added. The properties of the adhesive come from the selection of the monomers used to form the final polymer.

The two main types of synthetically designed hot melt adhesives are polyamides and polyesters. Polyurethanes are also synthesized into a form useful in hot melt adhesives, but this material is less often used. Urethane formation chemistry was discussed in Chapter 8. The synthetic schemes used to generate polyesters and polyamides are shown in Fig. 10.2. Polyamides are generated either through the reaction of diamine with a diacid or through the homopolymerization of an amino acid. Acids are employed as catalysts and the by-product of the reaction is water. In addition, and not shown in Fig. 10.2, is the ring opening polymerization of caprolactam to yield a polyamide. Polyester formation reactions are also shown in Fig. 10.2. In a manner analogous to the polyamide formation reactions, a diacid is reacted with a diol or an acid alcohol is self-polymerized to generate a polyester. Similarly to polyamide formation reactions, polyesters can be formed from the ring opening polymerization of caprolactone. Acids, antimony trioxide or anhydrous zinc chloride can be used to catalyze polyester formation. For both formation reactions, high temperatures are usually used and water is evolved. The degree of polymerization is controlled by the ratio of the monomers and by how far the equilibrium is driven by removal of water from the reaction mixture.

As discussed in the previous section, hot melts need to be optimized to have as large a range of temperature between T_g and T_m as possible. For copolymers of semicrystalline polyesters and polyamides, the T_m can be approximated by the Flory equation:

$$\frac{1}{T_{m,c}} = \frac{R}{\Delta H_m} \ln X + \frac{1}{T_{m,h}}$$

In this equation, R is the gas constant; ΔH_m is the heat of fusion of the homopolymer repeat unit; X is the mole fraction of the crystallizable unit in the copolymer; $T_{m,h}$ is the melt temperature of the homopolymer; and $T_{m,c}$ is the melt temperature of the copolymer [1]. For polyesters, the ratio of T_g to T_m is in the range of 0.5 to 0.7, depending upon the symmetry of the polymer. The use of these two relationships provides a maximum range over which the polyester can be a useful hot melt adhesive. The melt point of a copolymer, in general, decreases with the alkylene chain length of the diol used to form the polyester. The percent crystalline material in a polyester is dependent upon the alkylene chain length in the diol. The proportion of crystallization decreases as diol chain length increases, but the rate of crystallization increases as the alkylene chain length increases. The rate of crystallization can be important in applications in which the assembly is required to have a certain degree of strength in a certain time. By examining the curves in Fig. 10.1, it may be

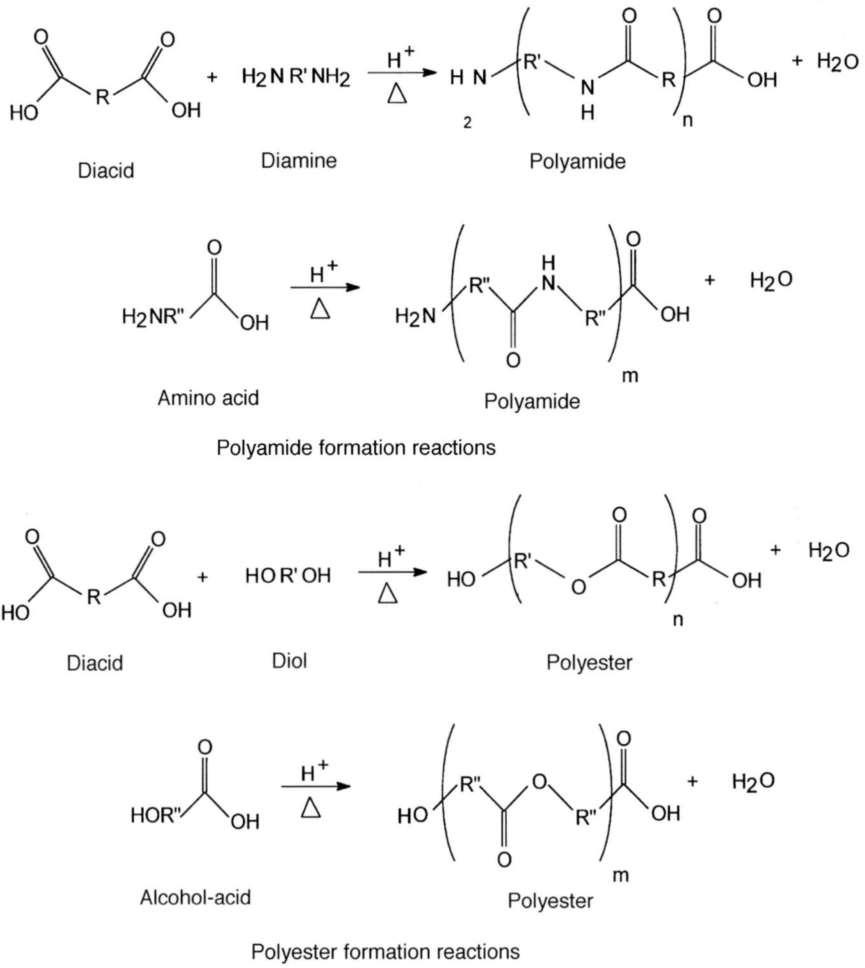

Figure 10.2   Reactions used in the formation of polyamides and polyesters

assumed that a high degree of crystallization is desired in a hot melt adhesive which translates to a high value of the modulus in the plateau region. This situation is somewhat problematic, in that crystallization is accompanied by molar volumetric shrinkage in the polymer. If the shrinkage is too great, then shear stresses build up at the interface between the adhesive and the adherend, which can cause the bond to delaminate. Thus, the balance which must be met when synthesizing a hot melt adhesive involves the following criteria:

- as large a range as possible between T_g and T_m
- a T_m that is as high as possible, but below the degradation point of the polymer and not too high that it damages equipment and adherends,
- a T_g below the use temperature

- as high a percent crystallization as possible, but within the tolerance of shrinkage of the bonded assembly
- a crystallization rate commensurate with the assembly process

Polyamides follow much of the same trends as for polyesters. However, poly-amides are helped as well as hindered by their ability to hydrogen bond. Polyamides have higher cohesive strength as well as higher melting points than polyesters of similar structure. However, polyamides are much more susceptible to moisture permeation than polyesters, since hydrogen bonds can break when water is absorbed by the polymer. A listing of the monomers commonly used for hot melt polyester and hot melt polyamide adhesives is shown in Table 10.2.

One particular type of diacid used to produce hot melt polyamide-based adhesives is the dimer acid. This name is applied to a series of acids that result from a dimeriza-tion reaction of natural unsaturated fatty acids. The fatty acids involved are C_{18}-doubly unsaturated, but non-conjugated. Examples of such acids are linoleic acid, oleic acid, and soybean oil acid. The C_{36} dimer of these acids is generated by many processes including high temperature dimerization through a Diels–Alder mechanism, and a free radical reaction. A proposed structure and thermal dimerization scheme for linoleic acid is shown in Fig. 10.3 [3]. Polyamides resulting from the polymerization of dimer acid with a diamine are flexible materials, due to the number of degrees of rotation available in these molecules because of their highly aliphatic character.

Polyester and polyamide based hot melt adhesives find uses in many industries. They are sold, as are the formulated adhesives, into markets where hand-held applicators are used. In addition, they are widely used in shoe manufacture. The performance of the synthetically designed hot melt adhesives is, in general, higher than that of the formulated adhesives.

Table 10.2   Monomers Commonly Used to Form Hot Melt Polyester and Polyamide Adhesives [2]

Polyamides	Polyesters
Acids	*Acids*
Dimer acid	Terephthalic
Sebacic	Adipic
Dodecanoic	Isophthalic
Azelaic	Phthalic
Adipic	Dimer acid
Diamines	Azelaic
Ethylene diamine	Sebacic
Hexamethylene diamine	*Diols*
Diethylene triamine	Ethylene glycol
Piperazine	1,4-butanediol
Polyoxypropylene diamines	1,6-hexanediol
	1,4-cyclohexanedimethanol

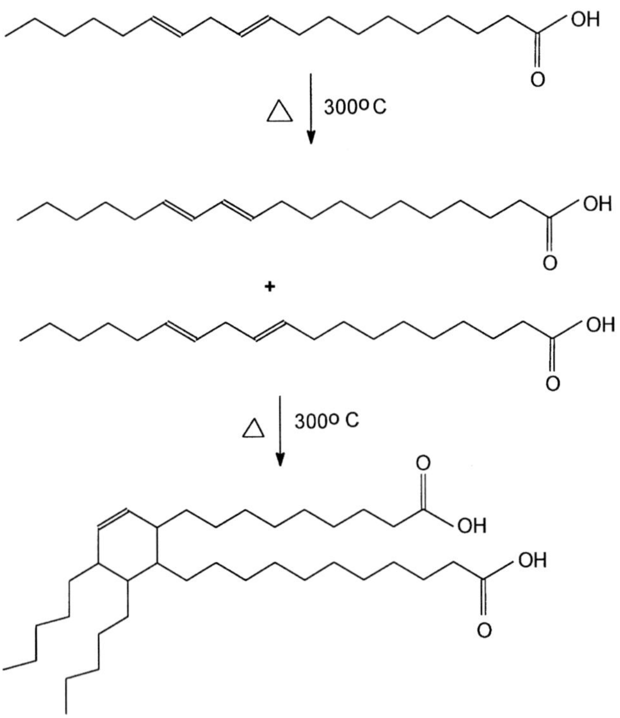

Figure 10.3   Thermal dimerization of linoleic acid

10.2.5   Curing Hot Melts

Hot melt adhesives have a number of drawbacks, however. The adhesives are thermoplastic, and are relatively low in molecular weight so that they can be dispensed from a gun type applicator. The molecular weight is not very much higher, if at all, than the entanglement molecular weight of the polymer. Therefore, creep is a major problem. Hot melt adhesives are also susceptible to water permeation and/or solvent penetration because of their thermoplastic character. Polyamide adhesives are particularly affected by water because much of the strength of the polyamide comes from intermolecular hydrogen bonds. Many of the problems associated with hot melt adhesives can be eliminated or ameliorated if the hot melt was not a thermoplastic but rather a thermoset (as described in Chapter 8). However, heating a thermoset causes it to cure and become infusible. If this should happen in an applicator, particularly some form of mechanized hot melt applicator, the results could be disastrous. Reactions for curing hot melts have to be stable in the applicator at the adhesive's melt temperature but occur at some reasonable rate application. In addition, the cure mechanism cannot attack the polymer in the melt or after application.

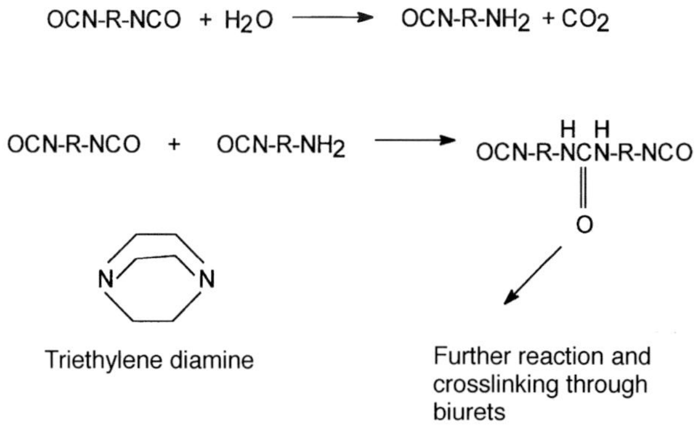
OCN-R-NCO + H2O → OCN-R-NH2 + CO2
OCN-R-NCO + OCN-R-NH2 → OCN-R-NCN-R-NCO
H H
O
N
N
Triethylene diamine
Further reaction and crosslinking through biurets

Figure 10.4 Reactions used in a moisture curing melt adhesive

One reaction for curing hot melt adhesives is the inclusion of free radically reactive double bonds and a photoiniator in the adhesive formulation. This formula can be stable under melt conditions, but then be photoactivated to cure the adhesive. The reaction most often used in curing hot melt adhesives involves moisture-reactive isocyanate.

The generation of a moisture curable hot melt adhesive involves the synthesis of an isocyanate-terminated polymer. The base polymer from which this is made is usually inherently useful as a hot melt adhesive. For example, a polyester polyol can be made from a stoichiometry slightly richer in the diol, yielding a polyester diol. This material can then be reacted with a diisocyanate at an isocyanate to alcohol mole ratio of 2:1. The moisture curing reaction of isocyanates is shown in Fig. 10.4. As shown, water reacts with the isocyanate to generate an amine and carbon dioxide. The resultant amine then reacts with another isocyanate to create a urea linkage. This reaction can continue as long as moisture can enter into the material and there are available isocyanate groups. Several catalysts for urethane formation are also useful catalysts for reacting water with isocyanates in a moisture curing reaction, including stannous octoate, dibutyl tin dilaurate and triethylenediamine. The structure of triethylenediamine is also shown in Fig. 10.4. The choice of catalyst depends, in part, on the stability of the reactive mixture at the temperatures in the hot melt applicator. The hot melt could also be formulated with other materials discussed earlier in this chapter. Those other materials must be compatible and stable with isocyanates and catalysts at the melt temperatures.

10.3 Polyvinyl Acetate-Based Adhesives

Many times in the previous chapters, certain polymers were referred to as "workhorses" of an industry or type of adhesive. This statement is particularly applicable to polyvinyl acetate (PVAc) in emulsion adhesives. Polyvinyl acetate is made by emulsion free radical polymerization. The basic polymer is quite brittle, but it can be modified by copolymerization with other monomers, in particular, ethylene. As the amount of ethylene in the copolymer increases, the more ductile the polymer becomes and the lower its glass transition temperature. However, its glass transition temperature cannot be made too low, because this may result in an adhesive with too little stiffness.

Poly(vinyl acetate) emulsions can also be made with a number of comonomers, such as various acrylates and dibutyl maleate. In addition to the synthesis of the base polymer, PVAc polymers and copolymers can be formulated through the addition of external plasticizers and tackifiers. Co-solvents may be added as well as crosslinking agents. External plasticizers, such as dioctylphthalate, can be added as long as they are in compatible emulsion. The same is true of tackifier emulsions. Co-solvents such as butyl cellsolve, which is soluble in both water and the PVAc emulsion, aid in the coalescence of the emulsion particles once the water has begun to evaporate.

Of importance in the formulation of stable PVAc emulsions are the surfactant and the protective colloid incorporated. These materials stabilize emulsions. Protective colloids can be certain polyurethanes known as "associative" protective colloids, or cellulosic materials such as hydroxy ethyl cellulose. In addition to stabilizing the colloid, the protective colloid increases the thixotropy of the adhesive. One material used as both a surfactant and part of a colloid protection system is hydrolyzed or partially hydrolyzed PVAc. The material is either polyvinyl alcohol (PVA) or PVAc-co-PVA. These combinations of surfactants and cellulosic protective colloids optimize properties, provide improved wettability on various surfaces, or have the potential for crosslinking. Crosslinking can also be obtained by copolymerizing vinyl acetate with a carboxyl-containing monomer such as acrylic acid. The carboxyl function can then be crosslinked by a number of materials including aminoplast resins, epoxies, etc. Crosslinking tends to improve creep resistance in the adhesive but it often imparts brittleness, which can be countered in a number of ways.

PVAc emulsion adhesives are well known to the consumer and the industry as "white glue". In wood bonding with PVAc adhesives, much of the drying of the adhesive takes place by sorption of water by the wood. White glues are also widely used in the packaging industry for the manufacture of cardboards and paper bags.

10.4   Polyvinyl Acetal Adhesives

Polyvinyl acetal is generated in two steps. PVAc is first hydrolyzed to a certain degree to yield a primarily PVA (polyvinyl alcohol) copolymer. The PVA is then reacted with formaldehyde or butyraldehyde to yield either polyvinyl formal or polyvinyl butyral, respectively. Neither of these polymers are actually homopolymers of polyvinyl acetal but are rather terpolymers of PVAc, PVA and polyvinyl acetal. Many of the properties of the resultant polymer depend upon the proportion of the monomers in this terpolymer, including crosslinkability, which depends upon the number of hydroxyl groups left in the polymer. The hydroxyl groups can be crosslinked with epoxy resins, aminoplast resins, diisocyanates, as well as dialdehydes. The use of polyvinyl acetals in the formulation of phenolic resins has already been described in Chapter 8. One of the primary uses of polyvinyl acetal adhesives is in the generation of safety glass.

10.5   Thermoplastic or Pseudothermoplastic Adhesives Based upon Natural Products

The oldest adhesives are based upon natural products. The use of proteins as base resin for a structural adhesive was described in an earlier chapter. However, a number of other natural product-based materials are also used as adhesives or as adhesive components and some are discussed in this section.

10.5.1   Starches [3]

Starches are obtained from roots and seeds and we classify them as pseudothermo-plastic materials, because starch is not actually soluble. Rather, starch is a branched polysaccharide consisting of amylose and amylopectin (structures are shown in Fig. 10.5). Since starches are highly branched, they are not soluble in water and most other materials. Because of their chemical structure, they swell considerably in water, particularly when the water is boiled. The water-swollen starch particles behave like a pseudoplastic emulsion which can be coated onto paper as well as other substrates to act as a re-moistenable adhesive. Starches can be formulated with a number of materials as plasticizer, such as glycerol, corn syrup or molasses. Borax is important in starch-based adhesives because it acts as a rheology modifier and at sufficiently high concentrations, as an antimicrobial.

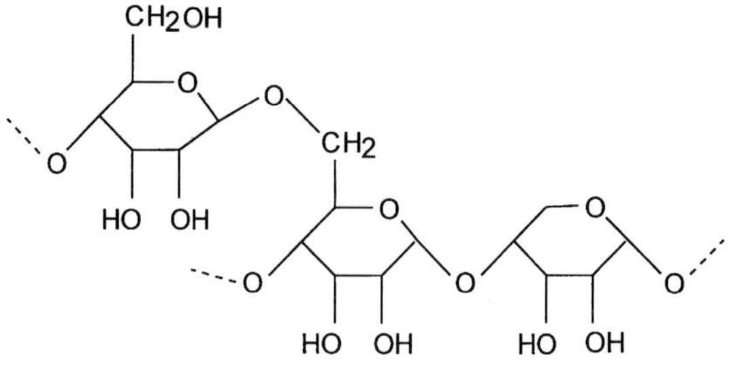

Figure 10.5   Structure of amylopectin

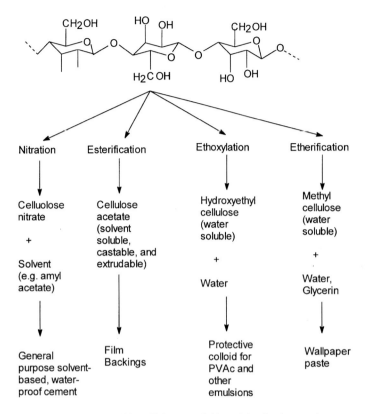

Figure 10.6   Reactions used to modify cellulose to yield useful adhesive products

10.5.2   Cellulosics [4]

The feedstock for cellulosic adhesive materials are wood pulp and cotton linters with the second providing higher quality. The best way to describe all the possible uses of cellulosics in adhesive technology is by the diagram shown in Fig. 10.6. Cellulose, since it is inherently insoluble, must be chemically modified to make useful adhesives. The oldest form of chemical modification is nitration. Reaction of cellulose with approximately a single nitration per ring yields cellulose nitrate. This form of cellulose is soluble in such solvents as amyl ketone and toluene. The solvated form of nitrocellulose is the well known adhesive; Duco[1] Cement sold for many years by the DuPont Company. Esterification of cellulose leads to cellulose acetate or triacetate. One use of these materials is for very clear, thin film products ("celluloid" or "cellophane"). These products formed the base for photographic films before the advent of polyethylene terphthalate and the backing for many pressure sensitive

---

[1] Duco is a registered trademark of E.I. DuPont de Nemours and Co., Inc.

adhesive tapes. Etherification of cellulose yields hydroxyethyl and hydroxy methyl cellulose. Their utility as protective colloids for emulsions, including those based upon PVAc, has been described. Hydroxymethyl cellulose also forms the basis for many wallpaper adhesives.

10.6   Summary

In this chapter, the chemistry of a number of adhesives classified as thermoplastic or pseudothermoplastic has been described. Most of the adhesives in this chapter start out as primarily thermoplastic but often are modified to be crosslinkable to impart properties such as creep and solvent resistance. The primary types of adhesives discussed are hot melts, emulsion adhesives, polyvinyl acetal adhesives and natural product-based adhesives. In general, these adhesives are moderate in strength with shear performances that are somewhat higher than that of rubber-based adhesives but substantially less than structural adhesives.

Bibliography

Handbook of Adhesives, 2nd Ed. Skeist, I. (Ed.) (1977), Van Nostrand Reinhold, New York

Weidener, R.A., in *Treatise on Adhesion and Adhesives*, Vol. 2, Patrick, R.L. (Ed.) (1969), Marcel Dekker, New York

Carpenter, A.T., and Taylor, J.R., in *Adhesion 1*, Allen, K.W. (Ed.) (1977), Applied Science Publishers, London

References

1. (a) Hardy, A., in *Synthetic Adhesives and Sealants*, Wake, W.C. (Ed.) (1986), John Wiley, Chichester. (b) Flory, P.J., *J. Chem. Phys.*, 17 (1949), p. 223
2. Rossito, C., in *Handbook of Adhesives*, Skeist, I.M. (Ed.) (1990), Van Nostrand Reinhold, New York, pp. 478–498
3. Cowan, J.C., *J. Am. Oil Chemists Soc.*, 39 (1962), p. 534
4. Williams, R.H., in *Modified Starches, Properties and Uses*, Wurzburg, O. (Ed.) (1987), CRC, Boca Raton, FL
5. (a) Hon, D.N.-S., in *Adhesives from Renewable Resources*, Hemingway, R.W., Conner, A.H., and Branham, S.J. (Eds.) (1989), American Chemical Society, Washington, DC. (b) Wint, R.F., and Shaw, K.G., in *Applied Polymer Science*, Tess, R.W., and Poehlein, G.W. (Eds.) (1985), American Chemical Society, Washington, DC. (c) Nicholson, M.D., and Merritt, F.M., in *Cellulose Chemistry and its Applications*, Nevell, T.P., and Zeronian, S.H. (Eds.) (1985), Ellis Horwood, Chichester, UK

11   The Basis for Adhesive Bond Design

11.1   Introduction

The last chapter of this book concerns itself with an attempt to put together many of the concepts discussed in the earlier chapters, providing a basis on which to design an adhesive joint. This chapter is not a manual for adhesive bond design, but rather, a checklist of considerations regarding the use of adhesives to create an assembly. The objectives of this chapter are to provide a means to connect chemistry with the physical properties of adhesives, a listing of items to consider when planning the use of adhesive bonding, and a simple set of rules for beginning the design of an adhesive bond.

11.2   Chemistry and Mechanical Properties of Adhesives

Before any type of adhesive is utilized, the level of mechanical load must be known. That information provides the starting point for the choice of adhesive. Table 11.1 lists many of the chemistries discussed in the previous three chapters, along with a few of the typical bond strength properties of those adhesives. The list is a guideline and not hard and fast, since there are exceptional adhesives in each class which can "push the envelope" in terms of performance. Observed shear strengths and peel strengths are highly dependent upon the adherends composition and thickness. Therefore, the values given in Table 11.1 are obtained when the most common adherend for that type of adhesive is used. For example, wood adherends are used with contact bond adhesives, fiberboard used with starch and cellulosics; and aluminum is used with epoxies. The list in Table 11.1 is provided in increasing order of overall strength.

The order of the list changes only slightly if the resistance of the adhesive to creep is considered. The more crosslinked the adhesive, the more likely the adhesive is resistant to creep. The load bearing capabilities of the adhesives in the list are roughly in the same order with the degree of aromatic character and potential degree of crosslinking. Thus, if the application is one in which a continuous load of 225 kg (500 pounds) is applied to an adhesive joint of small contact area (such as a few square centimeters or inches), it would be imprudent to consider using a PSA or even an RBA. However, an acrylic structural or possibly a structural urethane adhesive could do quite well with such a load.

Table 11.1   Chemistry and Mechanical Performance of Various Types of Adhesives

Adhesive chemistry or type	Room temperature lap shear strength, MPa (psi)	Peel strength, kN/m (piw)
Pressure-sensitive	0.01–0.07 (2–10)	0.18–0.88 (1–5)
Starch-based	0.07–0.7 (10–100)	0.18–0.88 (1–5)
Cellulosics	0.35–3.5 (50–500)	0.18–1.8 (1–10)
Rubber-based	0.35–3.5 (50–500)	1.8–7 (10–40)
Formulated hot melt	0.35–4.8 (50–700)	0.88–3.5 (5–20)
Synthetically designed hot melt	0.7–6.9 (100–1000)	0.88–3.5 (5–20)
PVAc emulsion (white glue)	1.4–6.9 (200–1000)	0.88–1.8 (5–10)
Cyanoacrylate	6.9–13.8 (1000–2000)	0.18–3.5 (1–20)
Protein-based	6.9–13.8 (1000–2000)	0.18–1.8 (1–10)
Anaerobic acrylic	6.9–13.8 (1000–2000)	0.18–1.8 (1–10)
Urethane	6.9–17.2 (1000–2500)	1.8–8.8 (10–50)
Rubber-modified acrylic	13.8–24.1 (2000–3500)	1.8–8.8 (10–50)
Modified phenolic	13.8–27.6 (2000–4000)	3.6–7 (20–40)
Unmodified epoxy	10.3–27.6 (1500–4000)	0.35–1.8 (2–10)
Bis-maleimide	13.8–27.6 (2000–4000)	0.18–3.5 (1–20)
Polyimide	13.8–27.6 (2000–4000)	0.18–0.88 (1–5)
Rubber modified epoxy	20.7–41.4 (3000–6000)	4.4–14 (25–80)

Table 11.2   Adhesives Types in Order of Their Resistance to High Temperatures while Under a Use Load

Adhesive chemistry or type
   Non-silicone pressure sensitive
   Starch-based
   Formulated hot melt
   Synthetically designed hot melt
   Rubber-based
   Cellulosic
   PVAc emulsion (white glue)
   Curing hot melt
   Cyanoacrylate protein-based urethane
   Rubber modified acrylic
   Anaerobic acrylic
   Rubber-modified epoxy
   Unmodified epoxy
   Modified phenolic
   Unmodified phenolics
   Silicone PSA
   Bis-maleimide
   Polyimide

The listing in Table 11.1 changes somewhat if it is made in terms of resistance to temperature. Indeed, some additions need to be made to properly characterize the adhesive types in order of their resistance to high temperatures for long periods of time. Table 11.2 provides a loose listing of adhesive types in order of their resistance to exposure to high temperatures under their use load.

Silicone PSAs have been specified in this list because of their excellent heat resistance. However, it should be noted that the strength of a silicone PSA is not structural in character. Phenolics have moved up the list while epoxies have moved down because of their poorer resistance to high temperatures for extended times. Table 11.2 provides a ranking in terms of *retention of strength* at high temperatures, not actual strength at those temperatures.

In each of the catagories of higher strength adhesives, consideration has to be made to the resistance of the adhesive to cleavage forces. As is seen in a later section in this chapter, bond designs try to minimize cleavage loading. However, it is only prudent to choose adhesives with the highest resistance to cleavage while retaining the stiffness necessary for the intended use. A good guideline for the proper choice of an adhesive for its mechanical performance is simply to choose an adhesive with the right stiffness (modulus) for the intended use but also with the highest possible strain energy release rate for that type of adhesive.

11.3 Application Criteria

Each type of adhesive described in this book has methodologies for how they must be used. If the intended use of the adhesive is to make an assembly which is sensitive to high temperatures, it makes no sense to use an adhesive requiring an oven cure. If there is a substantial mismatch between the coefficients of thermal expansion of the adherends, it is imprudent to avoid use of a heat-curing adhesive, as well. Table 11.3 provides a listing of possible cure or application conditions necessary for certain classes of adhesives.

It is unfortunate, but true, that those adhesives which exhibit the highest performance are those which require the most difficult application conditions. Pressure-sensitive adhesives, in tape form, are probably the easiest type of adhesive to use. There is no need to remove solvent or to carry out any other operations in order to make a bond. However, load bearing performance is limited to a few kilograms per square inch. For starches, cellulosics, rubber-based and protein-based adhesives, a means of application as well as a way of removing the carrier medium whether it be water or solvent are needed. In production environments, these types of adhesives are roll-coated onto the adherends. For starch-based adhesives, the adhesive is dried under heat lamps or in an oven. For cellulosics, a similar type of situation applies. If the adhesive is wallpaper paste, it is just applied and the water is allowed to evaporate into the atmosphere or into wallboard. Rubber-based adhesives are a very

Table 11.3   Cure or Application Conditions for Various Types of Adhesives

Adhesive type	Necessary application conditions
Pressure-sensitive	None, just finger pressure
Starch-based	A means to apply the adhesive, to remove water to yield a dry coated adhesive, to re-moisten before making the bond
Cellulosic	A means to apply the adhesive, to remove water or solvent
Rubber-based	A means to apply the adhesive, to remove water or solvent
Hot melt	A hot melt applicator; applied to a metal, a means to preheat the metal
PVAc emulsion	A means to apply the adhesive, to remove water, to fixture the bond during drying time
Cyanoacrylate	A means to apply the adhesive, a source of humidity or a primer, ventilation
Protein-based	A means to apply the adhesive, to remove water, possibly a heat source
Anaerobic acrylic	A means to apply the adhesive, ventilation
Rubber-modified acrylic, primer/liquid type	A means to apply the primer to one side of the bond and the monomer mix part to the other side of the bond, ventilation
Rubber-modified acrylic, 2-part type	A means to meter mix the two parts of the adhesive, to apply the mixed adhesive, ventilation
Modified phenolic	A means to refrigerate the adhesive before use, to apply the adhesive, to cure the adhesive as well as to apply pressure during the cure. Typically a hydraulic press or autoclave is needed. Cure temperatures usually 150°C or higher
2-part epoxy	A means to meter mix the two parts of the adhesive, to apply the mixed adhesive, to fixture the bond during the cure time. Could potentially use a post-cure for optimum properties
Heat-curing epoxy	A means to refrigerate the adhesive before use, to apply the adhesive, to cure the adhesive as well as to apply pressure during cure. Typically a hydraulic press or autoclave is needed. Cure temperatures usually 125–171°C, but could be as low as 82°C
Bis-maleimide	A means to refrigerate the adhesive before use, to apply the adhesive, to cure the adhesive as well as to apply pressure during cure. Typically a hydraulic press or autoclave is needed. Cure temperatures usually in excess of 171°C
Polyimides	A means to refrigerate the adhesive before use, to apply the adhesive, to cure the adhesive as well as to apply pressure during cure. Typically a hydraulic press or autoclave is needed. Cure temperatures usually in excess of 220°C

large class of materials and it is difficult to describe all of the possible application scenarios. These adhesives can be roll-coated onto substrates, but they can also be spray-applied. In general, heat lamps are used to evaporate solvent or water. However, if the RBA is a mastic, it is applied it to the piece to be bonded, and after a short time for solvent to flash off, the other adherend is applied. This is how an RBA is used as a tile or wallboard cement, which would require that the adhesive work well when placed on with a trowel.

Hot melt adhesives are used with some sort of manual or pneumatic hand-held applicator. In industrial situations, hot melt applicators can be robotic. In some cases, hot melt adhesives are foamed or patterned when applied to increase coverage of adhesive per pound or some level of strength.

PVAc emulsions are applied by roll coating or from hand held dispensers (such as plastic bottles). In home or woodworking applications, parts usually have to be fixtured for lengthy periods due to the length of time needed for water removal.

Cyanoacrylate and anaerobic adhesives are very easy to use, just apply and the cure takes care of itself. There are two provisos, however. The use of cyano-acrylates requires a supply of a nucleophilic agent. Water is sufficiently nucleophilic to initiate cure but ambient humidity may not always be sufficient. In addition, certain substrates are acidic enough to inhibit cure even if enough water is present in the atmosphere. For those situations, an amine-containing primer can be applied to the substrate before the adhesive to initiate polymerization. Anaerobic adhesives require only the exclusion of oxygen to effect a cure, but the substrate needs to be ferrous or some other metal which reduces the peroxide in the adhesive. If the part to be bonded cannot reduce the peroxide, a primer can be used, as discussed later for structural acrylics. Another matter of concern is the odor of acrylics, which can be objectionable. Therefore, they should be used only in well ventilated areas.

Certain types of acrylics require a primer on one surface and the monomer mix on the other to effect cure. As noted earlier, these adhesives require two chemicals, a peroxide and a reducing agent for cure. One of these can be applied to one substrate as a primer. The monomer mix, applied to the other substrate, contains the other chemical. However, there are also acrylics used as two-part adhesives, which must be mixed before application. In production environments, meter mixing equipment is a necessity to apply the mixed adhesive rapidly to parts. In low volume or non-production environments, hand-held dispensers with two syringe sections are an easy way to apply these adhesives. Acrylates cure very quickly, so extensive fixturing is seldom required.

Two-part epoxies and urethanes are applied in much the same way as the two-part acrylics. Similar meter mix production equipment and hand-held dispenser equipment are available for these two types of adhesives. In comparison to acrylates, these two types of adhesives cure much more slowly, so fixturing is often a requirement. Referring back to the section on T-T-T diagrams, it is obvious that a post-cure is required to get full performance from a two-part epoxy or urethane.

All of the remaining adhesive systems in Table 11.3 are much more difficult to use than those described above. These systems are latent curing in character and must be refrigerated to have a useful shelf life. The cure can be effected in a number of ways. Most often, the part is fixtured and placed in an oven for the required time at the required temperature. For more demanding applications, a heated press may be used. For the most demanding applications, such as aerospace bonding, an autoclave is used to effect the bond. When film form adhesives are used, they are usually cut into shape and applied by hand. The part is placed in a tool shaped like the final part and the entire assembly is "vacuum bagged." A vacuum is drawn on the part during the initial stages of cure, after which (or during which) a positive pressure is also applied. In the autoclave, a specific schedule of temperature rises and application of pressure is used. The usual cure temperatures for epoxies and phenolics are in the range of 82°C to 171°C. For bis-maleimides and polyimides, the temperatures are usually higher than 200°C. For polyimides, substantial pressure must be applied to eliminate water from the bondline.

One item discussed above is the need for certain types of rheology for many adhesive applications. If an adhesive is used on a vertical surface, it should be formulated so it exhibits a yield stress after which it flows easily. We call these materials "thixotropic." Such properties are desired with all mastics since the adhesive needs to stay in position until the second adherend is applied. In certain cases, the yield stress of the uncured adhesive should be low enough so that a bond can be easily executed. One such case is an anaerobic thread-locking adhesive. In film adhesives, flow is controlled by the molecular weights of the polymers used to formulate the adhesive and by the proper cure schedule with heat and pressure applied at specific times.

Several special types of adhesives have not been discussed in this book but are worthy of mention in this chapter. The first of these is the heat-curing PSA, which can be used in applications requiring greater load bearing. A heat-curing PSA can self-fixture a part but then after the application of heat, yield at least a semi-structural bond. Another type of adhesive not discussed earlier is the light-curing acrylic or epoxy. The acrylic's cure mechanism is free radical in nature but is initiated by light. For the epoxy, the light-initiated cure is usually cationic. For both, a UV or visible light source is necessary to effect the cure.

An interesting method to bond steel substrates is available which takes advantage of the fact that ferrous substances are susceptible to rapid increases in temperature when placed in electromagnetic fields, a method known as *induction heating.* Steel parts can be heated from room temperature to 200°C in seconds. Adhesives have been formulated which incorporate this heating method and provide fixturing strength in a short period of time.

11.4   Interfaces and Surface Preparations

Chapter 6 provided the basic surface chemical criteria for adhesive bonding and Chapter 7 provided a description of methods of surface preparation for a wide variety of substrates. Couched in terms of the rationalizations of adhesive bonding, the criteria for choosing the correct adhesive are:

- Choose an adhesive which is soluble in the adherends

or

- Choose an adhesive with a critical wetting tension less than the surface energy of the adherends to be bonded
- Choose an adhesive with a viscosity low enough so the equilibrium contact angle can be reached during the bonding time
- Provide a microscopic morphology on the adherends
- Choose an adhesive compatible with weak boundary layer materials or remove the weak boundary layer in some way

and, if the bond is to be subjected to environmental exposure,

- Choose an adhesive and/or primer for the adhesive which can provide covalent chemical bonds between the surface and the primer or adhesive

Even though "surface preparation is the key to bondment durability" it is not always true that rigorous surface preparation is necessary to effect a bond. For example, if the part is to be used in an interior application, it is likely that minimal or no surface preparation is necessary. It is also true that if the adhesive of choice is soluble in the adherend, then surface preparation may not be needed. *The primary guideline is to do the least costly surface preparation commensurate with the proposed use of the adhesive bond.* For example, if parts are being bonded for a pen cap, there is probably little need for a surface preparation. However, if the lives of people are dependent upon the retention of strength in an adhesive bond, such as in aircraft construction, the best possible surface preparation should be employed. In many cases, with proper choice of adhesive and with removal of obvious weak boundary layers, durable adhesive bonds can be attained. However, without the removal of weak boundary layers, significant chance for environmental damage and premature bond failure remains.

11.5   Miscellaneous Concerns

The remaining issues surrounding the choice of an adhesive are often just as important as the primary concerns listed earlier. For example, is the adhesive meant to be conductive or an insulator? Adhesives have been specially formulated to be conductors of heat or conductors of electricity, and to be insulators, as well as non-corrosive to sensitive electrical parts. If the bonding application involves electronics, the purity of the materials used in the adhesive is a major concern. For example, epoxy resins often have measurable quantities of sodium chloride remaining from synthesis. If the salt is not removed from the resin before it is used in an electronic application, corrosion and loss of the circuitry can result.

Other concerns include resistance of the adhesive itself to environmental or microbial attack. For example, urethane adhesives formulated from aromatic iso-cyanates, can potentially degrade in sunlight and moisture to yield a brown, partially hydrolyzed material. Acrylic adhesives, however, are considered to be color fast in sunlight. Other important factors regarding appearance include the optical clarity of the adhesive. For glass, mirror, and glazing applications, the adhesive must be optically clear when the bond is effected but must also retain that clarity and color for long times with exposure to sunlight. Most aromatic-based adhesives cannot meet this requirement.

Many natural product-based structural adhesives are not considered useful due to their proclivity for microbial attack and hydrolysis of their chemical structure in ambient conditions. In fact, this problem led to the rapid development of phenolic-based adhesives in exterior wood applications. Most natural product-based adhesives include microbial antagonists as additives in their formulations.

Thermal expansion coefficient is another concern. If the adherends to be bonded have the same thermal expansion coefficient, there is usually little need for concern unless that number is large. In that case, adhesives have to be chosen so the strain to failure is less than the expansion and contraction of the adherends during cure and use. A different concern comes about when dissimilar adherends are to be bonded. In this case, use of a heat-curing adhesive can yield curved parts due to this mismatch. A non-heat curing adhesive should be used for such an applications, or otherwise correct for the thermal expansion coefficient mismatch.

The final concern regarding to the choice of the adhesive is cost. In many cases, the cost of an adhesive is the final criterion for whether or not it is used. However, a better concern is a comparison of the *overall* cost of adhesive bonding versus that of alternative joining methods. The adhesive bonding user must consider not only the cost of the adhesive, but also the cost of surface preparation, the storage, the means of curing and production delays due to the need for fixturing. For some applications, the overall cost overcomes the benefits of adhesive bonding, and an alternative joining method is chosen. For the adhesive supplier, the task is to provide adhesive bonding technology which makes the overall process of joining parts as inexpensive as possible. The goal of the adhesive supplier is to eliminate as many cost deterrants as possible so that adhesive bonding is less expensive than alternative techniques. Developments in adhesive bonding technology have done just that; adhesives are used in a multitude of applications.

11.6   Basic Criteria for the Design of an Adhesive Bond

It is important for even the casual user of adhesives to know the pitfalls associated with improper bond design. It is also important that a book such as this, lay the

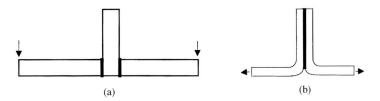

Figure 11.1   Improperly designed "Tee' joints

groundwork for further investigation into bond design. In this short section, some of the do's and don'ts of adhesive bond design are described, in terms of stress analysis of bonds discussed early in this book.

In Section 3.4.4, the Goland–Reissner analysis of the lap joint was described. The primary result of that analysis was that the ends of the lap joint bend away from the line of force through the joint, thus putting the edges of the adhesive into peel rather than shear. Earlier in this chapter, values of peel strength exhibited by various adhesives were listed. A glance at Table 11.1 clearly shows that the peel strength of an adhesive can be orders of magnitude less than its shear strength. One bond design criterion that is most important is: *design joints so they are in shear and minimize any cleavage loading.*

Look at a few examples. Figure 11.1 shows examples of some improperly designed "Tee" joints and Fig. 11.2 shows those same joints properly designed. The joint in Fig. 11.1(a) is particularly prone to cleavage failure. The joint in 11.1(b) is prone to cleavage failure if the adherends are pulled away perpendicularly to the bond axis, as shown in the drawing. However, placing of straps across the joint eliminates peel as a problem, as shown in Fig. 11.2.

There are a number of ways to minimize peel stresses in forming adhesive bonds. Figure 11.3 shows some ways, including (a), widening a thin adherend (which would be more susceptible to peel) at the edge. A wider bond has more resistance to peel forces. In the second method (b), the thinner adherend is wrapped around the edge of the thicker. The third way (c), shows a method often used in the aerospace industry: doublers and triplers. That is, extra adhesive bonds are applied in areas more susceptible to peel, fatigue or other damage. Another interesting way (d) is to provide an inset into which the thinner adherends fits. This way, there is no edge to initiate peel. Unfortunately, providing an inset also would require machining the

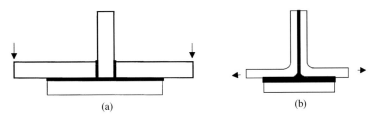

Figure 11.2   Properly designed "Tee" joints

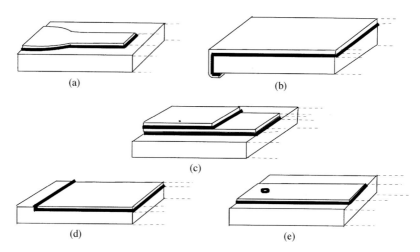

Figure 11.3   Drawings of some schemes for eliminating or reducing the chances of peel initiation at an edge of a bonded specimen. (a) shows widening the end of the thin adherent; (b) shows wrapping the thin adherend around the edge; (c) shows doubling the end of the specimen; (d) shows adding of an inset into which the thin adherend can fit; and (e) shows the judicious use of mechanical fasteners at appropriate points. The dashed lines indicate that the bonded specimen is actually bigger than drawn and that the drawings show the ends of specimens

part which increases cost. Another way (e) is to use a mechanical fastener at those points where peel is suspected to be a potential problem.

11.6.1   Hart-Smith Design Criteria for Double Lap Joints

The last section of this book describes one simple set of criteria for a bonded lap joint. These criteria were developed by L.J. Hart-Smith [1] who was also referenced earlier in this book. Reviewing the full Hart-Smith reports is essential for a detailed description of his bond design criteria. His computer programs provided predictions for optimized bond designs but, in this section, only a short description of his criteria can be provided. It is important to see how chemistry, mechanics, and physical properties of materials are combined to provide bond design criteria.

The Hart-Smith bond design criteria came from a U.S. Air Force-funded program called the PABST (Primary Adhesively Bonded Structure) program [2]. The objective of the research was to build a mock aircraft fuselage using adhesive bonding as the only construction technique. The research was to lead to methodology for the most efficient use of adhesives in aircraft construction. According to reports, the program was a complete success. The resulting mock fuselage was able to undergo the equivalent of an aircraft lifetime of pressurization and depressurization without a failure or fatigue crack growth. Because there were no "natural" failures, cracks were purposely added to the structure, and their progress followed

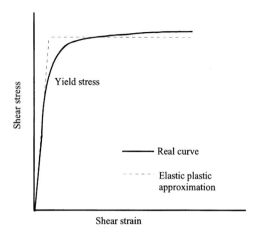

Figure 11.4   Figure showing a real stress–strain curve and the elastic–plastic approximation to that curve

by stop-action photography. The fuselage cracks propagated until they encountered the bonded joints and then they *actually turned back on themselves* instead of breaking the joint.

The Hart-Smith analysis starts with the Goland–Reissner analysis but then works with more realistic specimens such as the double lap shear specimen shown in the lower half of Fig. 3.8. Refer back to Figs. 3.15 and 3.16, where the edge of a lap joint is shown to have a substantial stress increase over the average stress in the joint, both in shear and in tension. For most adhesives, the shear stress at the edges of the joint may be above the yield point of the adhesive. To see what this means for bond design, turn to the elastic–plastic model for the stress strain curve of the adhesive shown in Fig. 11.4.

The elastic–plastic model says that the adhesive behaves elastically until the yield point at which it becomes plastic and yields at the same stress until failure. The dashed line in Fig. 11.4 shows an elastic–plastic approximation for the real stress–strain curve.The yield point is not well modeled. However, Hart-Smith adjusted his approximations so the *strain energy density* of the two curves agreed and then used the two straight lines. The analysis was analogous to Goland–Reissner, except that Eq. (3.6) was modified from Hooke's Law to one which was elastic–plastic in character. The reader is referred to the original Hart-Smith papers [1] for the complete description. A more pictorial description of the bond design methodology is used here.

In a short lap shear specimen, the chances that the adhesive yields at design loads is great. One tenet of the Hart-Smith design methodology is that the lap length of the bond should be long enough so much of the adhesive is *NOT* yielded under design loads. This statement comes with an important corollary: *the bond should always be designed so the adherends are the weakest part of the joint*. This situation harkens back to Fig. 3.9 which showed that even though "lap shear strength"

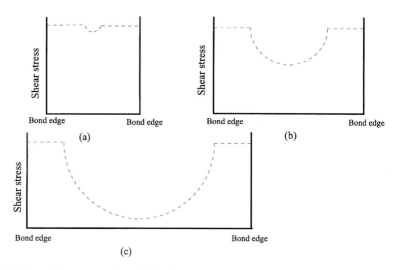

Figure 11.5 Pictorial representation of the shear stress in a lap joint as a function of lap length. For a short lap (a), most of the joint is above the yield stress of the adhesive. For the intermediate lap length (b), a portion of the joint is below the yield stress. For the long lap (c), most of the joint has the adhesive below its shear yield stress

decreases as a function of lap length, the failure in a joint eventually is failure in the adherend at long enough lap length. From Figs. 3.15 and 11.4, if σ_y is less than the shear stress at the edge of the joint, there is a region near the edges of the joint where the adhesive has yielded. Pictorially, this situation is represented as a function of lap length in Fig. 11.5.

For the short lap length, most of the adhesive in the joint is above its yield stress. For an intermediate lap length, some of the adhesive in the bond is below the yield stress. Note that the minimum occurs at the middle of the bond as expected from the Goland–Reissner analysis. Finally, for the long lap length, a substantial percentage of the adhesive is below its yield stress. Note that the region over which the adhesive has yielded is the same in all of the laps. In fact, the region over which this occurs is defined by the quantity

$$\frac{t}{2}\frac{\sigma_{ult}}{\tau_P}$$

where t is the thickness of the central adherend (remember, this is a double lap joint); τ_P is the shear yield stress of the adhesive; and σ_{ult} is the ultimate strength of the adhesive bond. Indeed, Hart-Smith also provides an expression for the distance from the edge of the plastic yielded region to the center of the trough:

$$3\sqrt{\frac{Et_A}{2G}}$$

where E is the modulus of the adherend; t is as above; t_A is the thickness of the adhesive; and G is the shear modulus of the adhesive.

The design of the joint then comes from several considerations based upon the analysis. First, a decision is made as to which adhesive stress–strain curve to use to determine τ_P. This may not seem to be a reasonable statement unless one remembers that adhesives are viscoelastic in nature and that adhesive/metal interfaces are thermodynamically unstable in harsh environments. Thus, one needs to use the shear stress–strain curve for the worst possible scenario: the shear stress–strain curve measured at high temperature and high humidity. In addition, since adhesives act more plastic at low rates of stress application, this shear stress–strain curve should be determined at a slow rate of extension. From the σ_{ult} and τ_P determined under these conditions, good design values can be derived. The thick adherend lap shear specimen shown in Fig. 3.7 is used for this determination. What is the significance of the elastic trough? Through the PABST program, it was found that adhesive bonds made with short lap lengths usually went to failure by creep. As the bond is loaded and unloaded under test conditions, the adhesive creeps. If the entire volume of the adhesive has yielded because of the short length of the joint, the adhesive cannot recover. Each additional loading then brings the joint closer to failure. However, if the lap is long enough so the center of the joint is essentially entirely elastic, then the joint recovers with loading and unloading. The question then is how much of the bond should remain elastic? This was experimentally determined in the PABST program as the point at which the minimum shear stress in the joint is about 10% of the yield stress of the adhesive. Therefore, the lap length should be increased so the length of the elastic trough is such that no creep can accumulate in the bond.

The Hart-Smith analysis brings together many of the factors discussed in this book and uses them to propose a reasonable set of bond design criteria from which one can make rational decisions about how to design an adhesive bond. Those factors come from both the Goland–Reissner analysis and the mechanical properties of adhesives.

11.7 Summary

The last chapter of this book has concerned itself with guidelines for the rational choice of adhesives and a method for beginning to design an adhesive joint. Simply, the criteria for choosing an adhesive are:

- high enough modulus for the application but as high as possible an ultimate strain energy density
- application and curing conditions commensurate with those available to the user
- economics appropriate for the end use

Bond design criteria include:

- surface preparation commensurate with the end use

- appropriate consideration for coefficient of thermal expansion mismatch
- minimization of peel at the edges of the bond
- design for adherend failure, NOT adhesive failure
- design so that adhesive is yielded only over a small region of the bond
- design based upon the properties of the adhesive under worst case conditions
- provide for a long enough lap so a substantial portion of the adhesive is elastically loaded rather than plastically loaded.

References

1. (a) Hart-Smith, L.J., in *Developments in Adhesives*, Kinloch, A.J., (Ed.) (1981), Applied Science Publishers, Essex, UK. (b) Hart-Smith, L.J., *Composites*, 25(9) (1994), p. 895. (c) Hart-Smith, L.J., *Adhesive-Bonded Single Lap Joints* (Jan., 1973), NASA Technical Report 112236. (d) Hart-Smith, L.J., *Adhesively-Bonded Double-Lap Joints* (Jan., 1973), NASA Technical Report 112235. (e) Hart-Smith, L.J., *Adhesively-Bonded Scarf and Stepped-Lap Joints* (Jan., 1973), NASA Technical 112237
2. Thrall, E.W., Jr., in *Bonded Joints and Preparation for Bonding*, AGARD Lecture Series No. 102 (1979), Harford House, London, UK

Index

structural adhesives
  acrylic-based, *195ff, 209ff*
  epoxy-based, *189ff, 202ff*
  phenolic-based, *185ff, 200ff*
  physical forms, *184*
  polyimide, *197ff*
  protein-based, *188ff*
  urethane-based, *193ff*
stud pull-off test, *38*
surface analysis methods, *98ff*
surface chemical functionalization, *152, 253*
surface energy, *77, 79*
surface energy of solids, *83*
surface forces apparatus, *86*
surface preparation, *147ff*
surface preparation
  of metals, *167ff*
  of plastics, *150ff*
surface tension, *82*
surface treatment
  by ion beam etching, *163*
  by sputter etching, *163*
  by ultraviolet radiation, *161*
  by wet chemical methods, *164ff*

T
tack, *217*
  and the Dahlquist criterion, *231*
  and viscoelasticity, *230–234*
  measurement techniques, *224–226*
tackification, *217*
tackifier, *217*
  C-5 aliphatic resin-based, *221–223*
  coumarone-indene-based, *221, 222, 241*
  MQ resin, *222–224*
  rosin acid based, *220*
  terpene-based, *221*
  tertiary butyl phenolic, *223–224, 241*
TEM, *100*
tensile measurement, *13*
test method
  described by ASTM, *37, 40, 56*
  for contact angles, *84*
thermal expansion coefficient, *268*

thermal transitions of polymers, *108ff*
thermoplastics, *105*
thermosets, *105*
thixotropic liquid, *24*
time-temperature equivalency, *106*
time-temperature superposition, *113*
time-temperature-transformation diagrams,
  192ff
T-peel test, *61*
Transmission Electron Microscopy, *100*

U
urethane resins
  in structural adhesives, *193ff*

V
van der Waals forces, *71*
viscoelastic, *24, 27*
viscosity, *23*

W
water break test, *156*
wedge test, *61*
  and adhesive bond durability, *170*
Williams-Landel-Ferry equation, *116*
WLF equation, *116*
work, *70*
work of adhesion, *81*
work of cohesion, *81*

X
XPS, *98*
X-ray Photoelectron Spectroscopy, *98*

Y
yield strength and toughening, *206*

Young equation, *85*
Young-Dupre equation, *86*

Z
zinc oxide in RBAs, *242, 243*
Zisman plot, *95*